ANALYTIC GEOMETRY

ALTERNATE EDITION

BY

W. A. WILSON, Ph.D.

PROFESSOR OF MATHEMATICS
YALE UNIVERSITY

AND

J. I. TRACEY, Ph.D.

ASSOCIATE PROFESSOR OF MATHEMATICS
YALE UNIVERSITY

D. C. HEATH AND COMPANY

BOSTON	NEW YORK	CHICAGO
ATLANTA	SAN FRANCISCO	DALLAS
	LONDON	

PREFACE

This alternate edition has been prepared in response to requests for a new set of problems. Accordingly the problem lists in the edition of 1925 have been revised as much as possible, by altering numerical and other data and adding some entirely new problems. The instances where changes have not been made are mostly cases where a loss in effectiveness would be involved.

The text has not been materially altered in deference to opinions by users of the book, who have probably had the experience of finding the first edition of a textbook better than any succeeding ones. The principal innovations are the addition of sections on cylindrical and spherical coördinates and space curves in the chapter on solid analytic geometry, the insertion of the method of moments as an alternative to the method of averages in the chapter on curve fitting, and the inclusion of a number of historical notes. These additions, certain minor changes in the chapters on the conics, and the increased number of problems account for the greater length of the book.

Finally, it is a pleasant duty to record the authors' appreciation of the great compliment paid them by the continued use of their book, and to thank those who have made suggestions regarding the revision.

W. A. W.
J. I. T.

December, 1936

CONTENTS

v

CHAPTER III — THE STRAIGHT LINE

CHAPTER IV — THE CIRCLE

CHAPTER XI — TANGENTS AND NORMALS

CONTENTS

INTRODUCTION

DEFINITIONS AND FORMULAS FROM ALGEBRA AND TRIGONOMETRY

1. The quadratic. An expression reducible to the form

$$Ax^2 + Bx + C,$$

where A, B, and C are any constants, is called a quadratic in x.

2. Solution of the quadratic equation. The roots of any quadratic equation may be found by completing the square, or by using the quadratic formula.

(a) To solve by completing the square, transpose the constant term to the right-hand member and divide both sides of the equation by the coefficient of x^2. In the resulting equation add to both members the square of half the coefficient of x and extract the square root.

(b) If the above rule is applied to the general quadratic equation $Ax^2 + Bx + C = 0$, we get

$$x = \frac{-B \pm \sqrt{B^2 - 4AC}}{2A},$$

which is known as the *quadratic formula*. To solve an equation by means of this formula simply substitute for A, B, and C in the formula their values in the given equation.

3. The discriminant. The expression under the radical, $B^2 - 4AC$, is called the *discriminant* of the quadratic. It is denoted by the Greek letter Δ. The quadratic formula shows that the roots of a quadratic equation are

imaginary,   if $\Delta < 0$;
real and equal,   if $\Delta = 0$;
real and unequal, if $\Delta > 0$.

4. Rules of proportion. If the proportion $a : b = c : d$ is true, then the following proportions are true:

xiii

$$b : a = d : c; \qquad \text{(Inversion)}$$
$$a : c = b : d; \qquad \text{(Alternation)}$$
$$a + b : a = c + d : c; \qquad \text{(Composition)}$$
$$a - b : a = c - d : c; \qquad \text{(Division)}$$
$$a + b : a - b = c + d : c - d. \qquad \text{(Composition and Division)}$$

5. Logarithms. The logarithm of a number to a given base is the exponent of the power to which the base must be raised in order that the result may be equal to the number. Thus if $b^x = N$, we say that x is the logarithm of N to the base b and write $x = \log_b N$.

The base b may be any positive number different from 0 and 1. Two systems of logarithms are in common use: the natural, or Naperian, where the base is $e = 2.71828 \ldots$; and the common, or Briggs, where the base is 10.

Important properties of logarithms to any base are the following:

$$\log_b 1 = 0; \qquad\qquad \log_b b = 1;$$

$$\log_b MN = \log_b M + \log_b N; \qquad \log_b \frac{M}{N} = \log_b M - \log_b N;$$

$$\log_b N^k = k \log_b N; \qquad\qquad \log_b \sqrt[k]{N} = \frac{1}{k} \log_b N;$$

$$\log_c N = \frac{\log_b N}{\log_b c} = \log_b N \cdot \log_c b.$$

6. Angles. In trigonometry an angle is supposed to be generated by revolving a line, called the *generating line*, about the vertex from one side of the angle, called the *initial line*, to the other side, called the *terminal line*. If the rotation is counter-clockwise, the angle is called positive; if clockwise, it is called negative.

Degree measure. The ordinary unit of angle measurement is one ninetieth part of a right angle, which is called a *degree*. One sixtieth part of a degree is called a minute and one sixtieth part of a minute is called a second. Thus

$$60'' = \text{one minute};$$
$$60' = \text{one degree};$$
$$360° = \text{one complete revolution} = \text{four right angles}.$$

Circular measure. The unit of circular measure is a central angle subtended by an arc equal to the radius of the circle. It is called a *radian.* We find at once that

$$\pi \text{ radians } = 180°;$$

$$1 \text{ radian } = \frac{180°}{\pi};$$

$$1° = \frac{\pi}{180} \text{ radians.}$$

From this definition we have the important result that in any circle the length of an arc equals the product of the measure of its subtended central angle in radians and the length of the radius.

7. Trigonometric functions. From any point P of the terminal line VP of the angle $\theta = AVP$ drop a perpendicular on the initial line of the angle (produced if necessary). The ratios of the sides of the triangle thus formed are called the trigonometric ratios or functions of the given angle.

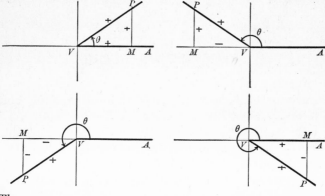

They are

$$\sin \theta = \frac{MP}{VP}; \qquad \cos \theta = \frac{VM}{VP}; \qquad \tan \theta = \frac{MP}{VM};$$

$$\csc \theta = \frac{VP}{MP}; \qquad \sec \theta = \frac{VP}{VM}; \qquad \cot \theta = \frac{VM}{MP}.$$

In these ratios the side of the triangle opposite the angle is considered positive if it extends up from the initial line, negative if down; the adjacent side is considered positive if it extends to the right of the vertex, negative if to the left; the hypotenuse is always positive.

8. Relations between the functions. For any angle,

$$\sec \theta = \frac{1}{\cos \theta}; \qquad\qquad \cot \theta = \frac{\cos \theta}{\sin \theta};$$

$$\csc \theta = \frac{1}{\sin \theta}; \qquad\qquad \sin^2 \theta + \cos^2 \theta = 1;$$

$$\cot \theta = \frac{1}{\tan \theta}; \qquad\qquad 1 + \tan^2 \theta = \sec^2 \theta;$$

$$\tan \theta = \frac{\sin \theta}{\cos \theta}; \qquad\qquad 1 + \cot^2 \theta = \csc^2 \theta.$$

9. Reduction of angles.

$$\sin (- \theta) = - \sin \theta; \qquad\qquad \sin \left(\frac{\pi}{2} \pm \theta\right) = \cos \theta;$$

$$\cos (- \theta) = \cos \theta; \qquad\qquad \cos \left(\frac{\pi}{2} \pm \theta\right) = \mp \sin \theta;$$

$$\tan (- \theta) = - \tan \theta; \qquad\qquad \tan \left(\frac{\pi}{2} \pm \theta\right) = \mp \cot \theta;$$

$$\sin (\pi \pm \theta) = \mp \sin \theta;$$
$$\cos (\pi \pm \theta) = - \cos \theta;$$
$$\tan (\pi \pm \theta) = \pm \tan \theta.$$

10. Special angles.

ANGLE	0	$\frac{\pi}{6}$	$\frac{\pi}{4}$	$\frac{\pi}{3}$	$\frac{\pi}{2}$	π	$\frac{3\pi}{2}$	2π
Sine	0	$\frac{1}{2}$	$\frac{\sqrt{2}}{2}$	$\frac{\sqrt{3}}{2}$	1	0	-1	0
Cosine	1	$\frac{\sqrt{3}}{2}$	$\frac{\sqrt{2}}{2}$	$\frac{1}{2}$	0	-1	0	1
Tangent	0	$\frac{\sqrt{3}}{3}$	1	$\sqrt{3}$	∞	0	∞	0

11. Formulas for the sum and difference of two angles.

$$\sin (\theta \pm \phi) = \sin \theta \cos \phi \pm \cos \theta \sin \phi;$$
$$\cos (\theta \pm \phi) = \cos \theta \cos \phi \mp \sin \theta \sin \phi;$$
$$\tan (\theta \pm \phi) = \frac{\tan \theta \pm \tan \phi}{1 \mp \tan \theta \tan \phi}.$$

12. Double and half angle formulas.

$$\sin 2\theta = 2 \sin \theta \cos \theta;$$
$$\cos 2\theta = \cos^2 \theta - \sin^2 \theta = 1 - 2 \sin^2 \theta = 2 \cos^2 \theta - 1;$$
$$\tan 2\theta = \frac{2 \tan \theta}{1 - \tan^2 \theta};$$

$$\sin \frac{\theta}{2} = \sqrt{\frac{1 - \cos \theta}{2}}; \quad \cos \frac{\theta}{2} = \sqrt{\frac{1 + \cos \theta}{2}};$$

$$\tan \frac{\theta}{2} = \sqrt{\frac{1 - \cos \theta}{1 + \cos \theta}} = \frac{1 - \cos \theta}{\sin \theta} = \frac{\sin \theta}{1 + \cos \theta}.$$

13. Triangle formulas. In any triangle ABC,

$$\frac{a}{\sin A} = \frac{b}{\sin B} = \frac{c}{\sin C}; \qquad \text{(Law of Sines)}$$

$$a^2 = b^2 + c^2 - 2bc \cos A. \quad \text{(Law of Cosines)}$$

14. The Greek Alphabet

LETTERS	NAMES	LETTERS	NAMES
A, α	Alpha	N, ν	Nu
B, β	Beta	Ξ, ξ	Xi
Γ, γ	Gamma	O, o	Omicron
Δ, δ	Delta	Π, π	Pi
E, ϵ	Epsilon	P, ρ	Rho
Z, ζ	Zeta	Σ, σ	Sigma
H, η	Eta	T, τ	Tau
Θ, θ	Theta	Υ, υ	Upsilon
I, ι	Iota	Φ, ϕ	Phi
K, κ	Kappa	X, χ	Chi
Λ, λ	Lambda	Ψ, ψ	Psi
M, μ	Mu	Ω, ω	Omega

ANALYTIC GEOMETRY

ALTERNATE EDITION

CHAPTER I

CARTESIAN COÖRDINATES

1. Introduction. The chief feature of analytic geometry, which distinguishes it from the geometry which the student has hitherto studied, is its extensive use of algebraic methods in the solution of geometric problems. Just as the use of symbols in algebra makes possible the ready solution of many problems which would be difficult if not impossible by the processes of arithmetic, so the use of algebraic reasoning simplifies much of geometry and widens its scope. The student is already familiar with some of these applications; for example, the theorems stating the numerical properties of a triangle are derived in whole or part by algebraic reasoning.

In trigonometry also the greater part of the reasoning is of the same character, and further simplification is gained by the introduction of negative numbers. Thus the law of cosines, $a^2 = b^2 + c^2 - 2bc \cos A$, states in compact language the contents of three theorems of plane geometry, since cosine A is positive or negative according as angle A is acute or obtuse. Other examples of a similar character may occur to the student.

2. Position; coördinates. Further extension of algebraic methods in geometry has been made possible by the device of locating points in a plane or in space by sets of numbers, called *coördinates*. To locate a point in a plane two such numbers are required; these may represent the distance and the direction of the point from a fixed reference point, or the distances of the point from two fixed perpendicular lines of reference. Both methods are commonly used in ordinary life. Thus we say, "Baltimore is 40 miles northeast (N 45° E) of Washington" or, "Go 5 blocks east of A Street and 3 blocks south of First Avenue to reach the library." Both methods

1

are used analytically; the second is simpler and will be discussed first.

3. Rectangular Cartesian coördinates. In this system there are two mutually perpendicular reference lines $X'X$ and $Y'Y$, as in the figure. These are called the **axes of coördinates** or **coördinate axes,** and their intersection O is called the **origin.** The two axes divide the plane into four quadrants numbered as in trigonometry. The coördinate axis $X'X$ is called the x-axis and $Y'Y$ is called the y-axis.

The position of a point P is determined by measuring its distance from $Y'Y$ along a parallel to $X'X$, and its distance from $X'X$ along a parallel to $Y'Y$. Distances measured to the right of $Y'Y$ or up from $X'X$ are called *positive*, those to the left or down *negative*. These distances, with the proper signs prefixed, are called the **coördinates** of the point; the one measured along a line parallel to $X'X$ is the **x-coördinate** or **abscissa;** the one parallel to $Y'Y$ is the **y-coördinate** or **ordinate.** Thus in the figure the abscissa of P is $BP = +4$, its ordinate is $AP = -3$. The content of this paragraph may now be stated compactly as follows:

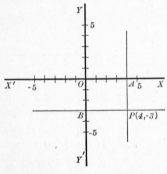

Definitions. *The abscissa or x-coördinate of a point is the distance from the y-axis to the point. The ordinate or y-coördinate of a point is the distance from the x-axis to the point.*

4. Notation. In naming a point by its coördinates we write them in parentheses, putting the abscissa first. Thus in the figure P is the point $(4, -3)$. If the coördinates are variable or unknown, the abscissa is denoted by the letter x, and the ordinate by y. This notation is used for every position of the point and the student is warned against the common mistake of denoting a variable point in the second quadrant by $(-x, y)$, etc. Fixed points of which the coördinates are not known or are arbitrary will be distinguished by means of subscripts, being lettered P_1, P_2, etc., and represented by the coördinates (x_1, y_1), (x_2, y_2), etc.

5. Plotting of points. It is clear that any point in a plane is fixed by means of its coördinates; for the abscissa locates it on a parallel to the y-axis and the ordinate on a parallel to the x-axis, and these meet in one point.

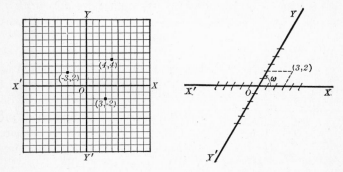

To locate a point whose coördinates are given (or as commonly stated, to *plot* the point), first mark the coördinate axes and choose a unit of measure, then measure off the abscissa on the x-axis and the ordinate from the end of the abscissa. Thus to plot $(-3, 2)$ count 3 units to the left on the x-axis and 2 units up. This is especially convenient when using coördinate paper, i.e., paper ruled with sets of equally spaced parallel lines.

The system of coördinates which has been described is the rectangular system and is the particular case of Cartesian coordinates which is usually employed. In the general Cartesian system the axes are not necessarily perpendicular, but may be oblique. The previous discussion is readily modified to fit the oblique system, which is illustrated above.

PROBLEMS

1. Plot each of the following groups of points, using a single set of coördinate axes:

(a) $(2, 6)$, $(6, 0)$, $(-3, 8)$;   (c) $(8, -2)$, $(-2, 0)$, $(5.5, 4.6)$;
(b) $(3, 5)$, $(8, -3)$, $(0, -4)$;   (d) $(7, 5)$, $(-3, -3)$, $(4\sqrt{2}, -1)$.

2. Draw the triangle whose vertices are as follows:

(a) $(5, 1)$, $(0, 7)$, $(-6, -2)$;   (c) $(1, 1)$, $(-7, -7)$, $(2, -10)$;
(b) $(0, 0)$, $(-8, 8)$, $(4, 10)$;   (d) $(-3, 2)$, $(4\sqrt{2}, 8)$, $(4, -3\sqrt{2})$.

3. Draw the quadrilateral whose vertices are as follows:

(a) $(-3, 0)$, $(3, 6)$, $(9, 0)$, $(3, -6)$;
(b) $(0, -5)$, $(10, 3)$, $(0, 5)$, $(-10, 3)$;
(c) $(6, 2)$, $(3, 6)$, $(-4, 2)$, $(1, -1)$.

4. Draw the triangle with the given vertices and find its area:

(a) $(6, 8)$, $(-4, 8)$, $(-4, 12)$;   (d) $(-5, -2)$, $(3, 4)$, $(6, -2)$;
(b) $(2, 7)$, $(-6, 7)$, $(-6, -2)$;   (e) $(3, 6)$, $(-2, 2)$, $(3, -4)$;
(c) $(3, 1)$, $(3, 9)$, $(-7, 9)$;   (f) (a, b), (a, c), (d, c).

5. Draw the triangle with the given vertices and find its area:

(a) $(7, -5)$, $(-4, -5)$, $(0, 3)$;   (c) $(1, 7)$, $(1, -3)$, $(8, 5)$;
(b) $(0, 4)$, $(12, 4)$, $(16, 8)$;   (d) (a, b), (c, b), (d, e).

6. Find the perimeter of each triangle in Problem 4.

7. Find the perimeter of each triangle in Problem 5.

8. Find the coördinates of a point 8 units to the right and 6 units below the point $(-3, 5)$.

9. Find the area of each triangle in Problem 2.

Hint. Draw a rectangle whose sides pass through the vertices of the given triangle and are parallel to the coördinate axes.

10. Find the area of each quadrilateral in Problem 3.

11. What is the abscissa of all points on the y-axis? the ordinate of all points on the x-axis? What are the coördinates of the origin?

12. To what quadrants is a point limited if its abscissa and ordinate have like signs? unlike signs?

13. If a point moves on a parallel to the x-axis, which of its co-ordinates remains constant? which if it moves on a perpendicular to the x-axis?

14. (a) What is the locus of a point whose abscissa is 6? whose ordinate is − 6?

(b) What is the locus of all points having the same abscissa? having the same ordinate?

15. What is the locus of points whose abscissas and ordinates are (a) equal; (b) numerically equal, but of unlike sign? Why?

16. A square whose side is a has one vertex at the origin and two sides along the axes. Find the coördinates of its vertices.

17. Two vertices of an equilateral triangle are (0, 0) and (a, 0). What is the third vertex?

18. The base of an isosceles triangle has the ends (0, 0) and ($2a$, 0). The tangent of each base angle is $\frac{3}{4}$. What is the third vertex?

19. A rhombus has one angle of 60° and two vertices at (0, 0) and (a, 0). Find the coördinates of the other vertices if (a) both are in the first quadrant; (b) one is in the second quadrant.

20. A regular hexagon of side a is placed so that one diagonal lies along the x-axis and the center is at the origin. Find the coördinates of the vertices.

21. Three vertices of a parallelogram are (0, 0), (a, 0), and (b, c). What is the fourth vertex?

22. The bases of an isosceles trapezoid have the lengths $2a$ and $2b$, and the altitude is h. If one base lies along the x-axis and is bisected at the origin, what are the coördinates of the vertices?

23. The sides of a parallelogram have the lengths a and b, and the included angle α is acute. If two vertices are (0, 0) and (a, 0), what are the other vertices?

6. Directed lines. We have referred to the advantage of using negative numbers in trigonometry and have defined the signs of coördinates. In analytic geometry we constantly use *directed lines*, that is, lines on which one direction is taken as positive and the opposite as negative. On such lines the lengths of segments are reckoned as positive or negative according to the direction in which they are read. For example, if the positive direction is from left to right, and AB is 8 units long, then

$$A\text{————————————————}B$$

$AB = 8$, while $BA = -8$. Thus, *changing the direction of reading a line changes its sign*, i.e., $BA = -AB$.

In adding or subtracting line segments great care should be taken to avoid errors of sign. It is advisable for beginners to read all segments in one direction in performing such operations, later reversing segments as required. For example, let us find the relation between AB, BC, and AC in the figure.

$$A\qquad\qquad C\qquad\qquad\qquad B$$

We have $\qquad AB = AC + CB = AC - BC.$

In the Cartesian coördinate system *the positive direction on all lines parallel to the x-axis is to the right; on lines not parallel to the x-axis the positive direction is upward.* It is clear that this convention contains the rules of signs of coördinates given in § 3 as special cases.

All line segments should be read in the positive direction unless it is intended that their lengths are to be considered negative. Hence the directed line segments whose lengths are the coördinates of a point must always be read *from* the axes *to* the point.

Exercise 1. Prove that, for any position of the point C on a directed line passing through the points A and B,

$$AB = AC + CB. \qquad\qquad \text{(Three cases)}$$

Exercise 2. Prove that, for any position of the point O on a directed line passing through the points A and B,

$$AB = OB - OA.$$

7. Projections of a directed segment on the coördinate axes. Theorem. *The projection on the x-axis or any line parallel to it of the segment P_1P_2 is $x_2 - x_1$. The projection on the y-axis or any line parallel to it of the segment P_1P_2 is $y_2 - y_1$.*

Proof. In the figure P_1P_2 is the given (directed) segment, and MP_1 and P_2B are parallel to the y-axis while P_1S and MP_2 are parallel to the x-axis.

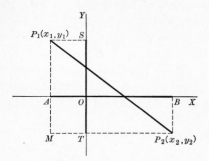

The projection on the x-axis is

$$AB = AO + OB = OB - OA = TP_2 - SP_1.$$

By the definition of abscissa $TP_2 = x_2$ and $SP_1 = x_1$. Substituting these values above we have

$$AB = x_2 - x_1.$$

In the same way the projection on the y-axis is

$$ST = P_1M = BP_2 + P_1A = y_2 - y_1.$$

Since the x-axis is usually drawn horizontally it will be convenient to refer to these projections as the *horizontal* and *vertical projections*. As this theorem is used constantly the proof should be worked out for several positions of the points P_1 and P_2 so as to show the validity of the formulas for all possible positions. Note that the horizontal projection of P_2P_1 is $x_1 - x_2$, and that its vertical projection is $y_1 - y_2$.

Exercise 3. Prove the above theorem when

(a) P_1 lies in the fourth quadrant and P_2 in the second;
(b) P_1 lies in the first quadrant and P_2 in the third;
(c) P_1 lies in the third quadrant and P_2 in the fourth.

8. Distance formula. Theorem. *The distance between any two points, $P_1(x_1, y_1)$ and $P_2(x_2, y_2)$, is given by the formula,*

$$d = \sqrt{(x_1 - x_2)^2 + (y_1 - y_2)^2}. \tag{1}$$

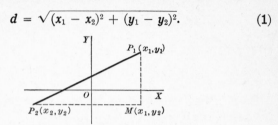

Proof. $\qquad d = P_2P_1 = \sqrt{\overline{P_2M}^2 + \overline{MP_1}^2}.$

But, by § 7, $\qquad\qquad P_2M = x_1 - x_2,$

and $\qquad\qquad\qquad MP_1 = y_1 - y_2.$

Substituting, we have the formula.

NOTE. The double sign is not used in Formula 1 because in this book the phrase "distance between P_1 and P_2" means the length of the segment in the ordinary sense, as distinguished from the (directed) "distance from P_1 to P_2."* If a segment is parallel to one of the coördinate axes, the theorem of § 7 should be used and care must be taken to name the points so that the result will be positive.

9. Point of division formulas. Theorem. *The coördinates (x, y) of a point P dividing a line segment from $P_1(x_1, y_1)$ to $P_2(x_2, y_2)$ in a given ratio $r_1 : r_2$ are given by the formulas*

$$x = \frac{r_1x_2 + r_2x_1}{r_1 + r_2}, \quad y = \frac{r_1y_2 + r_2y_1}{r_1 + r_2}. \tag{2}$$

The point P divides the directed segment P_1P_2 in the ratio $r_1 : r_2$ if $P_1P : PP_2 = r_1 : r_2$. If P lies between P_1 and P_2, the ratio is positive; if P lies on the segment produced in either direction, the ratio is negative, since P_1P and PP_2 have unlike signs.

* In the text this distinction is usually observed, but in later chapters, and especially in problems, the phrase "distance from A to B" is often used for the distance between the points for the sake of brevity.

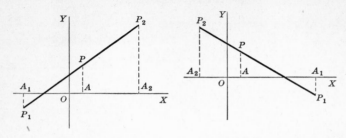

Proof. Since parallel lines cut off proportional segments on two transversals, we have

$$P_1P : PP_2 = A_1A : AA_2.$$

But $P_1P : PP_2 = r_1 : r_2$ by hypothesis. Also, by § 7, $A_1A = x - x_1$ and $AA_2 = x_2 - x$. This gives

$$\frac{r_1}{r_2} = \frac{x - x_1}{x_2 - x}.$$

Solving for x,

$$x = \frac{r_1x_2 + r_2x_1}{r_1 + r_2}.$$

The formula for y is derived in a similar manner, by drawing perpendiculars from P_1, P, and P_2 to the y-axis.

When P is the mid-point of the line, $r_1 = r_2$ and these formulas become:

$$x = \tfrac{1}{2}(x_1 + x_2), \quad y = \tfrac{1}{2}(y_1 + y_2), \tag{2a}$$

which are called the *mid-point formulas*.

Exercise 4. Derive the point of division formulas for one of the cases where P does not lie between P_1 and P_2.

Exercise 5. Derive the mid-point formulas directly from a figure.

EXAMPLE. A segment joins $(-3, 6)$ to $(13, 30)$. (a) Find the point on this segment which is $\tfrac{5}{8}$ the distance from the first to the second point. (b) To what point must the segment be extended beyond $(13, 30)$ in order to increase its length by one fourth?

Solution. Let P_1 be $(-3, 6)$ and P_2 be $(13, 30)$. (a) We must find $P(x, y)$ so that $P_1P = \tfrac{5}{8}P_1P_2$. If this relation exists, we see at once that $P_1P : PP_2 = 5 : 3$.

Then, in Formula 2, $r_1 = 5$, $r_2 = 3$, $x_1 = -3$, $y_1 = 6$, $x_2 = 13$, and $y_2 = 30$. Substituting, we have

$$x = \frac{(5)(13) + (3)(-3)}{5 + 3} = 7$$

and

$$y = \frac{(5)(30) + (3)(6)}{5 + 3} = 21.$$

Thus the first required point is $(7, 21)$.

(b) If, in this case, P denotes the end of the extended segment, we have $P_1P = \frac{5}{4}P_1P_2$. But since P lies without P_1P_2, P_1P and PP_2 are of unlike signs. Hence

$$\frac{P_1P}{PP_2} = \frac{5}{-1} = \frac{-5}{1}.$$

Taking $r_1 = 5$ and $r_2 = -1$, we find from the formula that

$$x = \frac{(5)(13) + (-1)(-3)}{5 - 1} = 17$$

and

$$y = \frac{(5)(30) + (-1)(6)}{5 - 1} = 36.$$

Hence the required point is $(17, 36)$. The same result is obtained if we take $r_1 = -5$ and $r_2 = 1$.

10. Applications to geometric proofs. By means of these formulas and others which will follow, many of the theorems of plane geometry can be proved in a very simple manner.

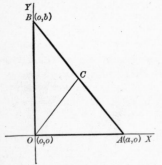

EXAMPLE. Show by analytic means that the mid-point of the hypotenuse of any right triangle is equidistant from the vertices.

Solution. Let the lengths of the legs be a and b. Let the coördinate axes be taken along the legs of the triangle. Then the vertices are $(0, 0)$, $(a, 0)$, $(0, b)$. Let C be the mid-point of the hypotenuse. By Formula 2a its coördinates are $\left(\frac{a}{2}, \frac{b}{2}\right)$. The distance formula gives,

$$OC = \sqrt{\frac{a^2}{4} + \frac{b^2}{4}} = \frac{1}{2}\sqrt{a^2 + b^2}.$$

The same result is obtained for CB and AC, which proves the theorem.

Note. In this problem the coördinates of the vertices were expressed by letters so as to insure that OBA should represent *any* right triangle. This procedure must be followed in all such problems in order to make the proof general and not merely a verification of a special case. The particular choice of coördinate axes obviously does not affect the size or shape of a figure.

PROBLEMS

1. Show that the triangle whose vertices are $(-4, 16)$, $(2, 6)$, and $(12, 12)$ is isosceles.

Solution. Using the distance formula, we let P_1 be $(-4, 16)$ and P_2 be $(2, 6)$. Then $x_1 = -4$, $y_1 = 16$, $x_2 = 2$, and $y_2 = 6$. Substituting, we have

$$d_1 = \sqrt{(-4 - 2)^2 + (16 - 6)^2} = \sqrt{136} = 2\sqrt{34}.$$

Applying the same formula to the points $(-4, 16)$ and $(12, 12)$, we find

$$d_2 = \sqrt{(-4 - 12)^2 + (16 - 12)^2} = \sqrt{272} = 4\sqrt{17}.$$

Similarly the distance between $(2, 6)$ and $(12, 12)$ is

$$d_3 = \sqrt{(2 - 12)^2 + (6 - 12)^2} = \sqrt{136} = 2\sqrt{34}.$$

Since $d_1 = d_3$, the triangle is isosceles.

In solving problems a figure should always be drawn, because it often suggests a means of solving the problem or of shortening the solution and it always furnishes a check on the accuracy of arithmetical work. In this problem a figure would show that d_2 cannot possibly be equal to either of the other sides and hence it was unnecessary to find its length.

2. Find the lengths of the sides of the triangles whose vertices are

(a) $(8, 6)$, $(4, 4)$, $(-6, 10)$; (d) $(4, 5)$, $(-4, -1)$, $(2, -9)$;
(b) $(-3, 1)$, $(5, 7)$, $(9, 4)$; (e) $(2, 5)$, $(8, -1)$, $(-4, -5)$;
(c) $(5, 4)$, $(0, -8)$, $(-6, 0)$; (f) $(0, 0)$, $(a, 0)$, (b, c).

3. Find the perimeter of each of the triangles in Problem 2.

4. Show that the following are the vertices of isosceles triangles:

(a) $(-7, -6)$, $(1, 6)$, $(5, -14)$; (c) $(0, 7)$, $(5, 2)$, $(-4, -2)$.

(b) $(-2, 2)$, $(5, -3)$, $(-7, -5)$;

5. Show that $(5, 5)$, $(-5, -5)$, $(5\sqrt{3}, -5\sqrt{3})$ are the vertices of an equilateral triangle and find the length of a median.

6. In each triangle in Problem 2 find the length of the median from the first vertex.

7. Show that $(4, 2)$, $(13, 14)$, $(-4, 8)$ are the vertices of a right triangle and find the area of the triangle.

8. Find the area of the triangle whose vertices are $(-2, -6)$, $(-7, 6)$ and $(5, 11)$.

9. Show that $(-4, 6)$, $(6, 10)$, $(10, 0)$, and $(0, -4)$ are the vertices of a square.

10. Show that $(-4, -5)$, $(10, -3)$, and $(2 + 5\sqrt{3}, 8)$ lie on a circle whose center is $(2, 3)$.

11. Show by the distance formula that $(-4, 1)$, $(2, -2)$, and $(10, -6)$ lie on a straight line. In what ratio does the second point divide the segment from the first to the third?

12. Find the coördinates of the point dividing in the ratio 2 : 3 the segment from the first point to the second:

(a) $(-5, 6)$ and $(10, -8)$; (c) $(0, 12)$ and $(12, -8)$;

(b) $(4, -1)$ and $(-8, 7)$; (d) $(0, 0)$ and $(-15, 4)$.

13. In each of the following find the coördinates of the point on the line through the given points whose distance from the first point is two thirds of the distance from the first point to the second:

(a) $(1, 8)$ and $(10, -4)$; (c) $(5, 0)$ and $(-9, -6)$;

(b) $(-2, 5)$ and $(8, -7)$; (d) $(0, 0)$ and (a, b).

14. Find two positions of the point $P(x, y)$ on the line passing through $A(-7, 4)$ and $B(3, -8)$ such that the distance between A and P is three times the distance between B and P.

15. In each triangle in Problem 2 find the coördinates of the point of intersection of the medians.

Hint. In plane geometry we learn that the point of intersection of the medians is two thirds of the distance from a vertex to the middle of the opposite side.

16. Two vertices of a parallelogram are $(0, 0)$ and $(a, 0)$, and the diagonals meet at (b, c). Find the coördinates of the other vertices.

17. What are the lengths of the segments into which the x-axis divides the segment joining $(0, -7)$ and $(8, 5)$?

18. If P, P_1, and P_2 lie on a directed line and $r = P_1P/P_1P_2$, prove that $x = x_1 + r(x_2 - x_1)$ and $y = y_1 + r(y_2 - y_1)$.

19. The ends of the base of an isosceles triangle are $(-5, 2)$ and $(2, -5)$ and the length of each of the other sides is 13. Find the coördinates of the third vertex.

Hint. In this and the three following problems let $P(x, y)$ be the unknown point and find two equations satisfied by x and y.

20. Find the coördinates of the point equidistant from the points $(16, 6)$, $(9, 13)$, and $(-1, -11)$.

21. Three vertices of a rectangle are $(0, 0)$, $(6, 3)$, and $(-2, 4)$. Find the coördinates of the fourth vertex.

22. Two vertices of an equilateral triangle are $(-5, 6)$ and $(5, -4)$. Find the coördinates of the third vertex.

23. Prove analytically that:

(a) the diagonals of a rectangle are equal;

(b) the diagonals of an isosceles trapezoid are equal;

(c) the diagonals of a parallelogram bisect each other;

(d) the medians from the ends of the base of an isosceles triangle are equal.

24. Prove analytically that in any triangle:

(a) the square of the side opposite an acute angle is equal to the sum of the squares of the other two sides decreased by twice the product of one of those sides and the projection of the other upon it;

(b) the sum of the squares of two sides is equal to twice the square of one half the third side, increased by twice the square of the median on that side;

(c) the sum of the squares of the medians is equal to three fourths the sum of the squares of the three sides.

25. Prove analytically that:

(a) the sum of the squares of the four sides of a parallelogram is equal to the sum of the squares of the diagonals;

(b) the sum of the squares of the four sides of any quadrilateral is equal to the sum of the squares of the diagonals increased by four times the square of the line joining the mid-points of the diagonals.

26. Let $O = (0, 0)$, $A = (a, 0)$, and $B = (a + b, 0)$. Let OCA, ADB, and OEB be isosceles triangles whose bases are on the x-axis and whose base angles are each 30°, C and D lying in the first quadrant, and E in the fourth. Prove that CDE is equilateral.

Hint. $\sin 30° = \frac{1}{2}$ and $\cos 30° = \sqrt{3}/2$.

11. Angle between two lines.

The angle of intersection of two directed lines is understood to be the angle between their

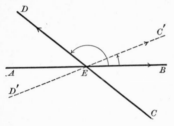

positive directions; i.e., if two lines intersect, their angle of intersection is that one of the four angles formed for which the sides are positive *if read from the point of intersection.* Thus, in the figure the angle of intersection of AB and CD is BED. The object of this convention is to avoid ambiguity and its effect is to keep the value of any angle between 0° and 180°. For example, suppose the line CD to be rotated around E so that the angle BED increases from 0° until ED reaches and passes the position EA. After that the positive direction on CD becomes EC' and the angle between the lines is BEC'.

12. Inclination and slope.

The inclination of a line is its angle of intersection with the x-axis. If it is parallel to the x-axis, its inclination is zero. By a well-known theorem of geometry, the angle of inclination of a line is also its angle of intersection with any line parallel to the x-axis.

The slope of a line is the tangent of its inclination. We denote the inclination by the Greek letter α (alpha), the slope by m. Thus $m = \tan \alpha$. When m is positive, α is acute and the line extends *upward* to the right; when m is negative, α is obtuse, and the line extends *downward* to the right.

The slope fixes the direction of a line. Hence a line is determined when its slope and one point on it are known.

13. The slope formula. Theorem. *The slope of a line passing through the points $P_1(x_1,\ y_1)$ and $P_2(x_2,\ y_2)$ is given by the formula*

$$m = \frac{y_1 - y_2}{x_1 - x_2}. \tag{3}$$

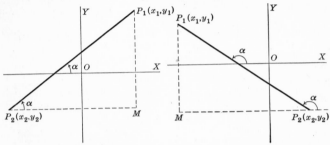

Proof. In both figures

$$\tan \alpha = \frac{MP_1}{P_2M}.$$

Now, by § 7, $\qquad MP_1 = y_1 - y_2,$

and $\qquad\qquad P_2M = x_1 - x_2.$

Substituting, we have the formula.

Exercise 6. Derive the slope formula when

(a) P_1 is in the fourth quadrant and P_2 in the second;

(b) P_1 is in the second quadrant and P_2 in the third;

(c) P_1 is in the third quadrant and P_2 in the fourth;

(d) both points are in the first quadrant and the inclination is greater than 90°.

Exercise 7. State in words the rule expressed by the slope formula.

14. Applications of the slope formula. 1. *To find the slope and inclination of a line through two given points.* To solve this problem we simply substitute the coördinates of the points in the formula and look up the corresponding inclination. For example, consider the line passing through $(-5, 6)$ and $(11, -6)$. Formula 3 gives at once

$$m = \frac{6 + 6}{-5 - 11} = -\frac{3}{4} = -0.7500.$$

The inclination is the angle whose tangent is $- 0.7500$. We recall from trigonometry that this is the supplement of the angle whose tangent is $+ 0.7500$, which is $36° 52'$. Hence $\alpha = 180° - 36° 52' = 143° 8'$.

2. *To draw a line through a given point with a given slope.* This is easily done with the aid of the slope formula and its

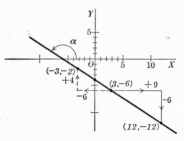

proof. For example, consider the line through $(3, - 6)$ with slope $- \frac{2}{3}$. Since the slope formula shows that the slope is merely the difference of the ordinates divided by the difference of the abscissas taken in the same order, another point on the line is that 3 units to the right and 2 units below $(3, - 6)$, namely $(6, - 8)$. As $- \frac{2}{3} = - \frac{4}{6} = - \frac{6}{9}$, etc., we also get points on the line by counting 6 units to the right and 4 down, or 9 to the right and 6 down, etc. We may also count 6 to the left and 4 up, etc.

15. Parallelism and perpendicularity. Theorem. *If two lines are parallel their slopes are equal, and conversely; if they are perpendicular their slopes are negative reciprocals, and conversely.*

Proof. If l_1 and l_2 are parallel, obviously $\alpha_1 = \alpha_2$; hence the slopes are equal.

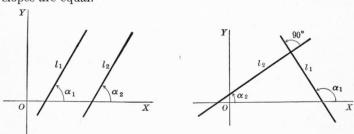

If l_1 is perpendicular to l_2, we have $\alpha_1 = \alpha_2 + 90°$. Since $\tan (\alpha + 90°) = - \cot \alpha$ by trigonometry,

$$\tan \alpha_1 = \tan (\alpha_2 + 90°) = - \cot \alpha_2 = - \frac{1}{\tan \alpha_2}.$$

Substitution of m_1 and m_2 gives

$$m_1 = - \frac{1}{m_2}, \quad \text{or} \quad m_1 m_2 = - 1.$$

Let the student prove the converse theorems.

Summarizing, we have:

Test for parallelism,

$$m_1 = m_2; \tag{4}$$

Test for perpendicularity,

$$m_1 m_2 = - 1. \tag{5}$$

16. The angle formula. Theorem. *The angle β between two lines is given by the formula*

$$\tan \beta = \frac{m_1 - m_2}{1 + m_1 m_2}, \tag{6}$$

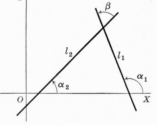

m_1 denoting the slope of the line of greater inclination.

Proof. Obviously $\alpha_1 = \alpha_2 + \beta$ and $\beta = \alpha_1 - \alpha_2$; hence

$$\tan \beta = \tan (\alpha_1 - \alpha_2) = \frac{\tan \alpha_1 - \tan \alpha_2}{1 + \tan \alpha_1 \tan \alpha_2} = \frac{m_1 - m_2}{1 + m_1 m_2}.$$

NOTE. When the inclinations are known, it is obvious from the above that $\beta = \alpha_1 - \alpha_2$ may be used as an alternative to Formula 6.

Exercise 8. Derive the angle formula for the case when the point of intersection is below the x-axis.

EXAMPLE. Find the angles of the triangle whose vertices are $A(7, 5)$, $B(- 11, 6)$, and $C(3, - 2)$.

Solution. The triangle is illustrated in the figure on page 18. By means of the slope formula we find at once that the slopes of AB, CB, and CA are respectively $- \frac{1}{18}$, $- \frac{4}{7}$, and $\frac{7}{4}$. Since the product of the last two is $- 1$, the angle BCA is 90° by Formula 5.

At A the angle given by Formula 6 is DAB, since the positive direction from A on the side CA is AD and not AC. The inclination of AD is acute and that of AB is obtuse, hence we set $m_1 = $ slope $AB = -\frac{1}{18}$ and $m_2 = \frac{7}{4}$. Then Formula 6 gives

$$\tan DAB = \tan \beta = \frac{-\frac{1}{18} - \frac{7}{4}}{1 - \frac{7}{72}} = -2.$$

The tables give $DAB = 180° - 63° 26'$, whence $BAC = 63° 26'$.

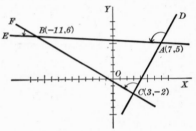

Since ABC is a right triangle, angle ABC is the complement of angle BAC. By finding it directly, however, we can use this fact as a check on our work.

At the vertex B angle "β" of Formula 6 is the angle EBF, which is equal to the required angle ABC. The larger inclination is that of AB; hence $m_1 = $ slope $AB = -\frac{1}{18}$ and $m_2 = -\frac{4}{7}$. Therefore

$$\tan ABC = \frac{-\frac{1}{18} + \frac{4}{7}}{1 + \frac{4}{126}} = \frac{1}{2} = 0.5000.$$

Hence $\qquad\qquad ABC = 26° 34'.$

Check: $\qquad\qquad ABC + BCA + CAB = 180°.$

PROBLEMS

1. Find the slope and the inclination of the line passing through

(a) $(-3, 5)$, $(7, 10)$;   (d) $(1, 8)$, $(5, 0)$;

(b) $(-1, -9)$, $(7, -3)$;   (e) $(-2, 5)$, $(10, -1)$;

(c) $(-2, -4)$, $(2, 8)$;   (f) $(1, 1)$, $(11, -3)$.

2. Find the slope and the inclination of the line passing through

(a) $(4, 4)$, $(13, -5)$;   (d) $(0, -4)$, $(-5\sqrt{3}, 1)$;

(b) $(-3, 2)$, $(4, 9)$;   (e) $(5, 0)$, $(-5, 10\sqrt{3})$;

(c) $(5, 0)$, $(9, -4\sqrt{3})$;   (f) $(0, 6)$, $(3\sqrt{3}, 3)$.

3. Prove that $(3, 2)$, $(7, -4)$, and $(-1, 8)$ are on the same straight line.

4. Prove without using the mid-point formulas that $(1, -1)$ is the mid-point of the segment joining $(6, 6)$ and $(-4, -8)$.

5. What are the inclinations of the lines perpendicular to those in Problem 2?

6. Prove that the line joining $(-3, 6)$ and $(9, 1)$ is perpendicular to the one joining $(0, 0)$ and $(5, 12)$.

7. Find the angle between a line of inclination $135°$ and each of the lines in Problem 2.

8. Find the angle between a line of inclination $40°$ and each of the lines in Problem 2.

9. Find the angle between a line of slope -3 and each of the lines in Problem 1.

10. Find the angle between a line of slope -2 and each of the lines in Problem 1.

11. Prove that the following points are vertices of a right triangle and find its acute angles:

    (a) $(5, 0)$, $(8, 4)$, $(-4, 13)$;

    (b) $(-6, -4)$, $(-1, 4)$, $(15, -6)$;

    (c) $(1, -6)$, $(8, 8)$, $(-7, -2)$;

    (d) (a, b), $(a + c, b + d)$, $(a + c - d, b + d + c)$.

12. Find the angles of the parallelogram which has the following vertices:

    (a) $(-6, -5)$, $(2, 1)$, $(14, 11)$, $(6, 5)$;

    (b) $(0, 3)$, $(9, 8)$, $(2, 11)$, $(-7, 6)$;

    (c) $(-2, -2)$, $(0, 2)$, $(8, 5)$, $(6, 1)$;

    (d) $(1, 1)$, $(-4, 7)$, $(4, 4)$, $(9, -2)$.

13. Find the angles of the triangle whose vertices are:

    (a) $(2, 6)$, $(6, 0)$, $(-3, 8)$;   (c) $(-2, 2)$, $(5, 5)$, $(8, -6)$;

    (b) $(0, 0)$, $(-8, 8)$, $(4, 10)$;   (d) $(0, 7)$, $(6, 1)$, $(-4, -3)$.

14. Find the slope of a line making an angle of $45°$ with each line in Problem 1.

15. The slopes of two lines are -2 and 3. Find the slope of the line bisecting the angle between them.

16. The base of a triangle extends from (0, 0) to (12, 0) and the slopes of the other sides are $\frac{3}{4}$ and $-\frac{2}{3}$. Find the coördinates of the vertex.

17. Find a point on the segment joining $(-7, -6)$ to $(9, 6)$ and 4 units distant from the former point.

18. Segments are drawn from two opposite vertices of a parallelogram to the points trisecting the diagonal joining the other vertices. Prove analytically that the figure thus formed is a parallelogram.

19. The broken line $ABCDE$ has somewhat the form of the letter W. The angles ABC and CDE are right angles, $AB = BC$, $CD = DE$, and the positions of points B and D are known. Show that it is possible to locate the position of the mid-point of the segment AE.

20. Prove analytically that

(*a*) the diagonals of any square are perpendicular;

(*b*) the median of a trapezoid is parallel to the bases;

(*c*) the lines joining the mid-points of the sides of any quadrilateral form a parallelogram;

(*d*) the lines joining the mid-points of the sides of a rectangle form a rhombus.

CHAPTER II

CURVES AND EQUATIONS

17. Introduction. The coördinates x and y, if no restriction is placed on their values, represent any point in the plane. If, however, the values of x and y are subject to certain conditions, points having these coördinates will lie upon certain lines or curves. For example, if y is unrestricted but x always equals -6, all such points will lie upon a line parallel to the y-axis and 6 units to the left. Again, the locus of all points whose abscissas and ordinates are equal is the bisector of the first and third quadrants. Such restrictions upon coördinates are expressed by means of equations. Thus, the equation of the first locus is $x = -6$, of the second $x = y$. As a general definition, we have:

An equation of a locus is an equation which is satisfied by the coördinates of each point on the locus, and by those of no other point. The last part of this definition is equivalent to the statement that all points whose coördinates satisfy the equation lie on the locus. *The curve which contains all points whose coördinates satisfy the given equation and no other points is called the locus or graph of the equation.**

The derivation of equations of loci and the study of graphs by means of their equations form the chief part of elementary analytic geometry.

REMARKS. It is clear from the above definitions that the locus of a given equation is unique. The situation with regard to equations of curves or loci is not so simple. It is easily seen that not only is $x = -6$ an equation of the line which is parallel to the y-axis and 6 units to the left, but so also are $x + 6 = 0$, $8x + 48 = 0$, and $(x + 6)^2 = 0$. However, it is shown in higher algebra that, if a curve has an algebraic equation,

---

* By this association of a curve with its equation Descartes (1596–1650) invented analytic geometry.

there is always a lowest degree such that any two equations of the curve of this degree can be transformed into each other by transposing terms and multiplying by a constant. In the above example this is true of $x = -6$, $x + 6 = 0$, and $8x + 48 = 0$. These are regarded as merely different forms of one equation and it is customary to call such an equation of lowest degree *the* equation of the locus. This usage will be followed here.

As already indicated, transposition of terms in an equation and multiplication or division of both members by a constant which is not zero do not alter the locus of the equation. Such operations are called *reversible*. On the other hand multiplication or division by an expression containing a variable and squaring an equation may change the locus. For example, the locus of the equation $x = y$ is not the same as that of $x^2 = xy$, since the latter equation is satisfied by the coördinates of all points on the y-axis, as well as those on the line whose equation is $x = y$. In practice the ordinary operations on equations give no trouble, if reasonable care is exercised.

18. Plotting of graphs. When a locus is given by its equation, the shape of the curve is sometimes evident from the form of the equation, as in examples mentioned above, and as we shall see in more complicated problems later. Usually the graph is constructed by a process called plotting the graph of the equation, in which we proceed as follows:

Solve the equation for y in terms of x.

Set x equal to convenient positive and negative values (generally integral) *and compute the corresponding values of y.* Each pair of values of x and y is a solution of the equation, and hence the point of which these are the coördinates lies on the curve by the definition of the locus.

Make a table of values by arranging these pairs in order according to the magnitudes of the values of x.

Plot the points thus tabulated and join them by a smooth curve in the order of the table. This gives an approximation to the true curve which becomes more exact when a large number of points is plotted.

REMARKS. It is sometimes more convenient to solve for x in terms of y. In this case the above is applicable on interchanging x and y.

If the solution for y in terms of x involves a square root, the double sign must be used with the radical and in general two points will be found for each value of x. A similar remark applies to a solution for x in terms of y.

The scale on which the curve is drawn must be small enough so that the tabulated points will fall within the limits of the paper, but it should not be chosen so small that the drawing cannot be well done.

Sometimes the values of either x or y will be so large that it is impossible to draw a smooth curve through the plotted points. In this case use one scale for x and another for y. This should not be done unless necessary, for the figure thus drawn will not be a true image of the locus, but will be a distortion much like the distortions produced by cylindrical mirrors.

When the points plotted do not appear to lie on a smooth curve, look for an error in the table of values. If there is no error, assume intermediate fractional values of x or y and plot the corresponding points.

The table of values should be extensive enough to show the form of the curve completely. If it extends to infinity, the plot should contain all parts with considerable curvature and should extend far enough to show the direction of the curve beyond the limits of the paper.

EXAMPLE 1. Plot the graph of $3x + y - 4 = 0$.

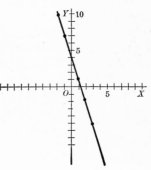

Solving for y,

$$y = -3x + 4.$$

x	y
-2	10
-1	7
0	4
1	1
2	-2
3	-5

Substituting $x = -2$, -1, 0, 1, 2, 3, we get $y = 10$, 7, 4, 1, -2, -5 respectively. Thus points on the line are $(-2, 10)$, $(-1, 7)$, $(0, 4)$, etc. The table of values is at the left and the plot at the right.

EXAMPLE 2. Plot the graph of $5y^2 - 10y = x - 15$.

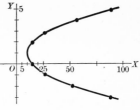

y	x
-3	90
-2	55
-1	30
0	15
1	10
2	15
3	30
4	55
5	90

Here it is easier to solve for x in terms of y:

$$x = 5y^2 - 10y + 15.$$

In the plot each unit on the y-axis has been taken equal to 10 units on the x-axis. This is because the values of x are so much larger than those of y that, if the same scale were used on both axes, it would be impossible to draw the curve on a small sheet of paper.

The scale used should be indicated on the graph.

EXAMPLE 3. Plot the graph of $4x^2 + y^2 = 20$.

Solving for y in terms of x, we get:

$$y = \pm \sqrt{20 - 4x^2}$$
$$= \pm 2\sqrt{5 - x^2}.$$

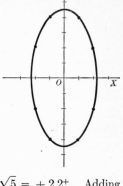

x	y
-3	imag.
-2	± 2
-1	± 4
0	$\pm 2\sqrt{5}$
	$= \pm 4.5$
1	± 4
2	± 2
3	imag.

Here y is imaginary when $x = \pm 3$, but there are two points corresponding to each of the values $x = \pm 2$. To find out where the curve crosses the x-axis, we set $y = 0$ in the equation and solve, getting $x = \pm \sqrt{5} = \pm 2.2^+$. Adding the points $(2.2^+, 0)$ and $(-2.2^+, 0)$ to the plot, we are able to draw the entire curve.

EXAMPLE 4. Plot the graph of $xy = -4$, or $y = -\dfrac{4}{x}$.

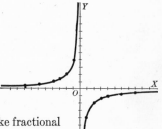

x	y	x	y
1	-4	-1	4
2	-2	-2	2
3	$-\frac{4}{3}$	-3	$\frac{4}{3}$
4	-1	-4	1
6	$-\frac{2}{3}$	-6	$\frac{2}{3}$
8	$-\frac{1}{2}$	-8	$\frac{1}{2}$

Since x cannot equal 0,* we must take fractional values of x between ± 1 in order to find the shape of the curve. These give additional points:

x	y	x	y
$\frac{1}{2}$	-8	$-\frac{1}{2}$	8
$\frac{1}{4}$	-16	$-\frac{1}{4}$	16

Adding these to the plot, we see that the curve extends to infinity along the x- and y-axes in the second and fourth quadrants.

* This is due to the fact that the substitution of $x = 0$ in the equation involves division by 0, an impossible operation. Since y becomes indefinitely great as x *approaches* 0, it is sometimes stated that for $x = 0$, $y = \infty$, but this abbreviation should not be allowed to obscure the fact that for $x = 0$ there is *no* point on the curve.

19. Equations containing arbitrary constants. Consider the equation $4x^2 + y^2 = a^2$. For each value of a this equation has a locus. When $a = \sqrt{20}$, we have the closed curve of Example 3 above; when $a = 5$, we have a similar curve, somewhat larger than the one in the figure, etc. The letter a is called an *arbitrary* constant, since real values may be assigned to it at pleasure. As we shall see later, the loci of equations of a given form constitute a class or *system* of curves having many properties in common and frequently of the same general shape. Thus the graph of any equation of the form $4x^2 + y^2 = a^2$ is an ellipse twice as long as it is wide.

In plotting such an equation we set the arbitrary constant equal to a convenient value and proceed as in § 18. The value of the arbitrary constant chosen should not be zero, as this value will generally not show the properties of the system. For a similar reason, if there are two arbitrary constants, the same value should not be used for both.

PROBLEMS

Plot the graphs of the following equations:

1. $x = 0$.
2. $y = 8$.
3. $y = -3x$.
4. $2x - 3y = 0$.
5. $x + y = 12$.
6. $5x - 4y = 40$.
7. $y = x^2$.
8. $y^2 = 12x$.
9. $4y = 16 - x^2$.
10. $4y = x^2 - 8x + 8$.
11. $9x + 2y^2 - 8y = 10$.
12. $x^2 + y^2 = 100$.
13. $x^2 - 12x + y^2 = 0$.
14. $x^2 + 4y^2 = 36$.
15. $25x^2 + 9y^2 = 225$.

16. $x^2 - 12x + 4y^2 = 0$.
17. $2x^2 + y^2 = 2$.
18. $4x^2 + y^2 - 6y = 16$.
19. $x^2 - y^2 = 16$.
20. $x^2 - y^2 + 9 = 0$.
21. $16x^2 - 9y^2 + 144 = 0$.
22. $x^2 - 6x - 4y^2 = 0$.
23. $y^3 = 8x$.
24. $x^3 + 4y^2 = 0$.
25. $10y = x^3 - 9x$.
26. $10y = x^3 + 9x$.
27. $2y = x^3 - 5x^2$.
28. $4y = (x + 4)(x - 2)(x - 3)$.
29. $10y = x^4 - 12x^2$.
30. $y^2 = x^4 - 9x^2$.

31. $x^2y + 16y = 64.$

32. $x^2y + 4y = 8x.$

33. $xy = 24.$

34. $xy + 24 = 0.$

35. $xy + 4y = 12.$

36. $xy + 2x - 3y = 30.$

37. $x^2y = 48.$

38. $(x + 4)y^2 = 16.$

39. $xy = x^2 + 6.$

40. $5xy = x^3 + 4.$

41. $x^2y - 4y = x.$

42. $(y - 4x)^2 = 8x^3.$

43. $y = mx.$

44. $y = ax^2.$ $(a > 0.)$

45. $y = ax^2.$ $(a < 0.)$

46. $y^2 = ax.$ $(a > 0.)$

47. $y^2 = ax.$ $(a < 0.)$

48. $y = ax^3.$ $(a > 0.)$

49. $y = ax^3.$ $(a < 0.)$

50. $y^2 = ax^3.$

51. $x^2 + y^2 = a^2.$

52. $\dfrac{x^2}{a^2} + \dfrac{y^2}{b^2} = 1.$

53. $\dfrac{x^2}{a^2} - \dfrac{y^2}{b^2} = 1.$

54. $xy = a.$ $(a > 0.)$

55. $xy = a.$ $(a < 0.)$

56. $y = x^3 - a^2x.$

57. $x^2y = a^2.$

58. $y = x^3 - ax^2.$

59. Which ones of the first twenty curves given above contain the origin?

60. Prove that, if $P(x, y)$ is any point on the locus of $y^2 = 8x$, then the distance between P and the point $(2, 0)$ is $x + 2$.

61. Prove that, if $P(x, y)$ is any point on the locus of $y = 2x$, then the difference of the squares of the distances of P from the points $(-2, 1)$ and $(4, -2)$ is 15.

62. Prove that, if $P(x, y)$ is any point on the locus of $x^2 + y^2 = 100$, then the lines joining P to $(10, 0)$ and $(-10, 0)$ are perpendicular.

20. Derivation of equations. When a curve is not given by means of its equation, it is often defined as the locus of a point satisfying certain definite conditions. Thus the circumference of a circle is the locus of a point at a given distance (the radius) from a fixed point (the center). To find the equation of a curve defined as a locus, we must translate the definition into algebraic language and obtain as a result an equation in x and y *satisfied by the coördinates of every point on the locus and by those of no other point.* No rule can be stated which will automatically yield a solution of every such problem, but the following general directions should be followed as far as practicable.

1. *Take the origin and axes in a convenient position.* The origin will usually be a fixed point mentioned in the problem, or the point midway between two such points, with one of the axes passing through them. This does not involve any loss of generality as far as the *locus* is concerned, since the locus is independent of the position of the coördinate axes; but a correct choice of axes will greatly simplify the form of the equation and the work of deriving it.

2. *Designate by P(x, y) any point satisfying the given conditions and therefore on the curve.* This must not be a point in some special position, as on one of the coördinate axes, unless the problem expressly requires such a location.

3. *Draw any lines suggested by the data of the problem.* These lines may suggest auxiliary construction. It is often helpful to draw the perpendiculars from P to the coördinate axes.

4. *Express the conditions of the problem in an equation which contains x, y, and the given constants, or which can be reduced to such a form.* For this purpose it will be necessary to find some formula or principle of geometry relating to the coördinates, the given constants, and the auxiliary lines.

5. *Simplify the equation.* It should contain all the given arbitrary constants, but *no variables other than x and y.*

EXAMPLE 1. Find the equation of the circle * of radius 6 whose center is $(7, -4)$.

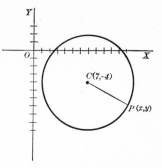

Solution. We are to find the equation of the locus of a point whose distance from the point $(7, -4)$ is always 6. Here the coördinate axes are fixed by the statement of the problem. Take any point $P(x, y)$ as one satisfying the conditions of the problem and draw PC. Then $PC = 6.$

* In analytic geometry the word *circle* always means the same thing as *circumference.*

Applying the distance formula gives at once

$$\sqrt{(x-7)^2+(y+4)^2} = 6,$$

or $$(x-7)^2+(y+4)^2 = 36.$$

We can either plot the curve by points, or, since we know that it is a circle, draw it with compasses.

EXAMPLE 2. A rock in the ocean lies 6 miles off a stretch of straight coast and a ship moves so as to be always equidistant from the rock and the coast. Find the locus of the ship.

Solution. Take the coast for the x-axis and let the y-axis pass through the rock, which will have the coördinates $(0, 6)$. Take a point $P(x, y)$ and draw its ordinate AP. Then $OA = x$, $AP = y$. P is to be equidistant from R and OX. This suggests drawing RP, AP being already drawn. By the conditions of the problem $RP = AP$. To get the length of RP use the distance formula, which gives

$$RP = \sqrt{x^2+(y-6)^2}. \quad \text{But its equal } AP = y.$$
$$\therefore \ \sqrt{x^2+(y-6)^2} = y, \text{ whence } x^2-12y+36 = 0.$$

We have now found the *equation* of the locus. To complete the solution, the graph of the equation should be plotted. As a partial check on the work, various points of the graph can be tested to see whether or not they satisfy the conditions of the problem. For example, in the figure below measurement shows that AP and RP have the same length.

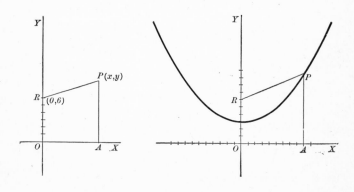

Example 3. A fixed point and a fixed line at a distance p from the point are given. Find the locus of a point which is always equidistant from the given point and the given line.

Solution. This is obviously a generalization of Example 2. Let the fixed line be the x-axis and the fixed point be $(0, p)$. We can use the figure of Example 2 if we understand that R designates $(0, p)$, which is any point on the y-axis except the origin. Then as before, we have

$$RP = AP,$$

whence

$$\sqrt{x^2 + (y - p)^2} = y,$$

or

$$x^2 - 2py + p^2 = 0.$$

The graph of this equation is the same as that of Example 2 when $p = 6$; for other values of p we have similar curves.

The derivation of the above equations shows that the coordinates of all points which lie on the locus satisfy the equation obtained. To show that the equation fulfills the second requirement of the definition of the locus, namely, that any point the coördinates of which satisfy the equation lies on the locus, it is sufficient to prove that the various steps taken in the derivation of the equation can be retraced. To illustrate, in Example 2 any point $P(x, y)$, whose coördinates satisfy the equation $x^2 - 12y + 36 = 0$, must also satisfy the previous equation since it can be reduced to that form by reversing the steps by which the latter was obtained. But the relation $\sqrt{x^2 + (y - 6)^2} = y$ simply says that the point P is equidistant from the x-axis and R, which was the condition stated in the problem.

PROBLEMS

1. What is the equation of a straight line

(a) parallel to the x-axis and 5 units below it;

(b) parallel to the y-axis and a units distant from it?

2. Solve Example 2 on page 28 when

(a) the origin is at the rock;

(b) the origin is midway between the rock and the shore.

3. Find and plot the equation of the locus of points equidistant from

(a) (5, 8) and (− 5, 4);
(b) (4, 7) and (10, 3);
(c) (2, 3) and (5, − 3);
(d) (6, 0) and (− 3, 3);
(e) (− 4, 2) and (8, − 4);
(f) (8, 6) and (6, 8);
(g) (a, 0) and (0, − a);
(h) (a, b) and (b, a).

4. Find and plot the equation of the circle which has

(a) the radius 4 and the center (5, 0);
(b) the radius 10 and the center (6, − 2);
(c) the radius 6 and the center (− 2, 4);
(d) the radius r and the center (h, k).

5. Find and plot the equation of the locus of points equidistant from

(a) the line y = − 8 and the point (0, 4);
(b) the line x = − 2 and the point (4, − 3);
(c) the line x = 12 and the point (0, 6);
(d) the line y = 0 and the point (0, p).

6. Find and plot the equation of the locus of points equidistant from

(a) the line y = 8 and the point (0, − 4);
(b) the line x = − 3 and the point (6, 6);
(c) the line x = 2 and the point (− 10, 0);
(d) the line x = − p and the point (0, 0).

7. Find the locus in Problem 5 when the distance from the point is twice that from the line.

8. Find the locus in Problem 6 when the distance from the point is twice that from the line.

9. Find the locus in Problem 5 when the distance from the line is twice that from the point.

10. Find the locus in Problem 6 when the distance from the line is twice that from the point.

11. Find the locus in Problem 6 when the distance from the point is 4 units less than the distance from the line.

12. Find the locus in Problem 5 when the distance from the point is 2 units less than the distance from the line.

13. Find the equation of the straight line of slope 3 which passes through

(a) (0, 4);   (b) (7, 3);   (c) (5, 4);   (d) (− 4, 6).

14. Find the equation of the straight line passing through each pair of points in Problem 3.

15. The base of a triangle is AB, where A is $(-4, 0)$ and B is $(4, 0)$. Find and plot the equation of the locus of the third vertex P, if

(a) the sum of the lengths of the other two sides is 10;

(b) the difference of the lengths of the other two sides is 6;

(c) the slope of AP is 2 less than the slope of BP;

(d) the sum of the slopes of the other two sides is 2.

16. The base of a triangle is AB, where A is $(-5, 0)$ and B is $(5, 0)$. Find and plot the equation of the locus of the third vertex P, if

(a) the vertical angle is $45°$;

(b) one base angle is twice the other;

(c) the product of the slopes of the other two sides is 1;

(d) the medians from A and B are perpendicular to each other.

17. The distance between two fixed points A and B is $2a$. Find and plot the equation of the locus of a point P moving so that

(a) $(AP)^2 + (BP)^2 = k$;   (b) $(AP)^2 - (BP)^2 = k$.

Hint. Let the points be $(\pm a, 0)$.

18. A fixed segment has the length $2a$. Find the locus of a point moving so that its distance from the mid-point of the segment is a mean proportional between its distances from the end points.

19. The base of a triangle is of length $2a$. Find the locus of the vertex if the vertical angle is $90°$.

20. The base AB of a triangle has the length a. Find the locus of the third vertex P, if AP is twice as long as BP.

21. One side of a rhombus is fixed in position and has the length a. Find the locus of the intersection of the diagonals.

21. Functional variables. The symbols used in mathematics represent two kinds of quantities, variables and constants.

A *variable* is a quantity which may have more than one value in the course of a discussion; e.g., the velocity of a falling body and the abscissa of a point moving along a curve are variable quantities.

A *constant* is a quantity having a fixed value. There are two kinds of constants: *absolute* constants, which have the same value in all problems, as 2, − 6, π; and *arbitrary* constants, which may have any value assigned, but keep the same value in a given discussion, as the quantities m_1 and m_2 in the discussion of parallel and perpendicular lines in § 15.

If one of two variables has one or more definite values corresponding to each value assigned to the other variable, the first variable is said to be a function of the second. The first variable is called the *dependent* and the second the *independent* variable. Thus the area of a circle is a function of the radius, the ordinate of a point on a curve is a function of the abscissa, the pressure of steam is a function of the temperature, etc. Such relations are commonly expressed by means of equations, as, in the case of the formula expressing the area of a circle, $A = \pi r^2$.

22. Functional notation. The expression $f(x)$ is used to denote any function of x; it is read "function of x," or "f of x." Similarly $f(x, y)$ stands for a function of both x and y. To denote a different function of x, some other letter is used, as $F(x)$ or $g(x)$. When it is possible, functional relations are usually expressed by means of equations and in this case the expression $f(x)$ may be regarded as an abbreviation for some combination of terms containing x and no other variable. It is in this sense only that we shall use the functional notation for the present.

If an equation in x and y is solved for y, we may regard x as the independent variable and y as a function of x. Thus, if x and y are connected by the relation $x^2 + 4y^2 = 4$, $y = \pm \frac{1}{2}\sqrt{4 - x^2}$ may be denoted by the abbreviation $y = f(x)$, where $f(x)$ stands for the expression $\pm \frac{1}{2}\sqrt{4 - x^2}$. The symbols $f(1)$, $f(- 2)$ represent the values of the function when 1 and − 2 respectively are substituted for x. For this function $f(1) = \pm \frac{1}{2}\sqrt{4 - 1} = \pm \frac{1}{2}\sqrt{3}$, and $\qquad f(- 2) = \pm \frac{1}{2}\sqrt{4 - 4} = 0$.

If it is not desired to solve the equation for either variable, we may transpose all terms to the first member and denote this form of the equation by the expression $f(x, y) = 0$.

PROBLEMS

1. Write the equation $2x^2 + y^2 = 4xy$ in the three forms $y = f(x)$, $x = g(y)$, and $F(x, y) = 0$.

Solution. To express y in terms of x, solve the equation for y. To do this we write the equation in the form $y^2 - 4xy + 2x^2 = 0$. This is a quadratic in y and the quadratic formula (see Introduction) gives at once:

$$y = \frac{4x \pm \sqrt{16x^2 - 8x^2}}{2} = 2x \pm x\sqrt{2}.$$

Hence $\qquad\qquad y = f(x) = 2x \pm x\sqrt{2}.$

In like manner $\qquad x = g(y) = y \pm \tfrac{1}{2}y\sqrt{2},$

and $\qquad\qquad F(x, y) = 2x^2 - 4xy + y^2 = 0.$

2. Write each of the following equations in the three forms $y = f(x)$, $x = g(y)$, and $F(x, y) = 0$:

(a) $xy - y = 4;$ (d) $4x^2 - y^2 = 4;$

(b) $x^2 + 4y^2 = 16;$ (e) $x^2 + y^2 = 6x;$

(c) $x^2 + 4x = y^2 - 6y;$ (f) $x^4 - 4x^2y + 4y^2 = 16.$

3. If $f(x) = x^4 - 3x^2 + 2$, find the value of $f(1)$, $f(2)$, $f(0)$, and $f(-x)$.

4. If $f(x) = \sin x$ and $g(x) = \cos x$, show that

(a) $f(2x) = 2f(x) \cdot g(x);$

(b) $f(x + y) = f(x) \cdot g(y) + g(x) \cdot f(y).$

5. If $f(x, y) = 3x^2 - x + y^2$, show that $f(x, -y) = f(x, y)$. Does $f(-x, y) = f(x, y)$?

6. Write a function of x and y such that

(a) $f(x, -y) = f(x, y)$ identically;

(b) $f(-x, -y) = f(x, y)$ identically;

(c) $f(-x, y) = f(x, y)$ identically.

23. Discussion of curves. Since it is possible to plot but a few points on a curve, the graph is always more or less inaccurate. Some of the properties of a curve can be found by an examination of its equation, sometimes called a *discussion*. The purpose of this discussion is threefold: it gives *exact* information regarding the curve, it furnishes a check upon the accuracy of the plot, and it usually facilitates the labor of plotting. A complete discussion of a curve in general requires the aid of the calculus. The properties that can be most conveniently studied without the calculus are the *intercepts, symmetry, extent,* and *asymptotes* of the curve.

24. Intercepts. *The intercepts of a curve are the distances from the origin to the points where it meets the axes.* In other words, the x-intercepts are the abscissas of the points where the curve meets the x-axis; the y-intercepts are the ordinates of the points where the curve meets the y-axis. Hence, to find the x-intercepts set $y = 0$ in the equation of the curve and solve for x; to find the y-intercepts set $x = 0$ and solve for y.

25. Symmetry. Definitions. *The* **axis of symmetry** *of two points is the perpendicular bisector of the line joining them. The* **center of symmetry** *of two points is the point midway between them.*

A curve is **symmetrical** *with respect to an axis (or center), if, for each point of the curve, its symmetrical point also lies on the curve.*

Thus the points $(3, 4)$ and $(-3, 4)$ are symmetrical with respect to the y-axis; $(3, 4)$ and $(3, -4)$ with respect to the x-axis; and $(3, 4)$ and $(-3, -4)$ with respect to the origin. From the figure we can readily establish the general principle:

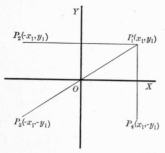

Two points are symmetrical with respect to the x-axis when their abscissas are the same and their ordinates differ only in sign; to the y-axis when their ordinates are the same and their abscissas differ only in sign; to the origin when their respective coördinates differ only in sign.

The proof is left to the student.

Applying this theorem to curves, we see that a curve is symmetrical with respect to the y-axis, if for each point (x, y) on the curve, the point $(-x, y)$ is also on the curve. The symmetry of a curve may be determined by inspection of the equation according to the following theorem:

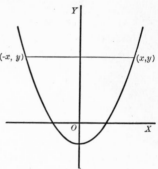

If an equation is unchanged * **by the substitution of $-x$ for x, its locus is symmetrical with respect to the y-axis.**

If an equation is unchanged by the substitution of $-y$ for y, its locus is symmetrical with respect to the x-axis.

If an equation is unchanged by the substitution of $-x$ for x and $-y$ for y, its locus is symmetrical with respect to the origin.

The proof of the first statement is as follows:

Let the equation be written in the form

$$f(x, y) = 0. \tag{1}$$

Let $P(x_1, y_1)$ be any point on the curve and $Q(-x_1, y_1)$ be its symmetrical point with respect to the y-axis. We must show that the coördinates of Q also satisfy equation (1).

If we substitute $-x$ for x in equation (1), we obtain

$$f(-x, y) = 0. \tag{2}$$

This equation is satisfied by the same values of x and y as equation (1) by hypothesis.

Now P is on the curve, hence its coördinates satisfy equation (1) and therefore equation (2). Hence the statement

$$f(-x_1, y_1) = 0$$

is true.

---

* That is, identical with the original equation or such that it is satisfied by the same values of x and y. For example, if the equation $f(x, y) = 0$ is not identical with $f(-x, y) = 0$, but $f(-x, y) = -f(x, y)$ identically, both equations are satisfied by the same values of x and y.

This means that equation (1) is verified by the substitutions $x = -x_1$, $y = y_1$. Therefore Q is also on the curve.

Thus the definition of symmetry is satisfied and the theorem is proved. The other two tests for symmetry are proved in exactly the same manner.

The figure at the top of page 35 is the graph of $x^2 - 2y - 1 = 0$, an equation satisfying the test for symmetry with respect to the y-axis. Solving for x, we have $x = \pm \sqrt{2y + 1}$, and the table of values illustrates various pairs of symmetrical points.

y	x
$-\frac{1}{2}$	0
0	± 1
1	$\pm \sqrt{3}$
2	$\pm \sqrt{5}$
4	± 3

A curve which is symmetrical with respect to both the x- and y-axes is symmetrical with respect to the origin, but the converse is not true (e.g., $y = x^3$). Moreover, a curve may have axes of symmetry other than the coördinate axes. In this case, if there are two perpendicular axes of symmetry, their intersection will be a center of symmetry.

Exercise 1. Prove that if $P_1(x_1, y_1)$ and $P_2(x_2, y_2)$ are symmetrical with respect to the x-axis, then $x_1 = x_2$, and $y_1 = -y_2$.

Exercise 2. Write a proof of the third test for symmetry.

26. Extent. To investigate the extent of a curve, we solve its equation for y in terms of x, and for x in terms of y. If either operation gives rise to radicals of even degree involving one of the variables, say x, then values of x which make the expression under the radical negative must be excluded, for the corresponding values of y would be imaginary.

EXAMPLE. Find the extent of the locus of $4x^2 - 9y^2 = 36$.

Solution. Solving for y and x, respectively, we have

$$y = \pm \tfrac{2}{3}\sqrt{x^2 - 9}, \qquad x = \pm \tfrac{3}{2}\sqrt{y^2 + 4}.$$

For $x^2 < 9$, or for values of x between ± 3, $x^2 - 9$ is negative, and therefore y is imaginary. Such values of x must be excluded from the table of values; but for any other value of x there are real values of y.

We express this by saying that the extent in x is from $-\infty$ to -3 and from $+3$ to $+\infty$.*

As $y^2 + 4 > 0$ for all values of y, no value of y needs to be excluded and the extent in y is from $-\infty$ to $+\infty$.

PROBLEMS

1. Discuss and plot the graph of $4x^2 + y^2 - 16x = 0$.

Solution. Setting $y = 0$, we find that the x-intercepts are 0 and 4; setting $x = 0$, we find that the only y-intercept is 0.

Symmetry: With respect to the x-axis.

x	y
0	0
1	± 3.5
2	± 4
3	± 3.5
4	0

Extent: Solving for x, we have

$$x = 2 \pm \tfrac{1}{2}\sqrt{16 - y^2}.$$

This shows that x is real if y^2 is not greater than 16; hence the extent in y is from -4 to $+4$.

Solving for y, we have

$$y = \pm\sqrt{16x - 4x^2} = \pm 2\sqrt{x(4 - x)}.$$

By factoring the expression under the radical, we make it easy to determine the sign of this expression for various values of x. If $x > 4$ or $x < 0$, the factors under the radical have unlike signs and their product is negative; for other values of x the product is positive or zero, and y is real. Hence the extent in x is from 0 to $+4$.

2. Discuss and plot the graph of $y = x^3 - a^2x$.

Solution. This equation contains an arbitrary constant a. It will have a different graph for each value given to a, but the properties obtained by the discussion will be common to all such curves. Therefore in treating any equation containing an arbitrary constant the discussion should be carried out without substituting a value for the arbitrary constant.

* As indicated in an earlier footnote, this does not mean that there is some point on the curve for which $x = +\infty$, but merely means that there is no upper bound to the values of x.

Intercepts: Setting $x = 0$, the y-intercept is 0. Setting $y = 0$, $x^3 - a^2x = 0$; the x-intercepts are 0, $\pm a$.

Symmetry: The substitution of $-x$ for x, or $-y$ for y, changes the equation, but if $-x$ is substituted for x and also $-y$ for y, we

get $\qquad\qquad -y = (-x)^3 - a^2(-x),$

or $\qquad\qquad -y = -x^3 + a^2x.$

This may be reduced to the original equation by multiplying through by -1. Hence the same values of x and y satisfy both equations and

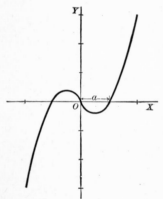

the curve is symmetrical with respect to the origin.

Extent: The equation is already solved for y and contains no radicals; hence the extent in x is from $-\infty$ to $+\infty$. Since the equation is of the third degree, there will be at least one real solution for each value of y; hence the extent in y is also from $-\infty$ to $+\infty$. If the equation is written in the form $y = x(x^2 - a^2)$, it becomes evident that when $x > a$, y is positive, and when x approaches infinity, y approaches infinity. Thus the curve extends to infinity in the first quadrant. Owing to the symmetry, the path where $x < 0$ is similar, extending to infinity in the third quadrant.

We could now sketch the curve *roughly*. A table of values for x positive gives a more accurate graph. In making the table we assign to a any convenient value, as 1.

x	y
0	0
$\frac{1}{2}$	$-\frac{3}{8}$
1	0
2	6 etc.

Discuss and plot the graphs of each of the following equations.

3. $12x - y^2 = 0$.

4. $x^2 + 8y = 0$.

5. $10y = x^2 - 25$.

6. $4y = 12 - x^2$.

7. $y^2 - 12x + 36 = 0$.

8. $5y = x^2 - 4x - 5$.

9. $4x^2 + 9y^2 = 144$.

10. $4x^2 - 9y^2 = 144$.

11. $x^2 + 4y^2 - 6x = 27$.

12. $4y^2 - x^2 = 16$.

13. $x^2 - y^2 + 8y = 0.$

14. $4x^2 - 24x + y^2 = 0.$

15. $4x^2 - 24x - y^2 = 0.$

16. $x^2 + 9y^2 - 54y = 0.$

17. $x^2 - xy + y^2 = 12.$

18. $8y = x^3.$

19. $y^2 = 8x^3.$

20. $3y = x^3 - 4x.$

21. $10y = x^3 + x.$

22. $x^2 + 2y^3 = 0.$

23. $x^3 + y^3 = 8.$

24. $x^2y + 4y = 8.$

25. (a) $y^2 = 2px;$ (b) $x^2 = 2py.$ (Parabolas)

26. $\dfrac{x^2}{a^2} + \dfrac{y^2}{b^2} = 1.$ (Ellipse)

27. (a) $\dfrac{x^2}{a^2} - \dfrac{y^2}{b^2} = 1;$ (b) $\dfrac{y^2}{a^2} - \dfrac{x^2}{b^2} = 1.$ (Hyperbolas)

28. $y = ax^3.$ (Cubical parabola)

29. $y^2 = ax^3.$ (Semicubical parabola)

30. (a) $2xy = a^2;$ (b) $2xy = -a^2.$ (Equilateral hyperbolas)

27. Horizontal and vertical asymptotes. In Example 4, page 24, we found that the curve extended indefinitely along the coördinate axes. In such cases we say that each axis is an *asymptote* of the curve. In general we have the definition:

An asymptote of a curve is a straight line approached by the curve as its tracing point recedes to infinity.

Not all curves which extend indefinitely have asymptotes (Example 2, page 28), but, when asymptotes exist, they are of considerable assistance in drawing the curve. For the present we shall consider only horizontal and vertical asymptotes, i.e., those parallel to the coördinate axes.

In order to develop a method for finding asymptotes let us take the equation $xy + x - 2y = 8$ as an example. If we solve first for y and then for x, we obtain

$$y = \frac{8 - x}{x - 2},$$

and

$$x = \frac{2y + 8}{y + 1}.$$

Inspection of the first solution shows that as x approaches 2, the numerator approaches 6 and the denominator 0; hence y be-

comes indefinitely great. Thus the line $x = 2$ is an asymptote
of the curve. In like manner the second solution shows that
$y = -1$ is an asymptote. Making a table of values and using
the asymptotes as guiding lines, we now draw the curve.

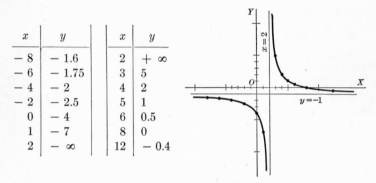

x	y		x	y
-8	-1.6		2	$+\infty$
-6	-1.75		3	5
-4	-2		4	2
-2	-2.5		5	1
0	-4		6	0.5
1	-7		8	0
2	$-\infty$		12	-0.4

The procedure employed in this example may be formulated
in the following rule:

*To find a vertical (horizontal) asymptote, solve the equation
for $y(x)$. If the solution is a fraction, set the denominator equal
to zero and solve for $x(y)$.**

In discussing the locus of an equation the asymptotes, if
any exist, should always be found.

---

* The horizontal asymptote can also be found from the solution for y in
terms of x by finding the value approached by y as x approaches infinity. If
the solution for y in terms of x contains x in both numerator and denominator,
both terms of the fraction should be divided by the highest power of x. Thus,
in the example just worked

$$y = \frac{8 - x}{x - 2}.$$

Dividing numerator and denominator by x, we have

$$y = \frac{\dfrac{8}{x} - 1}{1 - \dfrac{2}{x}}.$$

As x approaches infinity, $8/x$ and $2/x$ both approach 0; hence y approaches
$\dfrac{-1}{+1} = -1$, and $y = -1$ is the horizontal asymptote.

EXAMPLE. Discuss and plot the graph of $x^2y + 4a^2y = 8a^3$.

Solution. Solving for y and x, we have respectively:

$$y = \frac{8a^3}{x^2 + 4a^2} \quad \text{and} \quad x = \pm 2a\sqrt{\frac{2a - y}{y}}.$$

Intercepts: No x-intercept; y-intercept $2a$.

Symmetry: With respect to the y-axis.

Extent: The extent in x is obviously from $-\infty$ to $+\infty$. The solution for x shows that x is imaginary when y is negative or greater than $2a$; hence the extent in y is from 0 to $2a$.

Asymptotes: There is no vertical asymptote, since the equation $x^2 + 4a^2 = 0$ has no real root. The solution for x in terms of y shows that the line $y = 0$, or the x-axis, is an asymptote.

This curve is commonly called the *witch*. If we take a equal to 1, we obtain the following table of values and graph.

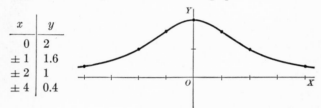

x	y
0	2
± 1	1.6
± 2	1
± 4	0.4

PROBLEMS

Find the horizontal and vertical asymptotes and plot the graphs of the following equations.

1. $xy + 4x = 8$.

2. $xy - 6y = 12$.

3. $(x - 3)^2y = x$.

4. $(x^2 - 9)y = 18$.

5. $(x^2 - 9)y = 3x$.

6. $(x - 3)^2y = x$.

7. $(x^2 - 16)y = x$.

8. $xy^2 = 8(x + 1)$.

9. $(x^2 + 9)y^2 = x^2 - 9$.

10. $x(x - 2)(x - 4)y = 3$.

11. $x^2y(y^2 - 4) = 10$.

12. $x^2y - 4y = x^2 - x$.

Discuss and plot the graphs of the following equations.

13. $xy = -a^2$.

14. $x^2y^2 = 144$.

15. $x^2y = 24$.

16. $xy^2 - y - 4x = 1$.

17. $x^2y = x^2 - 9$.

18. $x^2y = x^3 + 8$.

19. $xy = x^3 + 8$.   **21.** $x^2y + 4y = 2x^2$.

20. $x^2y + 4y = 4x$.   **22.** $x^2y = x^4 + 4$.

23. $y^2(2a - x) = x^3$. (Cissoid)

24. $y^2(a - x) = x^2(a + x)$. (Strophoid)

25. $(x - a)^2y^2 = x^3(2a - x)$. (Special case of the conchoid)

28. Symmetrical transformations. If the tests for symmetry of § 25 are not satisfied, the substitutions used will transform the given equation into a new equation.

For example, if we substitute $- x$ for x in the equation of a curve symmetrical with respect to the y-axis, the equation is unchanged; but if the curve is not symmetrical with respect to the y-axis, a new equation is obtained. The question at once arises: what relation has the locus of the new equation to that of the given equation?

In this case it can be shown as in the proof of § 25, that for any point $P(x_1, y_1)$ on the locus of the given equation $f(x, y) = 0$, the symmetrical point $Q(- x_1, y_1)$ lies on the locus of the new equation $f(- x, y) = 0$. For this reason the curves are said to be symmetrical to each other with respect to the y-axis, and the transformation is called a *symmetrical transformation*. Similar reasoning applies to the other substitutions.

Summarizing, we have the following definition and theorem:

Two curves are symmetrical to each other with respect to an axis or to a center, if, for each point of either curve, its symmetrical point lies on the other curve.

If in an equation substitution is made of

$$
\left.
\begin{array}{l}
- x \text{ for } x \\
- y \text{ for } y \\
- x \text{ for } x \text{ and } - y \text{ for } y
\end{array}
\right\}
\left\{
\begin{array}{l}
\textit{the locus of the new equa-} \\
\textit{tion is symmetrical to that} \\
\textit{of the old with respect to} \\
\textit{the}
\end{array}
\right.
\left.
\begin{array}{l}
y\text{-}axis; \\
x\text{-}axis; \\
origin.
\end{array}
\right\}
$$

EXAMPLE. Write the equation of the curve symmetrical to $y = x^2 - 5x + 6$ with respect to the y-axis, and plot both curves on the same axes.

Solution. Putting $-x$ for x, we get $y = x^2 + 5x + 6$. The continuous curve is the graph of the original equation, the dotted curve that of the new one.

Note that the table of values for $y = x^2 + 5x + 6$ may be obtained from that for $y = x^2 - 5x + 6$ by merely changing the signs of the values of x.

TABLES OF VALUES

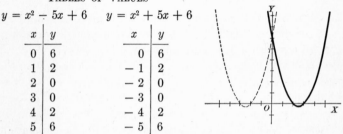

$y = x^2 - 5x + 6$		$y = x^2 + 5x + 6$	
x	y	x	y
0	6	0	6
1	2	-1	2
2	0	-2	0
3	0	-3	0
4	2	-4	2
5	6	-5	6

It is easy to see from this example that the effect of the substitution of $-x$ for x is to rotate the curve 180° about the y-axis, but the form of the locus is unchanged. Similar remarks apply to the other symmetrical substitutions. Another important transformation of like character is the interchange of x and y; this rotates the curve 180° about the line $x = y$.

29. Equations whose graphs cannot be plotted. Since real numbers alone are used as the coördinates of a point, an equation which is satisfied only by imaginary values of the variables does not define a real curve. Such equations may be most easily distinguished by transposing all terms containing variables to the left-hand member and completing the squares. If we then have the sum of several squares equal to a negative constant, the equation is obviously satisfied only by imaginary values of x and y.

EXAMPLE. Show that the equation $x^2 - 2x + 2y^2 + 8y + 14 = 0$ has no real locus.

Solution. Completing the squares in x and y, we have

$$(x - 1)^2 + 2(y + 2)^2 = -5.$$

For any real values of x and y, $(x - 1)^2$ and $(y + 2)^2$ are positive or zero; hence their sum cannot equal -5 and no real values of x and y can satisfy the equation.

PROBLEMS

1. Write the equation of the curve symmetrical to the given curve with respect to the x-axis, and plot both curves on the same axes.

(a) $4y = 16 - x^2$;

(b) $x^2 + 4y^2 - 16y = 0$;

(c) $4y = x^3 - 9x$;

(d) $xy - 4y = 12$.

2. Write the equation of the curve symmetrical to the given curve with respect to the y-axis, and plot both curves on the same axes.

(a) $y^2 = 8x$;

(b) $x^2 + 4y^2 - 12x = 0$;

(c) $4y^2 = x^3$;

(d) $y = x^2 - 4x$.

3. Write the equation of the curve symmetrical to the given curve with respect to the origin, and plot both curves on the same axes.

(a) $y = x^2 - 4x$;

(b) $x = y^2 + 6y$;

(c) $xy - 4y = 12$;

(d) $x + y = 8$.

4. Plot on the same axes the graphs of

(a) $y^2 = 8x$ and $x^2 = 8y$;

(b) $y^2 = x^3$ and $x^2 = y^3$;

(c) $y = x^3$ and $x = y^3$;

(d) $x^2 - y^2 = 16$ and $y^2 - x^2 = 16$.

5. What is the effect on the graph of substituting $- x$ for y and $- y$ for x in an equation? Test your answer by transforming one of the equations in Problem 3 in this way and plotting both curves.

6. Examine the following equations for the existence of a locus:

(a) $x^2 + y^2 + 4y + 3 = 0$;

(b) $x^2 + 4y^2 + 8y + 5 = 0$;

(c) $x^2 + 6xy + 9y^2 + 4 = 0$;

(d) $x^2 - 6x + y + 10 = 0$;

(e) $x^2y^2 - 2xy^2 + y^2 + 3 = 0$;

(f) $x^3 + y^2 = - 1$.

7. What is the locus of

(a) $x^2 + 4y^2 = 0$;

(b) $x^2 + y^2 - 6x - 4y + 13 = 0$?

8. For what values of k will the locus be imaginary, a point, or a curve in each of the following?

(a) $4x^2 + y^2 = k$;

(b) $x^2 + y^2 - 8y + k = 0$;

(c) $2x^2 + y^2 - 8x + k^2 = 0$;

(d) $x^2 - y^2 = k$.

30. Intersection of curves. It follows from the definition of the locus of an equation that a point lies on two curves if and only if its coördinates satisfy the equation of each. Hence we conclude that the coördinates of points of intersection may be obtained by solving the equations simultaneously. If there are no real solutions, the curves do not intersect.

EXAMPLE. Find the points of intersection of the curves whose equations are $x^2 + y^2 = 16$ and $y^2 = 6x$.

Solution. Solving simultaneously, we have $x^2 + 6x - 16 = 0$, whence $x = 2$ or $- 8$. When $x = 2$, $y = \pm \sqrt{12}$; when $x = - 8$, $y = \pm \sqrt{- 48}$. Thus there are but two pairs of real solutions, giving the two points $(2, \sqrt{12})$ and $(2, - \sqrt{12})$. The figure shows the curves and their points of intersection.

PROBLEMS

Find the points common to the loci of the following equations and check the results by plotting the loci.

1. $x + 3y = 12$,
$3x - 5y + 15 = 0$.

2. $4x - 3y = 24$,
$3x + 4y = 18$.

3. $2x - y = 6$,
$y^2 = 8x$.

4. $3x - 2y = 12$,
$4y = 8 + 2x - x^2$.

5. $x - y = 1$,
$x^2 + y^2 = 25$.

6. $x^2 + y^2 - 8x = 0$,
$x^2 + y^2 - 6y = 0$.

7. $x^2 + y^2 = 36$,
$y^2 = 3x + 8$.

8. $4y = 16 - x^2$,
$2y = x^2 - 6x$.

9. $y^2 = 2ax$,
$x^2 = ay$.

10. $y = 2x + 8$,
$x^2 + 4y^2 = 100$.

11. $4x^2 + 9y^2 = 144$,
$4x^2 - 9y^2 = 36$.

12. $x^2 + y^2 = 16$,
$y^2 = 2x + 20$.

13. $x + 2y = 12$,
$2xy = 35$.

14. $xy = - 9$,
$x^2 + 3y^2 = 36$.

15. $x^2 + y^2 - 6x = 0$,
$\quad y^2 = x^3$.

16. $3x + y = 0$,
$\quad y = x^3 - 9x^2$.

17. $y^2 = 8x$,
$\quad x^2 + y^2 - 10x = 0$.

18. $x^2 = 4ay$,
$\quad y(x^2 + 4a^2) = 8a^3$.

19. $y^2(2a - x) = x^3$,
$\quad x^2 + y^2 - 2ax = 0$.

20. $x^2 - y^2 = 36$,
$\quad x^2 = 6y$.

21. $x^2 - y^2 = 16$,
$\quad x^2 = 10y$.

22. $y^2 - 5y - 6 = 0$,
$\quad x^2 + 8y = 0$.

23. $xy - 2y = 12$,
$\quad y = x - 3$.

24. $x^2 + y^2 = 50$,
$\quad 2xy = 25$.

25. $y = x^3 - 4x$,
$\quad y = x^2 - 4$.

26. $y^2 = 4x$,
$\quad x = 12 + 2y - y^2$.

27. Find the area of the quadrilateral formed by joining the points of intersection of the curves whose equations are $x^2 + 4y^2 = 32$ and $y = 3x^2 - 50$.

28. Find the area of the triangle whose vertices are the points of intersection of the curves whose equations are $y = x^3 - x$ and $y = x - x^2$.

29. Find the length of the common chord of the curves whose equations are $x^2 + y^2 = 36$ and $y^2 = 9x$.

30. For what values of m do the loci of $y = mx$ and $4x^2 - y^2 = 64$ have real intersections? What happens when $m = \pm 2$?

31. For what values of m do the loci of $y = mx$ and $y = x^3 - x$ have only one real intersection?

32. Show that, if the loci of $y = mx$ and $y(1 + x^2) = x$ have three real intersections, they lie in a straight line.

33. Find in terms of m the coördinates of the points of intersection of the loci of $y = mx$ and $x^3 + y^3 - 3xy = 0$. Plot the points for m equal to 0, $\frac{1}{5}$, $\frac{1}{3}$, $\frac{1}{2}$, $\frac{2}{3}$, 1, $\frac{3}{2}$, 2, 3, and 5. Can you plot the curve?

CHAPTER III

THE STRAIGHT LINE

31. Introduction. So far we have obtained the equations of curves by treating each case as a locus problem and we have found the graphs of equations by plotting. These methods are general, but they are tedious except in the simplest cases. It is clear that the effectiveness of analytic geometry will be enormously increased if we can classify the simpler equations and curves, so that we can identify the curve at once from its equation and can write down the equation of a given curve at sight.

We begin with the straight line, for which various properties, such as its determination either by two points or by a point and a direction, lead to relations between the coördinates of its tracing point that can be expressed in the form of an equation. There are several forms of the straight line equation, but all are of the first degree and for a particular line each one may in general be reduced to any of the others.

32. The point slope and two-point forms. Let the line l be fixed by a point and a direction. Let the point be $P_1(x_1, y_1)$ and let the direction of l be given by the slope $m = \tan \alpha$. Let the tracing point be $P(x, y)$. By the slope formula,

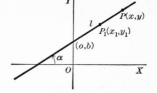

$$m = \frac{y - y_1}{x - x_1},$$

or $$y - y_1 = m(x - x_1). \qquad (7)$$

This is the *point slope form* of the straight line equation. It is used in writing the equation of a line when one point and the slope are known. It may also be used when two points

47

are known, for then the slope of the line can be found at once by the slope formula (3).

If in the latter case the line is determined by the points P_1 and P_2, the value of m is $\dfrac{y_1 - y_2}{x_1 - x_2}$. Substitution of this in Formula 7 gives

$$y - y_1 = \frac{y_1 - y_2}{x_1 - x_2}(x - x_1),$$

which may be written

$$\frac{y - y_1}{x - x_1} = \frac{y_1 - y_2}{x_1 - x_2}. \tag{7a}$$

This last equation is known as the *two-point form*.

33. The slope intercept form. If the slope and the y-intercept are given, the line is determined by a point on the y-axis $(0, b)$, and the slope m. Substituting in (7), we have

$$y - b = m(x - 0),$$

or $$y = mx + b, \tag{8}$$

which is called the *slope intercept form*.

This form can be used in finding the equation of a straight line when the slope and the y-intercept are known. Its most important use is in finding the slope of a line from its equation. For, if the equation of the line is reduced to form (8) by solving for y, the coefficient of x is then the slope of the line and the constant term is its y-intercept.

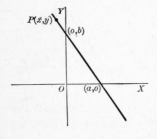

34. The intercept form. Suppose that the intercepts of the line are given; let the x-intercept be a and the y-intercept b.

Here the line is determined by two points $(a, 0)$ and $(0, b)$. We have at once,

$$m = -\frac{b}{a}.$$

Then by (7)
$$y - b = -\frac{b}{a}(x - 0),$$

which reduces to
$$\frac{x}{a} + \frac{y}{b} = 1. \tag{9}$$

This is called the *intercept form*. It is used in writing the equation of a straight line when the intercepts are known.

35. Lines parallel to the axes. The equation of a line parallel to the y-axis cannot be written in any of the forms so far given, since there is neither a y-intercept nor a slope. The equation of such a line is obviously

$$x = a.$$

Similarly the equation of a line parallel to the x-axis has the form
$$y = b.$$

Exercise 1. Derive the intercept form by means of the properties of similar triangles when

(a) a is positive and b is negative;

(b) a is negative and b is positive;

(c) both a and b are negative.

Exercise 2. If the coördinates of $P_1(x_1, y_1)$ and $P_2(x_2, y_2)$ satisfy the equation $y = mx + b$, prove without using § 32 that the slope of P_1P_2 is m.

PROBLEMS

1. Derive the equation of the line determined by the points (3, 1) and (5, 4).

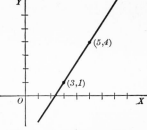

Solution. By the slope formula $m = \frac{3}{2}$. Using the point slope form,

$$y - 1 = \tfrac{3}{2}(x - 3),$$

which reduces to

$$3x - 2y - 7 = 0.$$

The same result is obtained if the two-point form is used.

Equations can be readily checked by substituting the coördinates of known points or drawing the line from the intercepts and observing whether or not it satisfies the given conditions.

2. Find the angle between the lines whose equations are $3x - 4y = 7$ and $2x + 3y = 8$.

Solution. Solving the equations for y in terms of x, we obtain $y = \frac{3}{4}x - \frac{7}{4}$ and $y = -\frac{2}{3}x + \frac{8}{3}$. Since these are in the slope intercept form, the slopes of the lines are $\frac{3}{4}$ and $-\frac{2}{3}$. Hence the angle between them is given by

$$\tan \beta = \frac{-\frac{2}{3} - \frac{3}{4}}{1 - \frac{1}{2}} = -\frac{17}{6},$$

and the value of the angle is $109° \ 26'$.

3. Derive the equation of the line determined by the given points in each of the following, and check the result by finding the intercepts and drawing the line.

(a) $(-3, 2)$, $(5, 6)$; (e) $(10, -10)$, $(-6, 0)$;
(b) $(4, 2)$, $(7, -6)$; (f) $(7, -8)$, $(-3, 7)$;
(c) $(6, 5)$, $(-3, -4)$; (g) $(-1, 8)$, $(7, -2)$;
(d) $(7, -4)$, $(-1, 8)$; (h) $(-8, -2)$, $(8, 10)$.

4. Write the equations of the lines satisfying the following conditions:

(a) passing through $(4, 8)$ and having the slope $-\frac{2}{3}$;
(b) passing through $(2, -5)$ and having the slope 2;
(c) passing through $(-3, -7)$ and having the slope 3;
(d) passing through $(0, 0)$ and having the slope $-\frac{1}{2}$;
(e) passing through $(6, 0)$ and having the slope $\frac{1}{2}$;
(f) passing through $(a, 0)$ and having the slope m;
(g) passing through $(7, -5)$ and having the slope -1;
(h) passing through $(-6, 4)$ and parallel to the x-axis;
(i) passing through $(-6, 4)$ and perpendicular to the x-axis;
(j) $a = 6$, $b = -4$; (n) $m = 1$, $b = -5$;
(k) $a = -4$, $b = \frac{5}{2}$; (o) $m = -2$, $b = 3$;
(l) $a = \frac{1}{2}$, $b = \frac{1}{3}$; (p) $m = \frac{2}{3}$, $b = -4$;
(m) $a = -\frac{7}{2}$, $b = 7$; (q) $m = -\frac{1}{2}$, $b = 6$.

5. Derive the equations of the lines satisfying the following conditions:

(a) passing through $(-4, -6)$ and having the inclination $45°$;
(b) passing through $(6, 3)$ and having the inclination $135°$;
(c) passing through $(5, 4)$ and having the inclination $30°$;

(d) passing through $(-5, 4)$ and having the y-intercept -6;

(e) $m = 2$, $a = -3$;   (h) $a = 6$, $\alpha = 135°$;

(f) $m = -3$, $a = 4$;   (i) $b = -4$, $\alpha = 60°$;

(g) $a = -5$, $\alpha = 45°$;   (j) $b = 5$, $\alpha = 150°$.

6. Reduce each of the following straight line equations to the slope intercept form, and draw the lines:

(a) $10x - 2y = 24$;   (e) $2x - 5y = 15$;

(b) $\dfrac{x}{5} - \dfrac{y}{4} = 1$;   (f) $3x + 2y = 12$;

                                          (g) $3y + 5 = 0$;

(c) $x + 2y = 6$;   (h) $x + 5y = 0$.

(d) $7x + 2y = 28$;

7. Find the angle between the line * $2x - 3y = 12$ and each of the lines in Problem 6.

8. Find the point of intersection of the line $2x - 3y = 12$ and each of the lines in Problem 6.

9. Find the area of the triangle bounded by the lines $y + 4 = 0$, $x - y + 1 = 0$, and $5x + 3y = 23$.

10. If $A(-1, 8)$, $B(3, -2)$, and $C(12, 4)$ are vertices of a parallelogram $ABCD$, find the equations of the sides AD and CD and the coördinates of D.

11. Two lines of slope $-\frac{4}{3}$ are tangent to a circle whose center is the origin and whose radius is 10. Find the equations of the lines.

12. Find the equation of the straight line which passes through the point $(5, 7)$ and has $b = 2a$.

13. Find the equation of a straight line which passes through the point $(3, 6)$ and forms with the coördinate axes a triangle of area 48.

14. Derive the straight line equation $x = ny + a$, where $n = \cot \alpha$ and a is the x-intercept.

15. A straight line of slope m passes through the point (c, d). Find the length of the segment intercepted by the coördinate axes in terms of m, c, and d.

16. In the triangle whose vertices are $(0, 0)$, $(8, 0)$, and $(6, 8)$ find

(a) the equations of its sides;

(b) the equations of the perpendicular bisectors of the sides;

---

* More properly we should say, "the line whose equation is $2x - 3y = 12$," but the close relation between a curve and its equation has given rise to the custom of using the abbreviated phrase.

(*c*) the equations of the perpendiculars from the vertices on the opposite sides;

(*d*) the equations of the medians.

17. In the triangle whose vertices are $(-2, -2)$, $(2, 6)$, and $(6, 2)$ find the information called for in Problem 16.

18. In the triangle of Problem 16 show that

(*a*) the perpendicular bisectors meet in a point;

(*b*) the medians meet in a point;

(*c*) the perpendiculars from the vertices on the opposite sides meet in a point.

(In each case find the coördinates of the intersection of two lines and show that they satisfy the equation of the third.)

19. Show that the three points of intersection found in Problem 18 lie in a straight line.

20. The distance between the fixed points A and B is $2c$. Find the locus of a point P, for which the square of its distance from A is k units greater than the square of its distance from B. What is the locus when $k = 0$?

21. A point lies on the line $x - 2y + 10 = 0$. Show that the difference of the squares of its distances from the points $(2, 8)$ and $(6, 0)$ is constant.

22. Prove that all straight lines for which $\dfrac{1}{a} + \dfrac{1}{b} = \dfrac{1}{5}$ pass through a common point.

23. The base of a triangle is fixed in length and position. Find the locus of the opposite vertex if the slope of one side is twice the slope of the other, and

(*a*) the base lies on the *x*-axis;   (*b*) the base lies on the *y*-axis.

24. The triangle OAB is equilateral. A point C is taken on OA so that CA is one third of OA, and a point E is taken on OB so that OE is one third of OB. If the lines BC and AE meet at F, prove by analytic means that OF is perpendicular to BC.

36. The linear equation. Theorem I. *Every straight line has an equation of the first degree, in one or two variables.*

Proof. This has already been proved. For, if the line cuts the *y*-axis, it has an equation of the form $y = mx + b$; and, if it is parallel to the y-axis, it has an equation of the form $x = a$. Both equations are of the first degree.

Theorem II. *Every equation of the first degree in one or two variables is the equation of a straight line.*

Proof. The general form of the equation of the first degree is

$$Ax + By + C = 0, \tag{10}$$

where A, B, and C may have any values, except that both A and B cannot be zero.

Case I. When $B \neq$ * 0, the equation can be solved for y, giving

$$y = -\frac{A}{B}x - \frac{C}{B}.$$

This is of the form $y = mx + b$ and therefore it is the equation of a straight line which has the slope $-\dfrac{A}{B}$ and the y-intercept $-\dfrac{C}{B}$.

Case II. When $B = 0$, we have $x = -\dfrac{C}{A}$. This is of the form $x = a$ and therefore it is the equation of a straight line which is parallel to the y-axis and has the x-intercept $-\dfrac{C}{A}$. Thus the theorem is proved for both cases.

NOTE. Equations of the first degree in any number of variables are called *linear equations*. The theorems just proved make this name especially appropriate when there are two variables.

Exercise 3. Transform the general equation $Ax + By + C = 0$ into the intercept form. When is this impossible?

37. Relations between two lines. The following theorems enable us to tell whether two lines are identical, parallel, or perpendicular by inspection of their general equations. For the sake of brevity certain exceptional cases are omitted in the statements and proofs; in practice these cause no trouble and the necessary modifications are left to the student.

---

* This symbol has the meaning, "is not equal to."

Theorem I. *If two linear equations in two variables have the coefficients of the variables proportional, the lines defined by the equations are parallel or identical,* and conversely.

Proof. Let the equations be

$$Ax + By + C = 0$$

and

$$A'x + B'y + C' = 0.$$

Solving for y,

$$y = -\frac{A}{B}x - \frac{C}{B} \quad \text{and} \quad y = -\frac{A'}{B'}x - \frac{C'}{B'}.$$

These are in the slope intercept form.

Hence

$$m = -\frac{A}{B} \quad \text{and} \quad m' = -\frac{A'}{B'}.$$

But by hypothesis $\quad A : A' = B : B'$

whence

$$\frac{A}{B} = \frac{A'}{B'} \qquad \text{by alternation.}$$

Thus we have $m = m'$, and the lines are parallel or identical, since their slopes are equal.

The conditions for the lines to be identical are given in Theorem III. The proof of the converse and the discussion of the trivial cases where the coefficients of x or y are zero are left to the student.

Exercise 4. Assume that the lines are parallel to each other, but not parallel to either coördinate axis, and prove that $A : A' = B : B'$.

Theorem II. *If in any two linear equations,*

$$Ax + By + C = 0$$

and

$$A'x + B'y + C' = 0,$$

$AA' = -BB'$, *the lines defined by the equations are perpendicular,* and conversely.

Proof. Solving the given linear equations for y, as before, we have

$$m = -\frac{A}{B} \quad \text{and} \quad m' = -\frac{A'}{B'}.$$

Then $$mm' = \left(-\frac{A}{B}\right)\left(-\frac{A'}{B'}\right) = \frac{AA'}{BB'}.$$

But by hypothesis $AA' = -BB'$, hence $mm' = -1$, and the test for perpendicularity is satisfied.

Exercise 5. Assume that the lines are perpendicular and prove that $AA' = -BB'$.

Theorem III. *If in any two linear equations*

$$Ax + By + C = 0$$

and $$A'x + B'y + C' = 0,$$

$A : A' = B : B' = C : C'$, *the lines defined by the equations are identical*, and conversely.

Proof. From the assumed proportions

$$\frac{C}{B} = \frac{C'}{B'}, \quad \text{or} \quad b = b'.$$

Also $$\frac{A}{B} = \frac{A'}{B'}, \quad \text{or} \quad m = m' \text{ as before.}$$

Hence the lines have the point $(0, b)$ in common and also have the same direction. They are therefore identical.

The proof of the converse and the discussion of the necessary modifications if any of the arbitrary constants are zero are left to the student.

Exercise 6. If $Ax + By + C = 0$ and $A'x + B'y + C' = 0$ are equations of a line which cuts both coördinate axes and does not pass through the origin, prove that $A : A' = B : B' = C : C'$.

These theorems can be used to advantage in solving problems. One use is to check solutions already obtained. For example, suppose that it is desired to find the equation of a line which passes through the point $(4, -2)$ and is perpendicular to the line $10x - 4y + 11 = 0$. The natural solution is first to find the slope of the given line from its equation; it is $\frac{5}{2}$. Then the slope of the required line is $-\frac{2}{5}$, and with the aid of the point slope equation we can obtain the required equation,

$2x + 5y + 2 = 0$. To check this result, we observe that this line is perpendicular to the given line, since $AA' = 20$ and $BB' = -20$. It also passes through the given point, since $2 \cdot 4 + 5(-2) + 2 = 0$.

Of greater importance is the fact that with these theorems we can often write down equations at sight. In the above problem we know by Theorem II that any line whose equation has the form $4x + 10y = k$ will be perpendicular to the given line $10x - 4y + 11 = 0$. Since the line is to pass through the point $(4, -2)$,

$$k = 4 \cdot 4 + 10(-2) = 16 - 20 = -4.$$

Hence the required equation is

$$4x + 10y = -4, \quad \text{or} \quad 2x + 5y + 2 = 0.$$

Similarly, by Theorem I the equation of the line which passes through the point $(4, -2)$ and is parallel to the line $10x - 4y + 11 = 0$ is $10x - 4y = 10 \cdot 4 - 4(-2) = 48$, or $5x - 2y = 24$. If a line passes through $(4, -2)$ and has the slope $-\frac{2}{3}$, then by Theorem II of the previous section its equation is $2x + 3y = 2 \cdot 4 + 3(-2) = 2$. Thus we can dispense with the point slope form entirely.

38. Application to the solution of linear equations. Two equations of the first degree in two variables are classified as

(a) *simultaneous* if they have one solution, which is usually the case;

(b) *incompatible* if they have no common solution, as

$$\begin{cases} 3x + 7y = 1, \\ 6x + 14y = 1; \end{cases}$$

(c) *dependent* if they have innumerable solutions, as

$$\begin{cases} 9x - 6y = 3, \\ 3x - 2y = 1. \end{cases}$$

It is sometimes convenient to determine the number of solutions without solving. The test by which the class of the equations can be determined is easily deduced from the relation between their loci, and from Theorems I and III, § 37.

(a) The equations have one and only one solution, if their lines intersect. This is the case when

$$A : A' \neq B : B'.$$

(b) The equations have no common solution, if their lines are parallel. This is the case when

$$A : A' = B : B' \neq C : C'.$$

(c) The equations have innumerable solutions, if their lines have more than one point in common and are therefore identical. This is the case when

$$A : A' = B : B' = C : C'.$$

PROBLEMS

1. Select two pairs each of parallel and perpendicular lines from the following:

(a) $y = 3x - 5$;
(b) $4x + 2y = 17$;
(c) $x = 2y$;
(d) $6x + 3y = 16$;
(e) $y = 9 - 2x$;
(f) $3x - y = 15$.

2. Choose from the following a pair of simultaneous equations, a pair of incompatible equations, and a pair of identical equations:

(a) $3x + 4y - 24 = 0$;
(b) $6x + 8y - 7 = 0$;
(c) $y = 6 - 0.75x$;
(d) $3x = 4y + 48$.

3. In each of the following cases find the equations of two lines which pass through the given point, one parallel and the other perpendicular to the given line:

(a) $(5, 5)$, $x - 2y = 15$;
(b) $(-2, 5)$, $3x - 4y = 24$;
(c) $(10, 1)$, $3x - y = 9$;
(d) $(-2, 10)$, $2x - 3y = 18$;
(e) $(1, -9)$, $5x + 12y = 66$;
(f) $(-3, -1)$, $2x + y = 12$;
(g) $(5, 10)$, $x + 3y = 15$;
(h) $(-4, -12)$, $3x + 5y = 30$.

4. Find the equation of the line which passes through the given point and is parallel to the given line in each of the following cases:

(a) $(-2, 4)$, $2x - y = 10$;
(b) $(2, 8)$, $x - 3y = 12$;
(c) $(-5, 13)$, $8x - 15y = 54$;
(d) $(12, 6)$, $4x - y = 8$;
(e) $(0, 0)$, $x + 2y = 10$;
(f) $(-6, -4)$, $x + y = 12$;
(g) $(-7, -1)$, $5x + 3y = 30$;
(h) $(-2, 0)$, $6x + 8y = 33$.

5. In each case in Problem 3 find the perpendicular distance between the line and the point.

6. In each case in Problem 4 find the equation of the line which passes through the given point and is perpendicular to the given line.

7. In each case in Problem 4 find the perpendicular distance between the line and the point.

8. Find the area of the triangle whose vertices are:

(a) $(0, 2)$, $(4, -3)$, $(12, 3)$;   (b) $(-2, -1)$, $(6, 7)$, $(10, -3)$.

9. Find the area of the triangle whose vertices are:

(a) $(2, 6)$, $(6, -2)$, $(10, 8)$;   (b) $(3, -2)$, $(-5, 4)$, $(11, 8)$.

10. For each triangle in Problem 9 find the center and the radius of the circumscribed circle.

11. Find the center and the radius of the circle circumscribed about the triangle whose vertices are:

(a) $(6, 0)$, $(-4, 0)$, $(10, 8)$;   (c) $(7, 4)$, $(3, 12)$, $(5, -2)$;
(b) $(0, 0)$, $(0, 8)$, $(12, 6)$;   (d) $(1, -1)$, $(-7, 5)$, $(9, 9)$.

12. The vertices of a parallelogram are $(0, 0)$, $(10, 0)$, $(3, 6)$, and $(13, 6)$. Lines are drawn from two opposite vertices to the mid-points of opposite sides. Show that they are parallel and that they trisect one of the diagonals.

13. Find the fourth vertex of a rectangle which has three vertices as follows:

(a) $(-3, 4)$ $(0, -2)$, $(16, 6)$;   (b) $(8, 1)$, $(11, 5)$, $(12, -2)$.

14. In each of the following cases one vertex and the equations of two sides of a parallelogram are given. Find the other vertices.

(a) $(-4, -2)$, $x + 3y = 15$, $2x - y = 8$;
(b) $(8, 10)$, $x + 2y = 10$, $3x - 4y = 24$.

15. Two opposite vertices of a square are $(-4, 6)$ and $(8, 1)$. Find the other vertices and the equations of the sides.

16. Find the equation of a straight line which passes through the point $(2, 3)$ and makes an angle of 45° with a line in Problem 1.

Hint. To find the slope of the required line use Formula 6 in Chapter I.

17. Find the equation of a straight line which passes through the point $(2, 3)$ and makes an angle whose tangent is $\frac{1}{3}$ with a line in Problem 1.

18. The base of an isosceles triangle lies on the line $x + 2y = 4$, the opposite vertex is $(5, 7)$, and the slope of one side is -3. Find the coördinates of the other vertices.

19. The base of an isosceles triangle lies on the line $x + 2y = 4$, the opposite vertex is $(5, 7)$, and the slope of one side is -2. Find the coördinates of the other vertices.

20. Find the equations of the bisectors of the angles made by the lines $3x + y + 2 = 0$ and $x - 3y = 0$.

21. The ends of the base of a triangle are at $(-6, 0)$ and $(8, 0)$, and the center of the inscribed circle is at $(0, 4)$. Find the coördinates of the third vertex.

Hint. The center of an inscribed circle lies on the bisectors of the angles of the triangle.

22. Show that the medians of a triangle meet in a point. (Let the vertices be $(0, 0)$, $(2a, 0)$, and $(2b, 2c)$.)

23. Show that the perpendicular bisectors of the sides of a triangle meet in a point. (Let the vertices be $(0, 0)$, $(2a, 0)$, and $(2b, 2c)$.)

24. Show that the perpendiculars from the vertices of a triangle on the opposite sides meet in a point. (Let the vertices be $(0, 0)$, $(2a, 0)$, and $(2b, 2c)$.)

25. Show that the three points of intersection found in Problems 22, 23, and 24 lie in a straight line.

26. Generalize Problem 12 by taking the vertices as $(0, 0)$, $(a, 0)$, (b, c), and $(b + a, c)$.

27. Show that the bisectors of the angles of a rectangle enclose a square. (Let the vertices be $(0, 0)$, $(a, 0)$, (a, b), and $(0, b)$.)

28. Show that, if the line $Ax + By + C = 0$ meets the line passing through $P_1(x_1, y_1)$ and $P_2(x_2, y_2)$, the point of intersection divides the segment P_1P_2 in the ratio $-(Ax_1 + By_1 + C) : (Ax_2 + By_2 + C)$.

29. Show that in any quadrilateral the segments joining the midpoints of opposite sides intersect in a point which is the mid-point of the segment joining the mid-points of the diagonals.

39. The normal form. The perpendicular from the origin to any line is called the *normal axis* of the line and the distance *from* the origin *to* the line measured along the normal axis is called the *normal intercept*. The inclination of the normal axis is denoted by ω and the normal intercept is denoted by p. It is obvious that the normal intercept and the y-intercept always have the same sign. The equation of the straight line determined by the constants p and ω is called the *normal form*.

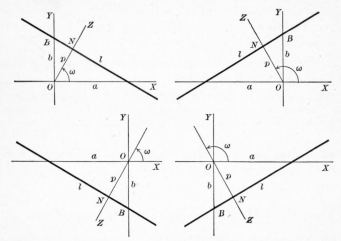

Derivation of the normal form. Referring to the above figures we can easily show that in any of the four possible cases $b = \dfrac{p}{\sin \omega}$. For any case, $\sin NBO = \dfrac{p}{b}$. But NBO is equal to either ω or $180° - \omega$, since the sides of these angles are mutually perpendicular; hence $\sin NBO = \sin \omega$. This gives $\sin \omega = \dfrac{p}{b}$, or $b = \dfrac{p}{\sin \omega}$.

Since the normal axis is perpendicular to the line, its slope is the negative reciprocal of that of the line. Hence

$$m = \frac{-1}{\tan \omega} = -\frac{\cos \omega}{\sin \omega}.$$

Substituting these values in the slope intercept equation $y = mx + b$, we have

$$y = -\frac{\cos \omega}{\sin \omega}x + \frac{p}{\sin \omega}.$$

Clearing of fractions and transposing gives the normal form:

$$x \cos \omega + y \sin \omega = p. \qquad (11)$$

The above proof does not cover the cases where the line is parallel to the y-axis, for there is then no slope intercept equation. For these cases we take $\omega = 0°$ and the equation is $x = p$. This agrees with (11) since $\sin 0° = 0$ and $\cos 0° = 1$.

Exercise 7. Derive the normal form directly from a figure by means of plane geometry and trigonometry.

Hint. In any of the figures of the previous page take a point P on the line l, draw a segment from P perpendicular to the x-axis and meeting it at K, and from K draw a segment perpendicular to the normal axis.

40. Reduction of a linear equation to the normal form. Let the equation of the given line l be

$$Ax + By + C = 0.$$

It is required to find the equation of l in the normal form.

Since the slope of the given line is $-\dfrac{A}{B}$, the slope of the normal axis is the negative reciprocal of this, $\dfrac{B}{A}$. Hence $\tan \omega = \dfrac{B}{A}$. Elementary trigonometry gives us at once

$$\sin \omega = \frac{B}{\pm \sqrt{A^2 + B^2}}, \quad \cos \omega = \frac{A}{\pm \sqrt{A^2 + B^2}}.$$

Since $\omega < 180°$, $\sin \omega$ is positive. Therefore the sign of the radical must be taken to agree with that of B. Thus we have determined $\sin \omega$ and $\cos \omega$ in terms of the coefficients of the given equation.

Dividing the given equation by $\pm \sqrt{A^2 + B^2}$, we have

$$\frac{A}{\pm \sqrt{A^2 + B^2}} x + \frac{B}{\pm \sqrt{A^2 + B^2}} y + \frac{C}{\pm \sqrt{A^2 + B^2}} = 0,$$

which is of the form

$$x \cos \omega + y \sin \omega - p = 0.$$

Comparing these equations, we see that p must be

$$\frac{-C}{\pm \sqrt{A^2 + B^2}}.$$

Summing up, we have the following working rule for the general case where neither A nor B is zero:

To reduce the linear equation $Ax + By + C = 0$ to the normal form, divide it by $\pm \sqrt{A^2 + B^2}$, giving the radical the sign of B.

In the special case that $A = 0$ it is readily seen that the rule also holds. When $B = 0$, the line is parallel to the y-axis and $\omega = 0$. Hence $\cos \omega = 1$ and the equation evidently assumes the normal form when it is solved for x; this may be regarded as giving the radical the sign of A.

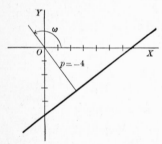

EXAMPLE. Reduce $3x - 4y - 20 = 0$ to the normal form.

Solution. Here $\sqrt{A^2 + B^2} = 5$, and B is negative. Therefore the required equation is

$$- \tfrac{3}{5}x + \tfrac{4}{5}y + 4 = 0.$$

This gives $\cos \omega = - \tfrac{3}{5}$, $\sin \omega = \tfrac{4}{5}$, and $p = - 4$. Plotting the equation affords an excellent check on the work.

The equation $Ax + By + C = 0$ can always be reduced to the normal form; for the division by the radical is always possible, since A and B cannot both be zero. This constitutes one of the two most important advantages of the normal form. The other consists in its convenience for use in finding the distance from a line to a point.

PROBLEMS

The sines and cosines of the angles used in this group of problems should be taken from the table in the Introduction.

1. Write the equations of the lines which satisfy the following data:

(a) $p = 6$, $\omega = 0°$;   (e) $p = 5$, $\omega = 90°$;

(b) $p = - 8$, $\omega = 30°$;   (f) $p = - 12$, $\omega = 120°$;

(c) $p = 10$, $\omega = 45°$;   (g) $p = 16$, $\omega = 135°$;

(d) $p = - 8$, $\omega = 60°$;   (h) $p = - 6$, $\omega = 150°$.

2. Write the equations of the lines which satisfy the following data:

(a) $p = -8$, $\omega = 0°$;

(b) $p = 12$, $\omega = 30°$;

(c) $p = -10$, $\omega = 45°$;

(d) $p = 5$, $\omega = 60°$;

(e) $p = -6$, $\omega = 90°$;

(f) $p = 8$, $\omega = 120°$;

(g) $p = 6$, $\omega = 135°$;

(h) $p = 16$, $\omega = 150°$.

3. Write the equations of the lines which satisfy the following data:

(a) $p = 10$, $\cos \omega = \frac{3}{5}$;

(b) $p = 12$, $\tan \omega = -\frac{5}{12}$;

(c) $p = 6$, $m = -2$;

(d) $a = -8$, $\omega = 135°$;

(e) $a = 15$, $\cos \omega = \frac{4}{5}$;

(f) $b = -5$, $\cos \omega = -\frac{4}{5}$.

4. Write the equations of the lines which satisfy the following data:

(a) $p = 8$, $\cos \omega = -\frac{5}{13}$;

(b) $p = -10$, $\tan \omega = 2$;

(c) $p = 5$, $m = \frac{1}{2}$;

(d) $a = 12$, $\omega = 60°$;

(e) $b = 6$, $\cos \omega = -\frac{3}{5}$;

(f) $b = -8$, $\omega = 120°$.

5. Reduce the following equations to the normal form:

(a) $3x - 4y = 24$;

(b) $12x - 5y = 60$;

(c) $15x + 8y = 120$;

(d) $4x + 3y = 0$;

(e) $x + y = 16$;

(f) $2x - 3y = 15$;

(g) $\sqrt{3}x - y = 12$;

(h) $x + 2y = 16$.

6. Reduce the following equations to the normal form:

(a) $4x + 3y = 12$;

(b) $5x - 12y = 65$;

(c) $8x - 15y = 120$;

(d) $2x - y = 24$;

(e) $3x + 5y = 0$;

(f) $x = y$;

(g) $6x + 8y = 75$;

(h) $3x + y = 5\sqrt{10}$.

7. Find the value of ω for each of the lines in Problem 6 correct to the nearest minute.

8. By transformation to the normal form find the (directed) distance of a line from the origin when it is determined as follows:

(a) $a = 8$, $b = -15$;

(b) $a = -8$, $b = 6$;

(c) $a = 5$, $b = 12$;

(d) $a = -6$, $b = -4$;

(e) $b = 5$, $m = -2$;

(f) $b = -6$, $m = \frac{1}{2}$;

(g) $a = 8$, $m = 3$;

(h) $a = 6$, $m = -3$.

9. Find the equation of the line which passes through the point $(10, -5)$ and has

(a) $\omega = 45°$;

(b) $\omega = 150°$;

(c) $\cos \omega = -\frac{5}{13}$;

(d) $p = 5$;

(e) $p = 2$;

(f) $p = -11$.

10. A circle has the center at the origin and the radius 10. Find the equations of the tangents to this circle which have the slope $\frac{3}{4}$.

11. Find p and $\tan \omega$ in terms of a and b.

12. Derive the normal form from the intercept form by finding a and b in terms of p and ω from the figures on page 60.

13. Find the coördinates of the foot of the perpendicular from the origin to a line in terms of its intercepts.

14. Find p in terms of m and b.

15. Transform the normal form into the intercept form.

16. Transform the normal form into the slope intercept form.

41. Distance from a line to a point. Let l be a line of which the equation is given and P_1 a point whose coördinates (x_1, y_1)

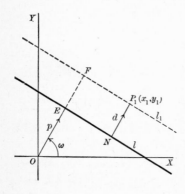

are given and let d be the distance NP_1 from the line to the point, *reckoned from the line.*

Through P_1 draw the line l_1 parallel to l and, if necessary, produce the normal p to meet it. The normal inclination ω is the same for l and l_1, and is known from the equation of l when it is reduced to the normal form. Denote OE by p and OF by p_1. Then

$$p_1 = OF = OE + EF = p + d.$$

Hence the normal equation of l_1 is

$$p + d = x \cos \omega + y \sin \omega.$$

This is satisfied by the coördinates of P_1; hence

$$p + d = x_1 \cos \omega + y_1 \sin \omega,$$

or $\qquad\qquad d = x_1 \cos \omega + y_1 \sin \omega - p.$ $\qquad\qquad$ (12)

But the equation of l is

$$x \cos \omega + y \sin \omega - p = 0.$$ $\qquad\qquad$ (11)

Thus the first member of (11) becomes the value of d when the coördinates of P_1 are substituted for x and y. Hence follows the rule:

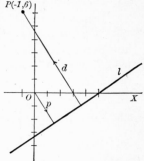

To find the distance from a line to a point, reduce the equation of the line to the normal form

$$x \cos \omega + y \sin \omega - p = 0$$

and substitute the coördinates of the given point for the variables. The value of the first member is the required distance.

EXAMPLE. Find the distance of the point $P(-1, 6)$ from the line

$$2x - 3y = 10.$$

Solution. The normal equation of l is

$$-\frac{2x}{\sqrt{13}} + \frac{3y}{\sqrt{13}} + \frac{10}{\sqrt{13}} = 0.$$

$$\therefore d = \frac{(-2)(-1)}{\sqrt{13}} + \frac{3 \cdot 6}{\sqrt{13}} + \frac{10}{\sqrt{13}} = \frac{30}{\sqrt{13}} = 8.32, \text{ approximately.}$$

Here p, being negative, is reckoned downward from the origin and d, being positive, is reckoned upward from the line l.

An obvious check is to draw the figure and measure the distance.

Exercise 8. Show that the distance formula can be written

$$d = \frac{Ax_1 + By_1 + C}{\pm \sqrt{A^2 + B^2}}$$

where the radical should have the sign of B. Also write the expression for the distance formula in terms of the slope intercept equation $y = mx + b$.

42. The bisectors of the angles between two lines. It is frequently desired to find the equations of the bisectors of the vertical angles formed by two intersecting lines. This can easily be done with the aid of the previous section, as illustrated on page 66.

EXAMPLE. Find the equations of the bisectors of the angles between the lines $3x - 4y = 12$ and $12x + 5y = 30$.

Solution. Let the lines meet at E; there are two bisectors, EF and EG. Let $P_1(x_1, y_1)$ lie upon EG, the bisector of the angle BEC. Then by plane geometry the perpendiculars HP_1 and KP_1 are of equal length.

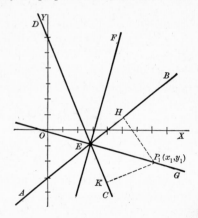

To find the length of HP_1 use Formula 12.

Then
$$HP_1 = \frac{-3x_1 + 4y_1 + 12}{5}.$$

Similarly
$$KP_1 = \frac{12x_1 + 5y_1 - 30}{13}.$$

But HP_1 is negative and KP_1 is positive.

Therefore
$$HP_1 = -KP_1,$$

or
$$\frac{-3x_1 + 4y_1 + 12}{5} = \frac{-12x_1 - 5y_1 + 30}{13}.$$

Simplifying and dropping subscripts, the equation of EG is
$$21x + 77y + 6 = 0.$$

In like manner the equation of EF is
$$99x - 27y - 306 = 0.$$

A convenient partial check on the accuracy of the work is to apply the test for perpendicularity to the two solutions.

PROBLEMS

1. In each case find the distance from the line to the point.

(a) $4x + 3y = 36$, $(-3, -4)$;   (d) $x - y = 10$, $(-5, 5)$;
(b) $x = 2y$, $(-5, 10)$;   (e) $2x + 3y = 18$, $(-2, -7)$;
(c) $5x - 12y = 120$, $(4, 8)$;   (f) $15x - 8y = 136$, $(0, 0)$.

2. In each case find the distance from the line to the point.

(a) $3x - 4y = 18$, $(-2, 7)$;   (d) $2x - y = 10$, $(-8, 4)$;
(b) $y + 3x = 0$, $(8, 0)$;   (e) $8x + 15y = 120$, $(0, -4)$;
(c) $12x + 5y = 40$, $(10, 10)$;   (f) $3x - 5y = 30$, $(2, 6)$.

3. Find the distance between each of the following pairs of parallel lines:

(a) $y = 2x + 5$,   (c) $3x + 4y + 24 = 0$,
    $y = 2x - 8$; $3x + 4y - 12 = 0$;
(b) $2x - 3y = 18$,   (d) $5x - 3y = 0$,
    $2x - 3y = 6$; $10x - 6y = 60$.

4. In each of the following find the distance between the intersection of the first two lines and the third line.

(a) $x - 2y = 12$, $2x + 3y = 12$, $3x - y = 9$;
(b) $9x + 16y = 156$, $5x - 2y = 5$, $3x - 4y = 24$;
(c) $x - 2y = 4$, $5x + 4y = 48$, $4x - y + 12 = 0$.

5. Find the areas of the triangles formed by the sets of lines in Problem 4.

6. Find the areas of the triangles whose vertices are

(a) $(0, 6)$, $(10, 7)$, $(5, -3)$;   (c) $(-4, 3)$, $(2, -5)$, $(7, 1)$;
(b) $(0, 0)$, $(8, -4)$, $(12, 8)$;   (d) $(5, 5)$, $(-10, -4)$, $(8, -8)$.

7. Find the areas of the quadrilaterals which have the following vertices:

(a) $(-7, 4)$, $(4, 6)$, $(11, -2)$, $(1, -4)$;
(b) $(-2, 10)$, $(5, 3)$, $(3, -4)$, $(-9, -5)$;
(c) $(-4, 1)$, $(5, 4)$, $(8, -3)$, $(0, -6)$;
(d) $(-3, -5)$, $(0, 5)$, $(7, 10)$, $(12, 0)$.

8. Find the equations of the bisectors of the angles between

(a) $5x - 12y + 35 = 0$,   (c) $x - 2y = 3$,
    $12x - 5y - 35 = 0$; $4x - 2y = 15$;
(b) $4x - 3y - 24 = 0$,   (d) $3x - 4y = 8$,
    $8x + 15y + 36 = 0$; $5x + 12y = 32$.

9. Find the locus of points twice as far numerically from the first line as from the second in each of the groups in Problem 8.

10. Find the locus of points the sum of whose directed distances from each of the pairs of lines in Problem 8 is 10.

11. Find the locus of points 5 units distant from the lines

(a) $4x - 3y = 20$;   (c) $8x - 15y = 90$;

(b) $5x + 12y = 60$;   (d) $x - y = 10$.

12. Find the equation of the line midway between each pair of parallel lines in Problem 3.

13. The equations of two parallel lines are $y = mx + b_1$ and $y = mx + b_2$. Find the equation of a line parallel to these and having the ratio of its (directed) distance from the first line to its (directed) distance from the second equal to $r_1 : r_2$.

14. Two vertices of a triangle are $(3, 0)$ and $(8, 12)$. Find the locus of the third vertex if the area is 65.

15. A triangle has the vertices $(0, 0)$, $(16, 12)$, and $(21, 0)$. Find the center and radius of the inscribed circle.

16. The equations of the sides of a triangle are $3x + 4y = 0$, $5x - 12y = 0$, and $4x - 3y = 33$. Find the equations of the bisectors of the exterior angles of the triangle and show that these lines meet the opposite sides in three points which lie in a straight line.

17. Show analytically that the sum of the lengths of the perpendiculars from a point of the base of an isosceles triangle to the sides is equal to the length of the perpendicular from one end of the base to the side opposite.

43. Geometric conditions determining a line. In each of the standard equations

$$y = mx + b, \quad \frac{x}{a} + \frac{y}{b} = 1, \text{ and } x \cos \omega + y \sin \omega - p = 0,$$

we note that there are involved two arbitrary constants which represent geometric conditions determining the line. Three of these, a, b, and p, represent distances, while the others, m and ω, determine the direction of the line. The direction may also be given by the inclination α.

Thus we associate with any straight line six constants; three, a, b, and p, representing distances, and three, m, α, and ω, representing directions. 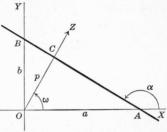 Any pair of them (one being a distance) will determine the line * (and also the other constants), and combined with its current coördinates they will furnish an equation of the line. Of the many possible equations involving these constants, only the three given above are commonly used.

44. Systems of straight lines. When one of the constants of a straight line equation is arbitrary and the other is absolute, as in $y = 3x + k$, the equation defines a line for each value assigned to the arbitrary constant, but each line so defined has the property given by the numerical constant.

Thus in the above equation k is the y-intercept, and it may have any value; but the slope of each line is 3, and by assigning 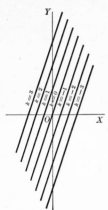 all possible values to k we have all possible lines of slope 3. Such a group of lines is called a *system*, and the arbitrary constant is called the *parameter* of the system. In the particular case under discussion we have a system of parallel lines of slope 3, of which several are drawn in the figure.

We have already seen that any of the standard forms of the straight line equation involves two arbitrary constants which correspond to the geometric conditions defining the line. Hence if one of these constants is given a numerical value and the other left arbitrary, we get a *system of straight lines* characterized by the geometrical property defined

* When b and p are given, there are two solutions.

by the numerical constant, and with one geometrical property left arbitrary or variable. This correspondence is general, as will be seen later in the case of the circle and the conics.

PROBLEMS

1. Draw the lines satisfying the following conditions:

(a) $a = 10$, $\alpha = 150°$;

(b) $b = -6$, $\alpha = 60°$;

(c) $p = 5$, $\alpha = 30°$;

(d) $a = 8$, $\omega = 120°$;

(e) $b = 6$, $\omega = 60°$;

(f) $p = -6$, $\omega = 135°$;

(g) $a = 15$, $p = 12$;

(h) $b = -10$, $p = -6$;

(i) $m = 3$, $p = 5$;

(j) $a = -10$, $m = 2$.

2. In each case in Problem 1 find the other four geometric constants.

3. Find the equation of each line in Problem 1.

4. Write the equations of the systems of lines defined as follows and draw several lines of each system:

(a) containing $(4, -2)$;

(b) containing $(-3, 4)$;

(c) having $p = 5$;

(d) having $\cos \omega = \frac{3}{5}$;

(e) having the y-intercept 4;

(f) having the x-intercept -6;

(g) having the slope $-\frac{1}{2}$;

(h) having equal intercepts.

5. Write the equations of the systems of lines defined as follows and draw several lines of each system:

(a) having the x-intercept equal to twice the y-intercept;

(b) having the inclination 135°;

(c) having the sum of the intercepts equal to 10;

(d) having the y-intercept equal to the reciprocal of the slope;

(e) having $b = a^2$;

(f) having $2p = a$.

6. What geometric conditions define the systems of lines represented by the following equations?

(a) $y - k = 0$;

(b) $x - 3y + k = 0$;

(c) $2x + ky - 12 = 0$;

(d) $kx - 3y + 12 = 0$;

(e) $kx + y\sqrt{1 - k^2} = 5$;

(f) $kx + 2ky = 12$;

(g) $y = kx - 3k$;

(h) $2x - k^2y = 8k$.

Hint. The condition is usually apparent if the equation is reduced to one of the standard forms or the slope and intercepts are found.

7. For each system in Problem 6 find the values of the parameter such that the line passes through the point $(4, -5)$, if it is possible.

8. For each system in Problem 6 find the values of the parameter such that the slope of the line is 2, if it is possible.

9. For each system in Problem 6 find the values of the parameter such that the line has the y-intercept equal to -5, if it is possible.

10. In Problem 6 find a system identical with the system

(a) $4x + ay = 4a$;   (b) $x + 2y = k$.

11. Write the equation of the system of lines whose normal axis has the slope $-\frac{3}{4}$.

12. Write the equations of two systems of lines, one parallel and the other perpendicular to the line whose equation is

(a) $3x - 4y = 12$;   (b) $x + 2y = 10$.

13. For each case in Problem 1 write the equation of the system of lines satisfying the first condition given, and then determine the value of the parameter such that the second condition is also satisfied.

14. Write the equation of the system of lines which passes through the point $(2, 6)$. Then find the value of the parameter for which the line forms with the coördinate axes a triangle of area 25.

15. Each line of a system forms with the coördinate axes a triangle of area 25. Write the equation of the system and find a value of the parameter such that the corresponding line passes through the point $(2, 6)$.

16. Find the equation of a straight line which passes through the point $(2, 11)$ and is tangent to the circle whose center is the origin and whose radius is 10.

17. Find the equation of a straight line which passes through the point $(18, -4)$ and has the sum of its intercepts equal to 20.

18. A line passes through the point $(5, 6)$ and cuts the lines $y = 2x$ and $y = 0$. Find the slope of the line if the segment intercepted by the given lines is bisected by the given point.

45. Systems of lines through the intersection of two given lines. Suppose that it is desired to find the equation of the system of lines through the intersection of two given lines. One way of doing this would be to solve the two given equations for the point of intersection and to use the point slope equation.

A method more expeditious and of great theoretical importance follows.

Theorem. *Let $l_1 = 0$ and $l_2 = 0$ be the equations* * *of two intersecting lines, and let k be an arbitrary constant. Then $l_1 + k \cdot l_2 = 0$ defines a system of lines passing through the intersection of the given lines.*

Proof. We first observe that $l_1 + k \cdot l_2 = 0$ defines a system of straight lines with k as a parameter, since it is obtained by adding two first degree equations.

Let the point of intersection P have coördinates (a, b). By the locus definition the equations $l_1 = 0$ and $l_2 = 0$ are both satisfied by $x = a$ and $y = b$, since $P(a, b)$ lies on both curves. Hence, the quantities $l_1(a, b)$ and $l_2(a, b)$ are both zero. Therefore $l_1(a, b) + k \cdot l_2(a, b) = 0$ for all values of k.

Hence every line of the system $l_1 + k \cdot l_2 = 0$ passes through P, since the coördinates of P satisfy the equation.†

EXAMPLE. Find the line containing the point $(2, 3)$ and the intersection of $l_1 : 3x + y - 5 = 0$ and $l_2 : x + 2y - 3 = 0$.

---

* The equation $l_1 = 0$ stands for an expression of the form
$$A_1 x + B_1 y + C_1 = 0,$$
and would more properly be written $l_1(x, y) = 0$, but the variables are omitted for convenience.

† We can also prove that *every* line passing through P (with the exception of $l_2 = 0$) belongs to the system. Let $l_3 = 0$ be another line through P, and let $P_1(x_1, y_1)$ be some other point on $l_3 = 0$. If the coördinates of P_1 be substituted in $l_1 + k \cdot l_2 = 0$, we obtain an equation
$$l_1(x_1, y_1) + k \cdot l_2(x_1, y_1) = 0$$
in which k, being the only unknown, can be found. For this value of k, the locus of the equation $l_1 + k \cdot l_2 = 0$ passes through P_1, since its coördinates make the left-hand member equal to zero. As it already passes through P, it must be identical with l_3, having two points in common with it.

When $k = 0$ the equation of the system becomes $l_1 = 0$, but for no value of k does it reduce to $l_2 = 0$. If we divide the equation through by k, we obtain $\frac{1}{k} l_1 + l_2 = 0$. This form of the equation shows that as k approaches infinity the corresponding lines of the system approach the line whose equation is $l_2 = 0$. In like manner the equation $y - 3 = m(x - 2)$ represents all lines passing through $(2, 3)$ except the one parallel to the y-axis. This one has an infinite slope and its equation is $x - 2 = 0$.

Solution. The system $l_1 + k \cdot l_2 = 0$ contains the intersection, and k may be found for the assumed point by substituting the coördinates of that point in the equation of the system, thus:

$$3x + y - 5 + k(x + 2y - 3) = 0$$

becomes $\qquad 6 + 3 - 5 + k(2 + 6 - 3) = 0,$

and $k = -\frac{4}{5}$; from which we have the result $11x - 3y - 13 = 0$.

Verification. Solving the given equations simultaneously, the intersection is $(\frac{7}{5}, \frac{4}{5})$. These coördinates and the coördinates $(2, 3)$ both satisfy the new equation.

The proof on page 72 will apply to any two equations of the form $f(x, y) = 0$, as well as to two linear equations. The general principle may be stated as follows:

The equation $f(x, y) + k \cdot g(x, y) = 0$ defines a system of curves passing through the intersections of the curves defined by the two equations $f(x, y) = 0$ and $g(x, y) = 0$.

PROBLEMS

1. A system of lines passes through the intersection of the lines $3x + y = 5$ and $x + 2y = 3$. Find the line of the system which has the slope $\frac{1}{2}$.

Hint. The equation of the system, $3x + y - 5 + k(x + 2y - 3) = 0$, can be written as $(3 + k)x + (1 + 2k)y - 5 - 3k = 0$. If this is solved for y, the coefficient of x is the slope.

2. Find the line of the system in Problem 1 which is parallel to the x-axis; also the line which is parallel to the y-axis.

3. Find by the method of the illustrative example the equations of the lines determined by

(a) $P(2, -1)$ and the intersection of $x - y = 10$ and $3x + 2y = 12$;

(b) $P(8, 1)$ and the intersection of $x + 2y = 8$ and $2x - 5y = 20$;

(c) $P(0, 3)$ and the intersection of $2x - y = 12$ and $y = 6$;

(d) $P(-1, -2)$ and the intersection of $3x - 4y = 12$ and $4x + 3y = 48$.

4. For each case in Problem 3 find the line which passes through the intersection of the given lines and has the slope $-\frac{2}{3}$.

5. For each case in Problem 3 find the line which passes through the intersection of the given lines and has the x-intercept -5.

6. For each case in Problem 3 find the line which passes through the intersection of the given lines and is parallel to the y-axis.

7. The sides of a triangle are given by each of the following sets of equations. Find the equations of the perpendiculars from the vertices to the opposite sides without finding the vertices.

(a) $4x - 2y = 7$, $x - 2y = 3$, $x + y = 8$;
(b) $3x - 2y = -15$, $3x + 2y = 0$, $5x + 4y = 20$;
(c) $3x + 2y = 5$, $3x - 5y = 10$, $x - y = 20$;
(d) $5x - 6y = 30$, $4x + y = 15$, $2x + 5y = 40$.

8. For each pair of lines in Problem 3 write the equation of the system of lines which pass through their intersection and plot the lines for which $k = \pm \frac{1}{2}$, ± 1, ± 2, ± 4. What happens when k approaches 0 and $+\infty$?

9. What can you say about the locus of the equation obtained by subtracting the equations $x^2 + y^2 - 10x = 0$ and $x^2 + y^2 - 20y = 0$?

10. Describe the system of lines whose equation is

$$3x - 5y + 7 + k(3x - 5y + 15) = 0.$$

What general theorem does this suggest?

11. Find and plot the equations of two curves which pass through the intersections of

(a) $x^2 + 4y^2 = 68$, (b) $2y = 12 - x^2$,
$\quad\ x^2 + y^2 = 10x$; $\qquad y = 4x - x^2$.

46. Plotting by factoring. Theorem. *If $l_1 = 0$ and $l_2 = 0$ define two lines, the locus of $l_1 \cdot l_2 = 0$ consists of these lines.*

Proof. This follows directly from the locus definition. For the coördinates of a point (a, b) on either line, say the first, satisfy its equation $l_1 = 0$. But if $l_1(x, y)$ vanishes for $x = a$ and $y = b$, the product of $l_1(x, y)$ and $l_2(x, y)$ must vanish for the same values, i.e., (a, b) lies on the locus of $l_1 \cdot l_2 = 0$.

Conversely, if (a, b) is on this locus, one of the factors $l_1(x, y)$, $l_2(x, y)$ must vanish for $x = a$, $y = b$. Hence the point (a, b) lies on the line defined by the equation formed by setting this factor equal to zero.

The utility of this theorem is made clear by the following illustration.

Consider the equation

$$x^2 - 4y^2 - x - 2y = 0.$$

Factoring, we have

$$(x + 2y)(x - 2y - 1) = 0.$$

Now the coördinates of any point on the line $x + 2y = 0$, as $(2, -1)$, make the first factor zero and hence the product is zero. Therefore all points on $x + 2y = 0$ lie on the locus of the given equation. The same is true of $x - 2y - 1 = 0$. Conversely, if a point lies on the locus of $x^2 - 4y^2 - x - 2y = 0$, its coördinates satisfy the equation and must make at least one of the factors of the left-hand member zero. Therefore each point of the given locus belongs to one of the lines $x + 2y = 0$, $x - 2y - 1 = 0$.

This reasoning applies to all equations of the form $f(x, y) = 0$, whether they define straight lines or not, although it is useful chiefly for linear factors. It leads to the following rule.

Rule for plotting by factoring. *Transpose all terms to the first member. Factor as far as possible; set each factor equal to zero, and plot the resulting equations on the same axes.*

NOTE. The above theorem makes it clear that, if we have an equation of a locus, we can form any number of other equations which have the same locus. All we have to do is to transpose all the terms to the left-hand member and multiply by a polynomial which is zero for no values of x and y or for only such values as are coördinates of points on the locus. For example, $(x - y)(x^2 + y^2) = 0$, $(x - y)(x^2 + y^2 + 6) = 0$, and $(x - y)(x^2 + y^2 - 2x - 2y + 2) = 0$ all have the same locus as $x - y = 0$. (See § 17, REMARKS.)

PROBLEMS

1. Plot by factoring the sets of lines defined by the following equations:

(a) $x^2 - 4y^2 = 0$;

(b) $x^2y + 3xy^2 - 10y^3 = 0$;

(c) $4x^2 + 2x - y^2 - y = 0$;

(d) $x^2 - y^2 + 2x + 4y - 3 = 0$;

(e) $3x^2 + 2xy - y^2 + 4x + 4y = 0$;

(f) $x^2 - 4xy + 4y^2 - 3x + 6y + 4 = 0$.

2. Draw the locus defined by

(a) $x^3 - 8y^3 = 0$;   (b) $x^4 - y^4 = 0$.

3. Find the area of the triangle defined by

(a) $2x^2y + xy^2 - 8xy = 0$;

(b) $x^2y + 8x^2 - 8y^2 - y^3 = 0$;

(c) $(x - 6)(x^2 - 4y^2 + 8x + 16) = 0$.

4. A quadrilateral is bounded by the loci of

$$9x^2 - 6xy + y^2 + 12x - 4y = 0$$

and $$(2x + y)^2 - 4(2x + y) - 12 = 0.$$

Find its angles.

5. Plot the locus of

(a) $x^3y + xy^3 = 25xy$;

(b) $x^4 - 32x^2 + 256 - y^4 = 0$;

(c) $(4x^2 + y^2 - 25)^2 - 16x^2y^2 = 0$.

6. What is the locus of $Ax^2 + Bx + C = 0$ when $B^2 - 4AC > 0$? when $B^2 - 4AC = 0$? when $B^2 - 4AC < 0$?

7. Write a single equation whose locus is one of the following pairs of lines:

(a) $3x + y = 5$, $3x - y = 5$;

(b) $x - 2y = 7$, $x = 2y$;

(c) $2x + y + 4 = 0$, $2x - y - 4 = 0$;

(d) $y = 2x - 10$, $y = 2x + 5$.

8. Show that the equation of a pair of parallel lines can be written in the form $(Ax + By)^2 + h(Ax + By) + k = 0$.

9. Show that the locus of $Ax^2 + Bxy + Cy^2 = 0$ is

(a) a pair of intersecting lines if $B^2 - 4AC > 0$;

(b) a single line if $B^2 - 4AC = 0$;

(c) imaginary if $B^2 - 4AC < 0$.

10. Choose the origin and the axes conveniently on a sheet of coördinate paper and write an equation whose locus contains the rulings on the paper.

11. Write a single equation whose locus is the bisectors of the angles between the lines defined by $4x^2 - y^2 + 12x + 6y = 0$.

12. The vertices of a triangle are $(-2, 1)$, $(3, 4)$, and $(-2, 6)$. Write a single equation whose locus contains the sides of the triangle.

CHAPTER IV

THE CIRCLE

47. The standard equation of the circle. While the equation of the straight line is expressed in several standard forms, depending on the choice of the geometric constants determining it, we use only one such form for the equation of a circle in rectangular coördinates. The constants used in determining the circle are the coördinates of its center and the length of its radius.

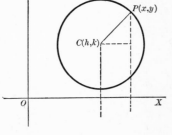

Let the coördinates of the center of the circle be (h, k), the length of the radius r, and the coördinates of the point tracing the circle (x, y). By the distance formula,

$$r = \sqrt{(x - h)^2 + (y - k)^2}.$$

This gives

$$(x - h)^2 + (y - k)^2 = r^2 \tag{13}$$

as the standard form of the equation of the circle.

When the center is at the origin, form (13) becomes

$$x^2 + y^2 = r^2. \tag{13a}$$

When properties involving circles are to be proved analytically, it is usually convenient to choose the origin so that this form can be used.

EXAMPLE. Prove that an angle inscribed in a semicircle is a right angle. (See figure on page 78.)

Solution. Let the radius of the circle be r; take the diameter as the x-axis and the center as the origin. Let $P(x, y)$ be any point on the circumference. We have to prove that BPC is a right angle.

77

Now the coördinates of B and C are $(-r, 0)$ and $(r, 0)$. Hence by the slope formula, the slope of BP is $\dfrac{y}{x + r}$; that of CP is $\dfrac{y}{x - r}$.

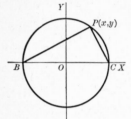

Calling these slopes m and m', we have

$$mm' = \frac{y^2}{x^2 - r^2}.$$

But $P(x, y)$ is on the circle. Therefore $x^2 + y^2 = r^2$, or $y^2 = r^2 - x^2$. This gives

$$mm' = \frac{r^2 - x^2}{x^2 - r^2} = -1,$$

which proves that BP and CP are perpendicular, or that BPC is a right angle.

In working problems of this kind the student should remember that the use of the equation of the circle is a necessary part of the solution; it is the essence of the analytic method of demonstration. If he does not use the equation, he is not using all the data and cannot expect to prove the theorem.

PROBLEMS

1. In each of the following cases write the equation of the circle in the standard form and simplify the result; also check the work by finding the intercepts and drawing the circle:

(a) center $(5, 8)$, radius 8;

(b) center $(5, -12)$, radius 13;

(c) center $(0, -7)$, radius 7;

(d) center $(5, 6)$, radius 10;

(e) center $(8, -6)$, radius 10;

(f) center $(-8, 0)$, radius 8;

(g) center $(-7, 5)$, radius 7;

(h) center $(-12, 7)$, radius 13;

(i) center $(-3, -3)$, radius 5.

2. Write the forms which the equation of the circle takes in the following cases:

(a) center on the x-axis;

(b) center on the y-axis;

(c) center on the x-axis and tangent to the y-axis;

(d) center on the y-axis and tangent to the x-axis.

3. Write the equations of the circles satisfying the following conditions and draw the figure in each case:

(a) tangent to the y-axis, radius 10, ordinate of center -6;

(b) tangent to both axes, radius 8, center in the second quadrant;

(c) passing through the origin, radius 10, abscissa of center 6;

(d) passing through the origin, x-intercept 8, y-intercept − 12;

(e) radius 10, x-intercepts 8 and − 4;

(f) tangent to the x-axis, y-intercepts 2 and 8.

4. Find the equation of the circle which has the segment joining the points (12, 6) and (− 3, − 2) as its diameter.

5. Find the equation of the circle which passes through the origin and has its x-intercept and y-intercept equal to a and b, respectively.

6. Find the equations of the circles which have their centers on the line $3x + 5y = 30$ and are tangent to both coördinate axes. (Two solutions.)

7. Find the equation of the circle which passes through the point (− 1, 7) and has its center at the point of intersection of the lines $2x + 3y = 12$ and $2x − 3y = 18$.

8. Find the equation of the circle which has its center at (− 10, 5) and is tangent to the line $3x + 4y = 20$.

9. Two opposite vertices of a regular octagon are (± r, 0). Find the coördinates of the other vertices and the length of a side.

10. Find the coördinates of the points of intersection of two circles, of which one has the center at the origin and the radius r and the other has the segment joining the origin to the point (a, 0) as a diameter.

11. Prove without the use of slopes that an angle inscribed in a semicircle is a right angle.

12. Prove that the sum of the squares of the distances of a point on a circle from the ends of a fixed diameter is a constant.

13. Prove that a line from the center of a circle bisecting a chord is perpendicular to it.

Hint. Let the ends of the chord be (− r, 0) and (b, c).

14. Prove that angles inscribed in the same segment of a circle are equal.

Hint. Let the ends of the segment be (c, d) and (− c, d) and prove that the tangent of the angle is constant.

48. The general equation of the circle. If we expand the standard form (13), we get

$$x^2 + y^2 − 2hx − 2ky + h^2 + k^2 − r^2 = 0.$$

This is of the form

$$x^2 + y^2 + Dx + Ey + F = 0, \qquad (14)$$

which may be called the *general form* of the circle equation. Conversely, this form represents a circle, since by completing the squares in x and y it is possible to reduce it back to form (13), which we know is the equation of a circle of center (h, k) and radius r. (Note exception, § 49.)

The general equation of the second degree has the form

$$Ax^2 + Bxy + Cy^2 + Dx + Ey + F = 0.$$

Comparison with (14) shows that this can be reduced to the same form if $B = 0$ and $A = C$, by dividing by A. Hence, if we extend the term "circle" to the degenerate forms discussed in § 49, we have the theorem:

An equation of the second degree in two variables defines a circle when, and only when, the coefficients of x^2 and y^2 are equal and the term in xy is missing.

49. Identification of center and radius. To find the center and the radius of a circle when the equation is given, reduce the equation to form (13).

EXAMPLE. Find the center and the radius of the circle

$$2x^2 - 8x + 2y^2 + 6y - 21 = 0.$$

Solution. Dividing by 2 and completing the squares, we have

$$x^2 - 4x + 4 + y^2 + 3y + \tfrac{9}{4} = \tfrac{21}{2} + 4 + \tfrac{9}{4},$$
or
$$(x - 2)^2 + (y + \tfrac{3}{2})^2 = \tfrac{67}{4}.$$

This is of form (13) and therefore represents a circle whose center is $(2, -\tfrac{3}{2})$ and whose radius is $\tfrac{1}{2}\sqrt{67} = 4.1$ approximately.

Degenerate forms. Sometimes on completing the squares the term corresponding to r^2 is negative, or zero. In the former case, it may be shown by the methods of § 29 that the locus is imaginary and we say that the graph is an *imaginary circle*. In the latter case, the radius of the circle is zero, and the graph is called a *point circle*. Such forms are sometimes known as degenerate forms.

50. Special forms. Comparing the general form (14) and the expansion of the standard form (13) in § 48, we see that,

$$D = -2h, \quad E = -2k, \quad \text{and} \quad F = h^2 + k^2 - r^2.$$

The first two of these relations enable us to determine the center by inspection. They also enable us to determine the following special forms:

if $D = 0$, $h = 0$ and the center is on the y-axis;
if $E = 0$, $k = 0$ and the center is on the x-axis;
if $D = 0$ and $E = 0$, the center is at the origin;
if $F = 0$, $h^2 + k^2 = r^2$, and the origin is on the circumference.

Exercise 1. Prove by considerations of symmetry that if $D = 0$, the center is on the y-axis.

51. A locus problem. In the problems of this kind so far given the equation of the locus could always be found by means of relations between the variable point tracing the locus and certain fixed points or lines. In more complicated problems the position of the tracing point may depend upon that of some variable point which lies on a given curve. The procedure illustrated below is often useful in such cases.

EXAMPLE. From a fixed point on a circle chords are drawn to the other points on the circle. Find the locus of the mid-points of the chords.

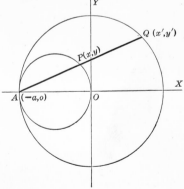

Solution. Let the given circle have its center at the origin and the radius a. Let the fixed point be $A(-a, 0)$. Let AQ be any chord from A and let P be its mid-point.

As we are required to find the locus of P, let its coördinates be (x, y). Let the coördinates of Q be (x', y'); then, by the equation of the circle

$$x'^2 + y'^2 = a^2.$$

With the aid of the mid-point formulas it is easily found that $x' = 2x + a$ and $y' = 2y$. Substituting these in the above equation, we have

$$(2x + a)^2 + 4y^2 = a^2.$$

Dividing this by 4, we obtain

$$\left(x + \frac{a}{2}\right)^2 + y^2 = \frac{a^2}{4}.$$

This shows that the locus is a circle, with the center at $(-a/2, 0)$ and the radius $a/2$; i.e., a circle whose diameter extends from the fixed point to the center of the given circle.

PROBLEMS

1. Find the center and the radius of each of the following circles. If the circle is real, illustrate by a figure.

(a) $x^2 + y^2 - 8x + 4y - 44 = 0$;   (f) $x^2 + y^2 - 10x + 7y + 9 = 0$;

(b) $x^2 + y^2 - 6x - 10y - 66 = 0$;   (g) $x^2 + y^2 + 16y + 28 = 0$;

(c) $x^2 + y^2 + 16x + 12y = 0$;   (h) $x^2 + y^2 + 4x - 6y - 33 = 0$;

(d) $2x^2 + 2y^2 = 9x$;   (i) $3x^2 + 3y^2 + 8x - 4y + 15 = 0$;

(e) $x^2 + y^2 + 16x - 12y + 36 = 0$;   (j) $x^2 + y^2 - 6x + 8y + 25 = 0$.

2. Find the center and the radius of each of the following circles. If the circle is real, illustrate by a figure.

(a) $x^2 + y^2 + 12x - 8y + 3 = 0$;   (f) $2x^2 + 2y^2 - 3x + 5y - 35 = 0$;

(b) $2x^2 + 2y^2 + 6x - 10y - 33 = 0$;   (g) $x^2 - 20x + y^2 - 125 = 0$;

(c) $x^2 + y^2 - 10x + 24y = 0$;   (h) $x^2 + y^2 - 18x + 8y + 17 = 0$;

(d) $x^2 + y^2 + 2x - 6y - 17 = 0$;   (i) $x^2 + y^2 - 6x + 4y + 13 = 0$;

(e) $x^2 + y^2 + 14y = 0$;   (j) $4x^2 + 4y^2 + 4x + 3 = 0$.

3. Determine by inspection which of the circles in Problem 1

(a) have their centers on the x-axis;

(b) have their centers on the y-axis;

(c) pass through the origin.

4. Determine by inspection the centers of the circles in Problem 2.

5. Determine the values of k for which the locus of each of the following equations is (i) a real circle; (ii) a point; (iii) an imaginary circle:

(a) $x^2 + y^2 + ky + 16 = 0$;   (b) $x^2 + y^2 + kx + 20 = 0$.

6. Draw several circles of each of the following systems:

(a) $(x - 4)^2 + (y - 5)^2 = k$;   (c) $x^2 + y^2 + Dx = 0$;

(b) $(x - h)^2 + y^2 = 25$;   (d) $x^2 + y^2 - 2rx - 2ry + r^2 = 0$.

7. Find the points of intersection and the equation of the common chord of the circles:

(a) $x^2 + y^2 + 8y = 64$,   (b) $x^2 + y^2 + 4x = 25$,

     $x^2 + y^2 - 6x = 16$; $x^2 + y^2 - 8y = -3$.

8. Find the equation of the locus of the vertex of a right triangle which has the ends of its hypotenuse at

(a) $(4, 0)$ and $(10, -8)$;   (b) $(0, 5)$ and $(5, -7)$.

9. The point $(5, 2)$ bisects a chord of the circle whose equation is $x^2 + y^2 + 2x + 14y = 80$. Find the equation of the chord and its length.

10. Find the equation of the circle which is tangent to the line whose equation is $4x - 3y = 24$ and which has its center at

(a) $(0, 0)$;   (b) $(-1, 1)$;   (c) $(-9, 0)$.

11. Find the equation of the tangent to each of the following circles at the point indicated.

(a) $x^2 + y^2 - 6x = 91, (-3, 8)$;   (c) $x^2 + y^2 + 10x = 60, (4, 2)$;

(b) $x^2 + y^2 + 8y = 153, (5, 8)$;   (d) $x^2 + y^2 - 12y = 36, (6, 0)$.

12. Find the angles of intersection between the line $x - 2y = 8$ and each of the following circles:

(a) $x^2 + y^2 - 12y = 64$;   (b) $x^2 + y^2 - 2x - 18y = 223$.

Hint. The angle of intersection between a line and a curve is defined as the angle between the curve and the tangent at the point of intersection.

13. In each of the following, tangents are drawn from the given point to the given circle. Find the coördinates of the points of contact.

(a) $x^2 + y^2 - 4y - 36 = 0, (4, 10)$;

(b) $x^2 + y^2 - 8x - 84 = 0, (9, -10)$;

(c) $x^2 + y^2 + 16y - 105 = 0, (-7, 9)$.

14. In each case in Problem 13 find the equations of the tangents.

15. For the corresponding circle in Problem 13 find the points of contact where the slope of the tangents is

(a) $\dfrac{1}{3}$;   (b) $\dfrac{4}{3}$;   (c) $-\dfrac{12}{5}$.

16. A segment of slope -1 in the first quadrant has its ends on the coördinate axes and is trisected by the circle $x^2 + y^2 = r^2$. Find the coördinates of its end points.

17. From the point $A(a, 0)$ a line is drawn cutting the circle $x^2 + y^2 = r^2$ in points P and Q. For what slope of the line will P bisect AQ? For what relation between a and r is there no solution?

General Hint. In the following, if the coördinate axes are not determined by the conditions of the problem, they should be chosen according to the directions of § 20. In each case, after deriving the equation of the locus, draw a figure to show the relation of the locus to the given conditions.

18. The base of a triangle has the ends $(a, 0)$ and $(-a, 0)$. Find the locus of the opposite vertex if

    (*a*) the vertical angle is 90°;

    (*b*) the vertical angle is 45°;

    (*c*) the tangent of the vertical angle is any constant k;

    (*d*) the median to one of the variable sides is a constant k.

19. Find the locus of a point from which the tangents to the circle $x^2 + y^2 = r^2$ are perpendicular to each other.

20. Find the locus of a point whose distance from the point $(a, 0)$ is k times its distance from the origin.

21. From the point $(a, 0)$ a line is drawn to the circle $x^2 + y^2 = r^2$. Find the locus of the mid-point.

22. A fixed point O and a fixed line whose distance from O is a are given. On any segment OQ joining O to a point on the line a point P is chosen, so that $OP \times OQ = k$, a constant. Find the locus of P.

23. The distance between two fixed points is $2c$. Find the locus of a point, which moves so that the sum of the squares of its distances from the fixed points is a constant, k.

24. The ends of a straight line of constant length a lie on two perpendicular lines. Find the locus of the middle point.

25. Find the locus of a point if the sum of the squares of its distances from (*a*) the sides, (*b*) the vertices, of a given square is constant.

26. From one end of a diameter of a circle whose radius is r chords are drawn and produced their own length. Find the locus of the ends of these lines.

27. Find the locus of a point P such that the line joining P to the origin makes equal angles with the lines joining P to the points $(4, 0)$ and $(-6, 0)$.

52. The equation of the circle derived from three conditions.
The correspondence between the geometric conditions which
determine a circle and the algebraic conditions which determine
its equation is analogous to that discussed for the straight line.
The number of independent constants in the general linear
equation

$$Ax + By + C = 0$$

is two, for if we divide each term by A, we have the form

$$x + B'y + C' = 0.$$

Geometrically, a straight line is determined by two points,
or in general by two geometric conditions. Both forms (13)
and (14) of the circle equation involve three arbitrary constants.
Geometrically a circle is determined by three points not on a
straight line. A circle may be determined in other ways than
by the condition of passing through three points, but the
determining condition is in any case threefold.

To derive the equation when the geometric conditions are
given, it is necessary to express these conditions in three equations
involving h, k, and r (or D, E, and F) and solve them
simultaneously. The method is illustrated by the following
examples.

EXAMPLE 1. Find the equation of the circle passing through $(1, 7)$,
$(8, 6)$, and $(7, -1)$.

Solution. Each pair of these coördinates must satisfy the standard
equation of the circle (13).

Hence
$$(1 - h)^2 + (7 - k)^2 = r^2,$$
$$(8 - h)^2 + (6 - k)^2 = r^2,$$
$$(7 - h)^2 + (-1 - k)^2 = r^2.$$

Solving these equations simultaneously,* we find that $h = 4$, $k = 3$,
and $r = 5$. Therefore the equation is $(x - 4)^2 + (y - 3)^2 = 25$.

---

* By expanding all three equations and subtracting the first in turn from
the second and third, we eliminate h^2, k^2, and r^2, and obtain

$$7h - k = 25$$
and
$$3h - 4k = 0.$$

From these we easily find that $h = 4$ and $k = 3$. Substitution of these values
in any one of the three original equations gives $r = 5$.

We may also solve the problem by using form (14), which gives

$$1 + 49 + D + 7E + F = 0,$$
$$64 + 36 + 8D + 6E + F = 0,$$
$$49 + 1 + 7D - E + F = 0.$$

Solving simultaneously, we have

$$D = -8, \quad E = -6, \quad \text{and} \quad F = 0.$$

Then the equation of the circle is $x^2 + y^2 - 8x - 6y = 0$, which may be reduced to $(x - 4)^2 + (y - 3)^2 = 25$ by completing squares.

EXAMPLE 2. Find the equation of a circle whose radius is $4\sqrt{5}$ and which is tangent to the line $x - 2y = 20$ at the point $(6, -7)$.

Solution. In this problem it is given that $r = 4\sqrt{5}$. Let the center C have the coördinates (h, k) as usual. Since the point $(6, -7)$ is on the circle we have at once

$$(6 - h)^2 + (-7 - k)^2 = r^2 = 80. \tag{1}$$

Since the tangent to a circle is perpendicular to the radius drawn to the point of contact, the slope of the line joining C to $(6, -7)$ is the negative reciprocal of the slope of the line $x - 2y = 20$. The former slope is $\dfrac{k + 7}{h - 6}$ and the latter is $\dfrac{1}{2}$. Hence

$$\frac{k + 7}{h - 6} = -2. \tag{2}$$

The simultaneous solutions of equations (1) and (2) are the values of h and k. From equation (2) we find that

$$k + 7 = 2(6 - h).$$

Substituting this in equation (1), we obtain

$$5(6 - h)^2 = 80.$$

This gives $6 - h = \pm 4$, whence $h = 2$ and $h = 10$. The corresponding values of k are 1 and -15.

There are then two solutions: one in which the center is at $(2, 1)$ and the other in which the center is at $(10, -15)$. The equations of the circles are

$$(x - 2)^2 + (y - 1)^2 = 80$$

and

$$(x - 10)^2 + (y + 15)^2 = 80.$$

We can also solve the problem by using the formula for the distance from a line to a point. By § 41 the distance from the line $x - 2y = 20$ to the center (h, k) is $\dfrac{h - 2k - 20}{-\sqrt{5}}$. This is equal to $+ 4\sqrt{5}$ or $- 4\sqrt{5}$ according to whether the center is above or below the line. Hence

$$h - 2k = 0 \quad \text{or} \quad h - 2k = 40.$$

Solving the first equation simultaneously with equation (2), we get the center $(2, 1)$. From the second equation we get the center $(10, - 15)$.

An effective graphical check in problems of this kind is to draw the circle with compasses and observe whether or not it satisfies the given conditions.

PROBLEMS

1. Find the equation of the circle which passes through the points:

(a) $(- 2, 5), (8, 5), (- 6, 9)$;

(b) $(0, 0), (8, 0), (- 2, - 6)$;

(c) $(- 6, 3), (- 6, 7), (10, 5)$;

(d) $(6, 3), (4, - 11), (- 10, - 9)$;

(e) $(7, - 8), (0, 9), (- 10, - 15)$;

(f) $(1, 7), (8, 6), (7, - 1)$.

2. Find the equation of the circle which passes through the points:

(a) $(0, 0), (9, 9), (4, 8)$;

(b) $(8, 1), (4, 9), (5, 10)$;

(c) $(- 3, 1), (- 3, 9), (5, 5)$;

(d) $(10, 0), (6, 8), (- 8, 6)$;

(e) $(9, - 1), (1, - 7), (5, - 9)$;

(f) $(3, 2), (- 2, - 3), (1, 9)$.

3. Find the equation of the circle which

(a) passes through the points $(0, 3)$ and $(0, 12)$ and is tangent to the x-axis;

(b) passes through the points $(- 3, 0)$ and $(5, 6)$ and has the radius $5\sqrt{2}$;

(c) circumscribes the triangle bounded by the lines

$$y = 4, \quad 4x - 5y + 20 = 0, \quad \text{and} \quad 4x - 7y + 20 = 0;$$

(d) passes through the points $(6, 4)$ and $(- 4, - 2)$ and has its center on the line $2x - 3y = 20$;

(e) is tangent to the line $4x + 3y = 27$ at the point $(3, 5)$ and passes through the point $(- 4, 6)$;

(f) is tangent to the line $3x + 2y = 16$ and passes through the points $(1, 0)$ and $(- 3, 6)$;

(*g*) is tangent to the lines $x + 2y = 10$ and $2x + y = 9$ and passes through the origin;

(*h*) is inscribed in the triangle bounded by the lines

$$12x - 5y = 0, \quad 4x + 3y = 48, \quad \text{and} \quad 5x - 12y = 0;$$

(*i*) is tangent to the circle $x^2 + y^2 - 10x = 0$ and passes through the points $(-5, 5)$ and $(3, 11)$;

(*j*) is tangent to the circle $x^2 + y^2 - 10x = 0$ at the point $(9, 3)$ and has the radius 13.

4. Find the equation of the circle which

(*a*) passes through the points $(8, 0)$ and $(10, 4)$ and is tangent to the *y*-axis;

(*b*) passes through the points $(5, 2)$ and $(10, -3)$ and has its center on the *y*-axis;

(*c*) passes through the point $(2, 9)$ and is tangent to both axes;

(*d*) is tangent to the line $4x - 3y = 18$ and has its center at $(-3, 5)$;

(*e*) is tangent to the line $x + 2y = 20$ at the point $(10, 5)$ and has the radius $4\sqrt{5}$.

5. How many circles are tangent to all three of the circles

$$x^2 + y^2 - 4 = 0,$$
$$x^2 + y^2 - 24x + 2y + 136 = 0,$$
and $\qquad x^2 + y^2 - 2x - 20y + 76 = 0?$

Write simultaneous equations whose solutions will give the center and radius of one of these tangent circles. What difficulties are encountered in solving these equations?

53. Length of a tangent. Let t be the length of the tangent P_1T, let (h, k) be the coördinates of the center C, and let r be the radius. Then

$$t^2 = CP_1^2 - CT^2.$$

Using the distance formula, this becomes

$$t^2 = (x_1 - h)^2 + (y_1 - k)^2 - r^2. \quad (15)$$

It is observed that the expression for t is the same in form as the equation of the circle, with the coördinates of P_1 substituted for the variables. Note the similarity of this to the formula for the distance from a line to a point.

Since the right-hand member of (15) is the same in form as the standard equation of the circle, it may also be written

$$t^2 = x_1{}^2 + y_1{}^2 + Dx_1 + Ey_1 + F. \qquad (15a)$$

EXAMPLE. Find the length of the tangent from (1, 4) to the circle

$$x^2 + y^2 - 4x + 6y - 12 = 0.$$

Also find the point of tangency.

Solution. Using Formula 15a, we have

$$t^2 = 1 + 16 - 4 + 24 - 12 = 25,$$
or $\qquad t = 5.$

Since the point of tangency is 5 units distant from (1, 4), it lies on the circle:

$$(x - 1)^2 + (y - 4)^2 = 25,$$
or $\qquad x^2 + y^2 - 2x - 8y - 8 = 0.$

But it also lies on the given circle:

$$x^2 + y^2 - 4x + 6y - 12 = 0.$$

Solving these equations simultaneously, we obtain the solutions (5, 1) and $(-2, 0)$ corresponding to the two possible tangents.

54. Common chord of two circles. To find the common chord of two circles we may solve the equations simultaneously, to get the points of intersection, and then use the two-point form of the line equation. A better method will now be illustrated.

Let the two circles have the equations

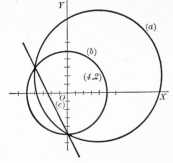

$$x^2 + y^2 - 8x - 4y - 44 = 0, \quad (a)$$
and $\qquad x^2 + y^2 - 25 = 0. \quad (b)$
Subtracting,
$$8x + 4y + 19 = 0. \quad (c)$$

By the theorem of § 45 the locus of (c) contains the points common to (a) and (b). Since it is of the first degree, it defines a straight line. Hence this line is the common chord.

The equation of the common chord of two circles can always be obtained by subtracting the equation of one of them from that of the other, as above. For, since nothing above the first degree appears in the equation of a circle except the characteristic terms $x^2 + y^2$, which are always present, these will be cancelled by subtraction, leaving a linear equation whose locus contains the points of intersection of the two circles.

Exercise 2. Derive the general equation of the common chord of two circles.

$$Ans. \quad (D - D')x + (E - E')y + (F - F') = 0.$$

Exercise 3. Prove that the common chord of two circles is perpendicular to their line of centers.

Hint. The line of centers of two circles is determined by the points (h, k) and (h', k'). Hence its slope is $\dfrac{k - k'}{h - h'}$. Compare this with the slope of the common chord found in Exercise 2 and express the result in terms of h, k, h', and k'.

55. Radical axis. Consider the following two examples.

Example 1. Find the equation of the common chord of the circles

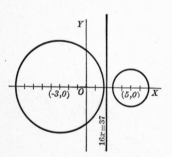

$$(x + 3)^2 + y^2 = 25$$
and $$(x - 5)^2 + y^2 = 4,$$

and the coördinates of the points of intersection of the circles.

Applying § 54, the equation is found to be $16x = 37$; but the points of intersection are imaginary, as is seen by inspection of the equations, since the sum of the radii is 7, while the distance between the centers is $3 + 5 = 8$.

Example 2. Find the equation of the common chord of the circles

$$(x + 3)^2 + y^2 = 25$$
and $$(x - 5)^2 + y^2 = 9.$$

Here the distance between the centers is the same as the sum of the radii and the circles are tangent to each other at the point (2, 0). Also we have by subtraction $x = 2$, whose locus, passing through the point (2, 0) and being perpendicular to the line of centers, is the common tangent.

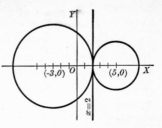

Thus we see that the application of the rule for finding a common chord gives a common chord when the two circles intersect, a common tangent when they are tangent, and finally, when they do not meet, a line which has no apparent significance. We shall find, however, that the line in all three cases has a common property; viz., it is the locus of the point from which tangents to the two circles are equal.

To prove this, let t and t' be the lengths of equal tangents from

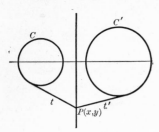

P to the circles C and C' respectively, of which the equations are

$$x^2 + y^2 + Dx + Ey + F = 0,$$

and $x^2 + y^2 + D'x + E'y + F' = 0.$

From § 53, Formula 15a,

$$t^2 = x^2 + y^2 + Dx + Ey + F.$$

Also $t'^2 = x^2 + y^2 + D'x + E'y + F'.$

Hence

$$t^2 - t'^2 = (D - D')x + (E - E')y + F - F'.$$

By hypothesis, $t = t'$, or $t^2 - t'^2 = 0.$

Therefore,

$$(D - D')x + (E - E')y + F - F' = 0 \qquad (16)$$

is the equation of the locus of P.

But this is the equation obtained by eliminating the terms in x^2 and y^2. Hence we have the theorem:

The locus of the point from which the tangents to two circles are equal is the line whose equation is obtained by eliminating the terms in x^2 and y^2 between the equations of the circles.

This locus is called the *radical axis*. When the circles intersect, it is their common chord; and when they touch, it is their common tangent.

56. Systems of circles. The geometric constants of the circle designated by h, k, and r determine the center and radius. If two of these constants are restricted by assigning conditions to them, numerical or otherwise, the equation will represent a *system of circles* defined more or less completely according to the nature of the conditions.

Thus, if $h = 2$ and $k = 4$, we have a system of concentric circles of varying radius. Again, if $h = k$ and $r = 10$, we have a system of equal circles whose centers lie on the line $x - y = 0$.

Systems having the same radical axis. If we use the theorem of § 45, we find that $C + k \cdot C' = 0$, where k is any constant and $C = 0$ and $C' = 0$ are the equations of two circles, will define a system of circles passing through the points of intersection of C and C'. But the radical axis of any two circles passes through the points of intersection, real or imaginary; hence this equation defines a system of circles having the same radical axis.

The figure on page 93 illustrates the system of circles having the same radical axis as

$$x^2 + y^2 + 4x - 96 = 0,$$
and $$x^2 + y^2 - 21x + 54 = 0.$$

These meet at the points $(6, 6)$ and $(6, -6)$; the equation of the radical axis is $x = 6$. The equation of the system is

$$x^2 + y^2 + 4x - 96 + k(x^2 + y^2 - 21x + 54) = 0.$$

In the figure the circles drawn in heavy lines are the given circles and the others are the circles corresponding to

$$k = \tfrac{1}{4}, 1, 4, -\tfrac{1}{5}, -\tfrac{1}{2}, -1, -\tfrac{5}{3}, -3, -6.$$

Note that when k approaches -1, the circle becomes of infinite size and approaches as a limit the radical axis.

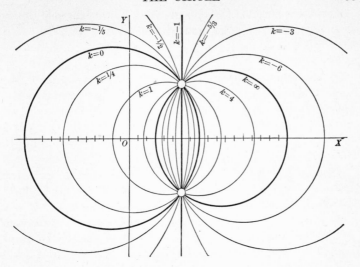

PROBLEMS

1. Find the least distance from the point (5, 10) to each circle of Problem 2, page 82.

2. Find the length of the tangent from the point (5, 10) to each circle of Problem 2, page 82.

3. Solve each case of Problem 13, page 83, by the method of the illustrative example in § 53.

4. Find the locus of a point such that the tangent from this point to the circle $x^2 + y^2 + 4x + 6y = 7$ has the length 7.

5. Prove that, if two different circles are concentric, there is no point from which the tangents to the two circles are of equal length.

6. Find the equations of the radical axes and the points of intersection of the following pairs of circles:

(a) $x^2 + y^2 + 8x + 12y = 28$,
$\quad x^2 + y^2 - 4x - 12y + 20 = 0$;

(b) $x^2 + y^2 + 12x - 288 = 0$,
$\quad x^2 + y^2 - 18x - 30y + 252 = 0$;

(c) $x^2 + y^2 + 10x + 18y + 8 = 0$,
$\quad 3x^2 + 3y^2 + 26x + 44y + 12 = 0$;

(d) $x^2 + y^2 + 6x + 5y - 23 = 0,$
$\quad x^2 + y^2 + 5x + 7y - 18 = 0;$

(e) $x^2 + y^2 - 4x + 8y - 8 = 0,$
$\quad x^2 + y^2 - 4x + 6y - 14 = 0;$

(f) $x^2 + y^2 + 9x - 7y + 6 = 0,$
$\quad x^2 + y^2 + 10x - 6y + 9 = 0;$

(g) $x^2 + y^2 = 100,$
$\quad x^2 + y^2 + 4x - 8y = 220;$

(h) $x^2 + y^2 - 10x - 10y = 150,$
$\quad x^2 + y^2 + 30x + 10y + 350 = 0.$

7. Find the point from which equal tangents can be drawn to each of the following sets of circles:

(a) $x^2 + y^2 + 8y = 20,$ \qquad (b) $x^2 + y^2 + 12y + 24 = 0,$
$\quad x^2 + y^2 - 8x = 48,$ \qquad\qquad $x^2 + y^2 + 12x - 16y + 90 = 0,$
$\quad x^2 + y^2 - 24x = -128;$ \qquad $x^2 + y^2 - 16x - 12y - 64 = 0.$

8. For each pair of circles in Problem 6 find the line of centers, and prove that it is perpendicular to the radical axis.

9. Prove that the radical axes of any three circles taken in pairs meet in a point or are parallel.

10. For each pair of circles in Problem 6 find the equation of the circle which passes through their points of intersection and also through the point (2, 2).

Hint. First write the equation of the system of circles passing through the points of intersection.

11. For each pair of circles in Problem 6 find the equation of the circle which passes through their points of intersection and has its center on the x-axis.

Hint. If the center is on the x-axis, what must be the coefficient of the first degree term in y?

CHAPTER V

THE PARABOLA

57. Definition. *The parabola is the locus of a point such that its distance from a fixed point is equal to its distance from a fixed line.*

The fixed point is called the *focus* and the fixed line the *directrix*. The line through the focus perpendicular to the directrix is called the *principal axis*. The point on the principal axis midway between the focus and the directrix lies on the locus and is called the *vertex* of the parabola.

58. Equations of the parabola. If the origin is taken at the vertex and the principal axis is one of the coördinate axes, very simple equations are obtained for the parabola.

Let us first use the principal axis as the x-axis and take the case that the focus is on the positive half of the axis. In the figure AB is the directrix, F is the focus, and O is the vertex. Call the distance between the directrix and the focus p. Then the coördinates of F are $\left(\dfrac{p}{2},\ 0\right)$, and the equation of the directrix is $x = -\dfrac{p}{2}$.

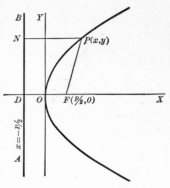

Let $P(x, y)$ be any point on the locus. Draw NP perpendicular to AB, and join FP. By definition $FP = NP$, that is,

$$\sqrt{\left(x - \frac{p}{2}\right)^2 + y^2} = x + \frac{p}{2}.$$

Squaring and reducing, we have

$$y^2 = 2px.\qquad(17)$$

If the principal axis is taken as the y-axis, with the vertex at the origin and the focus on the positive half of the axis, the variables are interchanged and the equation is

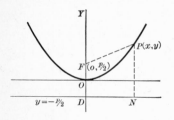

$$x^2 = 2py.\qquad(17a)$$

If the focus is taken in the negative direction from the vertex, we get two other forms corresponding to these. They are

$$y^2 = -2px,\qquad(17b)$$

and

$$x^2 = -2py.\qquad(17c)$$

The simplicity of these equations is due entirely to the choice of the coördinate axes. If the axes are chosen in any other way, a different and more complicated equation is obtained, but the curve itself is unaltered.* Therefore we shall study the properties of the parabola by means of the simple forms and reserve the general equations for a later chapter.

Exercise 1. Derive equation ($17a$) from a figure.

Exercise 2. Derive equation ($17b$) from a figure.

59. Discussion of the parabola. The form of equation (17) shows that the parabola is symmetrical with respect to the principal axis, and that the parabola crosses this axis at the vertex only.

Since negative values of x make y imaginary, the curve lies wholly to the right of the vertex and has no point nearer the directrix. It recedes indefinitely from both axes, since $y = \pm \sqrt{2px}$ increases indefinitely with x. A different parabola is obtained for each value assigned to p.

* The student should review Example 2, § 20, and Problem 2, page 29, to see the truth of this statement.

60. Latus rectum. A line joining the focus F to any point of the parabola is a *focal radius;* a chord of the parabola passing through F is a *focal chord.* The focal chord $L'L$ parallel to the directrix is called the *latus rectum.* By definition of the parabola, the distance of L from the focus is the same as that from the directrix.

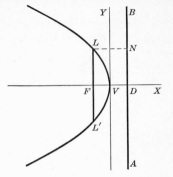

Hence

$$FL = LN = FD = p$$

and the length of the whole latus rectum is $2p$.

Exercise 3. If $P(x, y)$ is any point of the parabola whose equation is $y^2 = 2px$, show that the length of the focal radius to P is $x + \dfrac{p}{2}$.

61. Construction of the parabola. Consider the equation $x^2 = -8y$. This is of the form $x^2 = -2py$, and hence is the equation of a parabola. To draw the curve we can make a table of values as usual, or proceed according to one of the three following methods.

1. *A sketch.* From the form of the equation, $2p = 8$, or $p = 4$. Since the sign before $2p$ is minus, the curve lies wholly below the x-axis.

Hence the focus is $\left(0, -\dfrac{p}{2}\right)$, or $(0, -2)$, and the equation of the directrix is $y = 2$. Measuring off $p = 4$ to the right and left of the focus gives the ends of the latus rectum. These together with the vertex O make three points on the curve, which suffice for a sketch, as the general shape of a parabola is known. The sketch can be improved easily by also locating the points $(\pm 2p, -2p)$.

2. *A construction by ruler and compasses.* If a more accurate graph is desired, find the focus and directrix as before. Then with the focus as a center and a radius $r > \dfrac{p}{2}$ draw an arc. This will cut the line parallel to the directrix and r units from it in two points which lie on the parabola by definition. By using coordinate paper and varying r, as many points as are desired may be readily constructed.

3. *A mechanical construction.* Place a right triangle with one leg CE on the directrix. Fasten one end of a string whose length is CD at the focus F and the other end to the triangle at D. With a pencil at P keep the string taut. Then $FP = CP$; and as the triangle is moved along the directrix the point P will describe a parabola.

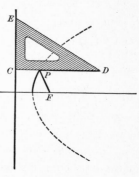

62. The parabola as a conic section. In the right circular cone O–AB pass a plane through the vertex O and the diameter of the base AB. It will be perpendicular to the base and will contain the elements OA and OB, and also the axis and the center of every section parallel to the base.

Draw a plane perpendicular to the plane OAB intersecting it in the line MN parallel to OA, and cutting the surface of the cone in CND.

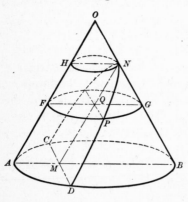

Through P, any point of CND, and N pass planes parallel to the base, intersecting the plane OAB in HN and FG, which are the diameters of the circular sections thus formed.

Now QP, the intersection of the planes FPG and CND, is perpendicular to OAB and hence to the lines FG and NM. Taking N as the origin and NM as the x-axis, the coördinates of P are $x = NQ$ and $y = QP$.

Then $$y^2 = \overline{QP}^2 = FQ \cdot QG.$$

By elementary geometry,

$$FQ = HN, \quad \text{and} \quad \frac{QG}{NQ} = \frac{HN}{OH}, \quad \text{or} \quad QG = \frac{HN}{OH}x.$$

Substituting, $$y^2 = \frac{\overline{HN}^2}{OH}x.$$

As HN and OH are constants, being independent of the position of P, $\dfrac{\overline{HN}^2}{OH}$ may be taken as $2p$. Thus the section CND is a parabola.

63. Properties and applications. The parabola, ellipse, and hyperbola were well known to the Greek geometers, who obtained them as plane sections of a conical surface and discovered most of their geometrical properties. (The proof in § 62 is essentially a special case of the more general proof by Apollonius for an oblique cone.) Menaechmus (*circa* 350 B.C.) is believed to have discovered the curves; his solution of the problem of duplicating the cube is indicated in Problem 11, page 101. Euclid (*circa* 300 B.C.) and Aristaeus (before Euclid) wrote books on them; one of the achievements of Archimedes (287–212 B.C.) was to find the area of a parabolic segment. The works of Euclid and Aristaeus were lost, but are apparently embodied in the first part of the great work of Apollonius of Perga (*circa* 230 B.C.), which became the standard treatise on the subject. To him are due the names of these curves.

In addition to properties already given the following may be mentioned here. The mid-points of all chords which have the same slope are on a line parallel to the principal axis. (See § 148.) The area of the segment formed by a parabola and any chord is equal to two thirds the area of the parallelogram having the given chord for one side and the opposite side tangent to the parabola.

The importance of the curve today is due chiefly to its scientific applications, which in turn are a consequence of its purely mathematical properties. Unfortunately a complete discussion of most of these applications cannot be given without the aid of the calculus, but it may be of interest at this point to state a few without proof.

If a parabola is rotated about its axis a parabolic surface is formed. Rays of light parallel to the axis and meeting the concave side of this surface are reflected so as to pass through the focus. Conversely, if a source of light be placed at the focus, all rays which meet the surface will be reflected parallel to the axis. It is for this reason that parabolic reflectors are used in searchlights. (See § 146.)

A projectile which is fired at any elevation traces a path which is approximately a parabola. If there were no atmosphere to retard the progress of the projectile, the path would be a true parabola. (See § 130.)

Several different types of bridges involve the use of a parabolic arch, with the vertex either above or below the roadbed of the bridge. The cable of a suspension bridge whose total weight is uniformly distributed over the length of the bridge also takes the form of a parabola.

PROBLEMS

1. From each of the following equations find the coördinates of the focus, the equation of the directrix, and the length of the latus rectum, and draw the parabola to scale:

(a) $y^2 = 16x$;

(b) $x^2 = 12y$;

(c) $x^2 = -12y$;

(d) $5y^2 + 36x = 0$;

(e) $y^2 = -6x$;

(f) $x = 9y^2$;

(g) $x^2 = 24y$;

(h) $x^2 + 16y = 0$;

(i) $y^2 = 4ax$;

(j) $y = 4ax^2$.

2. The same as Problem 1 for the following equations:

(a) $y^2 = 10x$;

(b) $y^2 = -10x$;

(c) $x^2 = 18y$;

(d) $5x^2 + 36y = 0$;

(e) $x^2 + 4ay = 0$;

(f) $x = ky^2$;

(g) $y^2 + 20x = 0$;

(h) $x^2 - 9y = 0$;

(i) $x^2 + 15y = 0$;

(j) $y^2 = 24x$.

3. Write the equations of parabolas satisfying the following data:

(a) directrix $y = 4$, focus $(0, -4)$;

(b) directrix $x = -5$, focus $(5, 0)$;

(c) vertex $(0, 0)$, focus $(0, a)$;

(d) vertex $(0, 0)$, one point of the curve $(10, -10)$;

(e) vertex $(0, 0)$, directrix $y = -6$;

(f) vertex $(0, 0)$, focus $(-6, 0)$.

4. Write the equations of parabolas satisfying the following data:

(a) directrix $y = 5$, focus $(0, -5)$;

(b) directrix $x = -a$, vertex $(0, 0)$;

(c) vertex $(0, 0)$, focus $(0, -6)$;

(d) vertex $(0, 0)$, one point of the curve $(8, -6)$;

(e) directrix $x = 3$, focus $(-3, 0)$;

(f) vertex $(0, 0)$, focus $(4, 0)$.

5. In the parabola $y^2 = 2px$ an equilateral triangle is inscribed with one vertex at the origin. Find the length of a side.

6. In the parabola $y^2 = 2px$ an isosceles right triangle is inscribed with the vertex of the right angle at the origin. Find its area.

7. In Problem 6 find the length of the hypotenuse of the right triangle.

8. In Problem 5 find the area of the triangle.

9. Find the equation of the circle which circumscribes the portion of the parabola $x^2 = 2py$ cut off by the latus rectum.

10. Find the formulas for the focal radius of a point analogous to that in Exercise 3, page 97, in the case of the equations $x^2 = 2py$ and $x^2 = -2py$.

11. Find the points of intersection of the parabolas $y^2 = 2ax$ and $x^2 = ay$. (This gives a solution of the problem of "duplicating a cube.")

12. A parabola has its vertex at the origin and its axis is the y-axis. If one end of a focal chord is $(-6, -4)$, find the other end.

13. A circle of radius 10 has its center at the focus of the parabola $y^2 = 12x$. Where does it intersect the parabola?

14. One end of a focal chord of the parabola $y^2 = 2px$ is $(2p, 2p)$. Find the other end.

15. The focal radius of a certain point on the parabola $y^2 = 2px$ has the same length as the latus rectum. Find the coördinates of the point.

16. What condition must be imposed on the arbitrary constant a in order that the circle $x^2 + y^2 - 2ay = 0$ and the parabola $x^2 = 2py$ meet in exactly one point?

17. Show that the mid-points of all chords of the parabola $y^2 = 2px$ which have the slope m have the same ordinate, namely $\dfrac{p}{m}$.

18. From any point of the parabola $x^2 = 2py$ lines are drawn to the ends of the latus rectum. Show that the difference of their slopes is 1.

19. Show that the lines drawn from the intersection of the directrix and the principal axis of a parabola to the ends of the latus rectum are perpendicular to each other.

20. Show that the distance of the mid-point of any focal chord of a parabola from the directrix is one half the length of the chord.

21. With any point of the parabola $x^2 = 2py$ as a center a circle is drawn so as to pass through the point $(0, p)$. Show that it intercepts a segment on the x-axis of length $2p$.

22. A right triangle is inscribed in the parabola $x^2 = 2py$ with the vertex of the right angle at the origin. Find the point where the hypotenuse cuts the y-axis.

Hint. Take the slopes of the legs as k and $-\dfrac{1}{k}$.

23. The radius of a right circular cone is 12 and its altitude is 16. How should a plane section be cut so as to make a parabola with the latus rectum 6?

24. Find the locus of a point whose distance from the point $(-3, 0)$ is two units less than its distance from the line $x = 5$.

25. Find the locus of a point whose distance from the point $(0, -5)$ is 5 units less than its distance from the line $y = 10$.

26. The ends of the base of a triangle are the points $(\pm a, 0)$. Find the locus of the opposite vertex if the ratio of the length of the base to that of the altitude is equal to the slope of the median to the base.

27. Two vertices of a triangle are $A(2a, a)$ and $B(-2a, a)$. Find the locus of the third vertex C if the slope of BC is one unit less than the slope of AC.

28. Find the locus of the center of a circle which is tangent to a given line and passes through a fixed point whose distance from the given line is $2a$.

29. Find the locus of the mid-points of the ordinates of the parabola $x^2 = 2py$.

30. In the parabola $y^2 = 16x$ chords are drawn from the vertex to each point of the curve. Find the locus of the mid-points.

31. Find the locus of the ends of the latus rectum of the parabola $y^2 = 2px$ when p is allowed to vary.

32. Find the locus of the centers of circles which are tangent to the y-axis and to the circle $x^2 + y^2 = 2rx$.

33. The vertex of a triangle is fixed at the point $(0, a)$ and the base is a segment of the x-axis of length $2a$. Find the locus of the center of the circle circumscribed about the triangle.

34. From the definition of the parabola derive its equation when:

(a) the x-axis is the principal axis and the origin is at the focus;

(b) the y-axis is the principal axis and the origin is on the directrix.

35. From the definition of the parabola derive its equation when:

(a) the y-axis is the directrix and the x-axis is the principal axis;

(b) the y-axis is the principal axis and the origin is at the focus.

36. The directrix of a parabola is the line $x + y = 0$ and the focus is the point $\left(\dfrac{a}{2}, \dfrac{a}{2}\right)$. Find the equation of the parabola.

37. The directrix of a parabola is the line $y = 5$ and the focus is the point $(4, -3)$. Sketch the curve by locating the vertex and the ends of the latus rectum and derive its equation.

Solution. Since the principal axis is perpendicular to the directrix and passes through the focus, it is the line $x = 4$. The vertex, midway between the focus and directrix, is the point $(4, 1)$. In this case $p = 8$, and the extremities of the latus rectum are $(12, -3)$ and $(-4, -3)$.

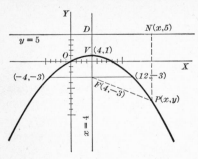

If $P(x, y)$ is any point on the parabola, its distance from the focus $(4, -3)$ is

$$\sqrt{(x - 4)^2 + (y + 3)^2},$$

its distance from the directrix $y = 5$ is $y - 5$. Hence:

$$\sqrt{(x - 4)^2 + (y + 3)^2} = y - 5.$$

Squaring and collecting terms, we have $x^2 - 8x + 16y = 0$.

38. The same as Problem 37 for the following:

(a) directrix $y = -3$, focus $(0, 7)$; (c) directrix $y = 4$, focus $(4, 6)$;
(b) directrix $x = 8$, focus $(-4, 3)$; (d) directrix $x = -2$, focus $(5, 3)$.

39. The same as Problem 37 for the following:

(a) directrix $x = -6$, vertex $(-8, 2)$; (c) directrix $x = 0$, focus $(6, 2)$;
(b) directrix $y = -6$, vertex $(4, 0)$; (d) vertex $(0, 2)$, focus $(0, 6)$.

40. Locate the directrix, the focus, and the ends of the latus rectum for each of the parabolas. Sketch the curve. (How many solutions in each case?)

  (a) principal axis $x = -4$, vertex $(-4, 2)$, latus rectum 16;
  (b) principal axis $y = 4$, vertex $(6, 4)$, latus rectum 10;
  (c) principal axis $x = 2$, vertex $(2, 3)$, latus rectum 16.

41. Find the equation of the parabola whose vertex is the point (h, k) and whose directrix is the line $x = h - \dfrac{p}{2}$.

42. Find the equation of each parabola in Problem 40.

CHAPTER VI

THE ELLIPSE

64. Definition. *The ellipse is the locus of a point such that the sum of its distances from two fixed points is constant.*

The two fixed points are called the *foci*. In the following we denote the distance between the foci by $2c$ and the sum of the distances of any point on the ellipse from the foci by $2a$. Obviously $2c < 2a$, or $c < a$.

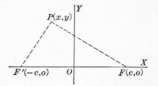

65. The equation of the ellipse. Take the origin midway between the foci F' and F, and let the line joining these two points be the x-axis. Then the coördinates of the foci are $(\pm c, 0)$, and any point $P(x, y)$ on the ellipse must satisfy the relation

$$F'P + FP = 2a,$$

or

$$\sqrt{(x + c)^2 + y^2} + \sqrt{(x - c)^2 + y^2} = 2a.$$

Transpose the second radical, square both sides, and collect terms. We get

$$4cx = 4a^2 - 4a\sqrt{(x - c)^2 + y^2}.$$

Solving for the radical gives

$$\sqrt{(x - c)^2 + y^2} = a - \frac{c}{a}x.$$

Squaring again and collecting terms, we have

$$\frac{a^2 - c^2}{a^2}x^2 + y^2 = a^2 - c^2,$$

or

$$\frac{x^2}{a^2} + \frac{y^2}{a^2 - c^2} = 1.$$

105

Since $c < a$, $a^2 - c^2$ has a positive value for every ellipse, and if we set $b^2 = a^2 - c^2$, then b will be a real number. The equation of the ellipse then becomes

$$\frac{x^2}{a^2} + \frac{y^2}{b^2} = 1, \tag{18}$$

or $$b^2x^2 + a^2y^2 = a^2b^2.$$

66. Discussion of the ellipse. The locus of equation (18) has intercepts $\pm a$ on the x-axis, and $\pm b$ on the y-axis. It is

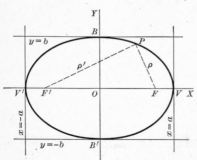

symmetrical with respect to both axes and hence is symmetrical with respect to the origin O.

Solving for y, we have

$$y = \pm \frac{b}{a}\sqrt{a^2 - x^2},$$

a form which shows that all values of x numerically greater than a must be excluded. Similarly all values of y numerically greater than b must be excluded. Hence the ellipse lies wholly within the rectangle whose sides are $x = \pm a$, $y = \pm b$.

The line $F'F$ through the foci is called the *principal axis*, and the points V and V' where the principal axis intersects the ellipse are called the *vertices*. The segment $V'V$ of the principal axis intercepted by the ellipse is called the *major axis*. The segment $B'B$ of the y-axis is called the *minor axis*. The major axis is of length $2a$ and the minor axis of length $2b$. O is called the center of the ellipse and is the mid-point of every chord of the ellipse which passes through it, since it is the center of symmetry. From the definition of b (§ 65) we have

$$a^2 = b^2 + c^2 \tag{19}$$

a relation connecting the semimajor axis, the semiminor axis, and the distance of either focus from the center.

Exercise 1. Show that the distance from either focus to one end of the minor axis is a.

Exercise 2. Show that the semiminor axis is the mean proportional between the segments into which either focus divides the major axis.

67. Limiting forms of the ellipse. If $c = 0$ the two foci F' and F coincide at the center, and $b = a$. The equation of the ellipse is then $\dfrac{x^2}{a^2} + \dfrac{y^2}{a^2} = 1$, or $x^2 + y^2 = a^2$, the locus of which is a circle with the center at the origin and the radius a. Hence the circle may be considered as a limiting form of an ellipse whose foci coincide at the center.

If $c = a$, then $b = 0$ and the two foci F' and F coincide with the vertices V' and V respectively. As c approaches a the ellipse "flattens out" and approaches the line segment $V'V$. Hence a line segment may be considered as a limiting form of an ellipse whose foci are at the extremities of the segment.

68. Eccentricity. From the previous section it is evident that the shape of an ellipse depends on the relative values of c and a. The fraction $\dfrac{c}{a}$ is called the *eccentricity* and is denoted by e.

Hence $$c = ae \tag{20}$$

and, since c cannot be greater than a by § 64, the eccentricity of an ellipse will have some value between 0 and 1. If we take a fixed line segment $V'V$ as the major axis of an ellipse and let e vary from 0 to 1, the ellipse will vary accordingly from the circle having $V'V$ as a diameter to the line segment $V'V$.

69. Latus rectum. The chord through either focus perpendicular to the major axis is called the latus rectum. If in the equation of the ellipse we put $x = \pm c$, we have

$$\frac{c^2}{a^2} + \frac{y^2}{b^2} = 1, \quad \frac{y^2}{b^2} = \frac{a^2 - c^2}{a^2} = \frac{b^2}{a^2}.$$

Therefore $$\frac{y}{b} = \pm \frac{b}{a}, \quad \text{or} \quad y = \pm \frac{b^2}{a}.$$

Hence the length of the latus rectum is $2b^2/a$.

As in the case of the parabola, the location of the ends of the latus rectum is a considerable aid to accuracy in sketching an ellipse of given dimensions.

Exercise 3. Show that the length of the minor axis is a mean proportional between the lengths of the major axis and the latus rectum.

PROBLEMS

1. Find the lengths of the semimajor axis, the semiminor axis, and the latus rectum, the eccentricity, the foci, and the vertices of the following ellipses, and sketch each curve.

(a) $9x^2 + 25y^2 = 225$.

Solution. Dividing by 225, we have

$$\frac{x^2}{25} + \frac{y^2}{9} = 1,$$

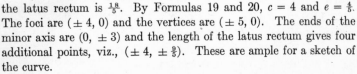

which is of the standard form. Hence $a = 5$, $b = 3$, and by § 69 the length of the latus rectum is $\frac{18}{5}$. By Formulas 19 and 20, $c = 4$ and $e = \frac{4}{5}$. The foci are $(\pm 4, 0)$ and the vertices are $(\pm 5, 0)$. The ends of the minor axis are $(0, \pm 3)$ and the length of the latus rectum gives four additional points, viz., $(\pm 4, \pm \frac{9}{5})$. These are ample for a sketch of the curve.

(b) $x^2 + 4y^2 = 100$;	(f) $25x^2 + 169y^2 = 4225$;
(c) $4x^2 + 9y^2 = 144$;	(g) $x^2 + 2y^2 = 72$;
(d) $x^2 + 9y^2 = 36$;	(h) $9x^2 + 49y^2 = 441$;
(e) $7x^2 + 16y^2 = 448$;	(i) $4x^2 + 25y^2 = 400$.

2. The same as Problem 1 for the following ellipses:

(a) $4x^2 + 9y^2 = 225$;	(f) $x^2 + 5y^2 = 80$;
(b) $5x^2 + 9y^2 = 180$;	(g) $9x^2 + 16y^2 = 576$;
(c) $x^2 + 4y^2 = 80$;	(h) $3x^2 + 7y^2 = 252$;
(d) $16x^2 + 49y^2 = 784$;	(i) $x^2 + 3y^2 = 81$;
(e) $25x^2 + 64y^2 = 1600$;	(j) $16x^2 + 36y^2 = 625$.

3. Write the equation of the ellipse with the center at the origin, given:

(a) one vertex $(6, 0)$, minor axis 6;

(b) major axis 16, one focus $(4, 0)$;

(c) one vertex (10, 0), latus rectum 10;

(d) one end of minor axis (0, 5), latus rectum 6;

(e) minor axis 10, one focus (5, 0).

4. Write the equation of the ellipse which has its center at the origin and the principal axis as the x-axis, given:

(a) $a = 20$, $e = \frac{4}{5}$;

(b) $b = 12$, $e = \frac{3}{4}$;

(c) $c = 6$, $e = \frac{2}{3}$;

(d) $c = 4$, latus rectum $\frac{18}{5}$;

(e) $e = \frac{4}{5}$, latus rectum 10;

(f) one end of a latus rectum (12, 7).

5. Find the relation between a and b if the length of the latus rectum is equal to

(a) the length of the semimajor axis;

(b) the length of the semiminor axis.

6. Find b in terms of a and e.

7. Find b in terms of c and e.

8. If two ellipses have the same eccentricity, show that the lengths of their major and minor axes are proportional.

9. Find the equation of an ellipse whose center is the origin, if it passes through (4, 3) and has the eccentricity $\frac{3}{4}$.

10. The earth's orbit is an ellipse of eccentricity 0.01674, with the sun at the focus. The semimajor axis is 93,000,000 miles. Find (a) the distance of the sun from the center; (b) the shortest distance from the sun to the earth.

11. Find a point on the ellipse $5x^2 + 9y^2 = 180$ such that the angle between the lines joining this point to the foci is 45°.

12. In a certain ellipse the distance between the foci and the length of the latus rectum are both 6. Find the eccentricity, and write the equation if the foci are $(\pm 3, 0)$.

13. Find the locus of a point the sum of whose distances from the points $(\pm 4, 0)$ is 10.

14. Find the locus of a point whose distance from the point $(-4, 0)$ is half its distance from the line $x = -16$.

15. The base of a triangle is fixed in position and is 12 units long, and the product of the tangents of the base angles is $\frac{9}{16}$. Find the locus of the vertex.

16. From points on the circle $x^2 + y^2 = 64$ perpendiculars are drawn to the x-axis. Show that the locus of the mid-points of these perpendiculars is an ellipse.

17. Lines are drawn from the center of the ellipse $x^2 + 4y^2 = 144$ to points on the ellipse. Show that the locus of the mid-points of these lines is an ellipse, and that its eccentricity is the same as that of the given ellipse.

18. The base of a triangle has its ends at $(\pm a, 0)$. Find the locus of the opposite vertex if the product of the slopes of the sides is $-\dfrac{b^2}{a^2}$.

70. Ellipse with foci on y-axis. If the foci are on the y-axis, this becomes the principal axis. Calling the major axis and

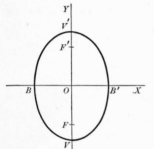

minor axis of the ellipse $2a$ and $2b$ respectively as before, the effect on the equation of the ellipse is merely to interchange the variables x and y. It is then

$$\frac{y^2}{a^2} + \frac{x^2}{b^2} = 1, \qquad (18a)$$

or $b^2y^2 + a^2x^2 = a^2b^2.$

In this form it is readily seen that the coördinates of the vertices are $(0, \pm a)$, and the coördinates of the foci are $(0, \pm c)$.

Exercise 4. Prove as in § 65 that the central equation of an ellipse having the foci on the y-axis is $b^2y^2 + a^2x^2 = a^2b^2$.

71. Focal radii and directrices. The distances of any point on an ellipse from the foci are called the *focal radii* of the point. If $P(x, y)$ is any point of the ellipse $b^2x^2 + a^2y^2 = a^2b^2$ and ρ_1 is the distance between P and the focus $(-c, 0)$, we have

$$\rho_1 = \sqrt{(x + c)^2 + y^2}.$$

If we solve the equation of the ellipse for y^2 and make the substitutions $b^2 = a^2 - c^2$ and $c = ae$, we obtain

$$\rho_1 = \sqrt{(x + ae)^2 + (1 - e^2)(a^2 - x^2)}$$
$$= \sqrt{a^2 + 2aex + e^2x^2} = a + ex.$$

Similarly, the distance between P and the focus $(c, 0)$ is $\rho_2 = a - ex$, and we may combine these results as a formula for the focal radii:

$$\rho = a \pm ex. \tag{21}$$

The sum of the focal radii is clearly $2a$; hence every point on the curve $b^2x^2 + a^2y^2 = a^2b^2$ satisfies the requirements of the definition of the ellipse. This is really necessary to complete the derivation of the equation in § 65, since some of the operations there used were not reversible. (See § 17.)

If we write $a + ex$ in the form $e\left(x + \dfrac{a}{e}\right)$, we see that the distance of each point of the curve from the focus $(- c, 0)$ is e times its distance from the line $x = -\dfrac{a}{e}$. This line is called a *directrix* of the ellipse. Similarly, the relation $a - ex = e\left(\dfrac{a}{e} - x\right)$ shows that the line $x = \dfrac{a}{e}$ is also a directrix, corresponding to the focus $(c, 0)$. If, as in the case of the parabola, we call the distance between the directrix and the corresponding focus p, we have the formula $c + p = \dfrac{a}{e}$.

In like manner we find that the focal radii of the ellipse $b^2y^2 + a^2x^2 = a^2b^2$ are $a \pm ey$ and that the directrices are the lines $y = \pm \dfrac{a}{e}$.

72. Construction of an ellipse. When a careful drawing of an ellipse is required, it is always possible to form the equation and compute a table of values. This, however, entails considerable labor, and it is sometimes better to proceed according to one of the following methods.

1. *A construction by points.* Lay off the major axis on coordinate paper. Then with a radius $\rho < 2a$ and a focus as a center draw an arc. With the other focus as a center and $\rho' = 2a - \rho$ as a radius, draw another arc cutting the first in

two points. These are points of the ellipse by § 64. By varying ρ we get as many points as are desired.

2. *A mechanical construction.* The relation of the focal radii may be used to construct the ellipse mechanically. On a

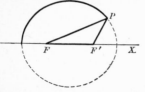

drawing board fasten two tacks at the foci F and F', and tie a string about them of length equal to $2a + 2c$. If a pencil is placed in the loop FPF' and moved so as to keep the string taut, then $PF + PF'$ is a constant equal to $2a$, and P describes an ellipse (§ 64).

73. Applications. Like the parabola the ellipse is a section of a right circular cone, an ellipse being formed if the cutting plane cuts all the elements of the cone (see § 74). It is also the curve formed when a right circular cylinder is cut by a plane not parallel or perpendicular to the base (see Problem 18, page 116). Among the applications of the ellipse in the arts and sciences the following may be mentioned.

If the focal radii are drawn to any point of an ellipse they make the same angle with the ellipse. (See § 147.) Hence if a surface is formed by rotating an ellipse about its major axis, any rays of light, or sound waves, proceeding from either focus will be reflected from the surface so as to converge at the other focus. This is the principle of some so-called "whispering galleries."

The paths of the planets in their motion around the sun are ellipses with one focus at the sun. The earth's orbit is an ellipse with an eccentricity of approximately $\frac{1}{60}$.

In the construction of bridges, elliptic arches are used as well as parabolic arches. They are also used in architecture.

74. The ellipse as a section of a cone. Let $V-AEBD$ be a right circular cone, and VAB a plane determined by the vertex V and the diameter of the base AB. This plane will be perpendicular to the base and will contain the elements VA

and VB, and also the axis of the cone and the center of every section parallel to the base.

Pass a plane perpendicular to the plane VAB, intersecting VA and VB at M and N. Through C, the mid-point, and Q, any other point of MN, pass planes parallel to the base, intersecting the plane VAB in FG and HK; these sections are circles and FG and HK are their diameters.

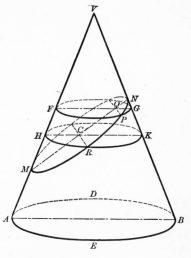

QP, the intersection of the planes FPG and MPN, is perpendicular to the plane VAB, and hence it is also perpendicular to the lines FG and MN. In the circles FPG and HRK,

$$\overline{QP}^2 = FQ \cdot QG \quad \text{and} \quad \overline{CR}^2 = HC \cdot CK.$$

The lines FQ and HC are parallel, hence the triangles FQM and HCM are similar.

$$\therefore \frac{FQ}{HC} = \frac{MQ}{MC} \quad \text{and} \quad \frac{QG}{CK} = \frac{QN}{CN}.$$

Hence
$$\frac{\overline{QP}^2}{\overline{CR}^2} = \frac{MQ}{MC} \cdot \frac{QN}{CN}. \qquad (a)$$

Let $CR = b$ and $MC = CN = a$, and we have

$$\frac{\overline{QP}^2}{b^2} = \frac{MQ \cdot QN}{a^2}. \qquad (b)$$

Now as Q moves along MN, P moves along the intersection of the conical surface and the cutting plane. Calling MN the x-axis and CR the y-axis, the coördinates of P will be $x = CQ$

and $y = QP$. Therefore $MQ = a + x$ and $QN = a - x$. Substituting in (b), we have

$$\frac{y^2}{b^2} = \frac{(a + x)(a - x)}{a^2},$$

which reduces to

$$\frac{x^2}{a^2} + \frac{y^2}{b^2} = 1.$$

Thus the section of the cone is an ellipse.

PROBLEMS

1. Find the vertices, foci, eccentricity, and length of the latus rectum of the ellipse and sketch the curve.

(a) $25x^2 + 9y^2 = 225$.

Solution. Dividing by 225, we have

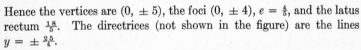

$$\frac{x^2}{9} + \frac{y^2}{25} = 1.$$

Since a is always $> b$, $a = 5$ and $b = 3$, and the equation is of the form

$$\frac{y^2}{a^2} + \frac{x^2}{b^2} = 1.$$

Hence the vertices are $(0, \pm 5)$, the foci $(0, \pm 4)$, $e = \frac{4}{5}$, and the latus rectum $\frac{18}{5}$. The directrices (not shown in the figure) are the lines $y = \pm \frac{25}{4}$.

(b) $25x^2 + 4y^2 = 100;$ (e) $16x^2 + 7y^2 = 448;$
(c) $9x^2 + 36y^2 = 324;$ (f) $64x^2 + 25y^2 = 1600;$
(d) $9x^2 + y^2 = 144;$ (g) $2x^2 + y^2 = 64.$

2. Investigate the following equations as in Problem 1:

(a) $4x^2 + y^2 = 64;$ (d) $9x^2 + y^2 = 36;$
(b) $25x^2 + 16y^2 = 400;$ (e) $x^2 + 5y^2 = 75;$
(c) $49x^2 + 16y^2 = 784;$ (f) $9x^2 + 5y^2 = 180.$

3. Write the equation of the ellipse with the center at the origin, given:

(a) vertex $(0, 6)$, focus $(0, 4)$;
(b) vertex $(0, 10)$, latus rectum 8;
(c) vertex $(0, 10)$, $e = \frac{4}{5}$;

(d) directrices $y = \pm 16$, foci $(0, \pm 8)$;

(e) one end of minor axis $(5, 0)$, focus $(0, -7)$.

4. Write the equations of the following ellipses with the center at the origin, the foci being first on the x-axis and second on the y-axis:

(a) $a = 8$, $b = 3$;

(b) $b = 5$, $c = 12$;

(c) $c = 8$, $e = \frac{4}{5}$;

(d) $b = 6$, latus rectum 9;

(e) $c = 4$, latus rectum 12;

(f) $b = 8$, $e = \frac{15}{17}$;

(g) $e = \frac{2}{3}$, latus rectum $\frac{20}{3}$;

(h) $a = 12$, latus rectum 6;

(i) $p = 8$, $e = \frac{3}{4}$;

(j) $p = 6$, $c = 6$.

5. Find the directrices of the ellipses in Problem 2.

6. Derive the formula for the length of the latus rectum of an ellipse by means of the formulas for the focal radii and the relations between the constants a, b, c, and e.

7. Two focal radii to the same point of an ellipse are perpendicular to each other and their respective lengths are 6 and 8. Find the equation of an ellipse with the center at the origin for which this is true and the coördinates of all points of this ellipse which satisfy these conditions.

8. An ellipse has its center at the origin and its foci on the y-axis. The point $(6, 8)$ lies on the ellipse and the focal radii to this point are perpendicular to each other. Find the equation of the ellipse.

9. Find in terms of a and e a point on the ellipse $b^2x^2 + a^2y^2 = a^2b^2$ such that the focal radii to this point are perpendicular to each other. What is the smallest value of e for which this problem has a solution?

10. Find a point on the ellipse $9x^2 + 25y^2 = 900$ such that the length of one focal radius to this point is three times that of the other.

11. Find the eccentricity of an ellipse when:

(a) the length of the latus rectum is three fourths that of the minor axis;

(b) the length of the latus rectum is two thirds that of the major axis.

12. Write the equation of an ellipse whose center is at the origin if it passes through the points:

(a) $(-4, 1)$ and $(1, 6)$;

(b) $(4, 2)$ and $(-3, 5)$;

(c) $(10, 0)$ and $(4, 4)$;

(d) $(3, 6)$ and $(-4, -4)$.

13. A rectangle is inscribed in an ellipse, so that its sides are parallel to the axes of the ellipse and the lengths of the sides are proportional to the lengths of the axes of the ellipse. Find the area of the rectangle.

14. Find the locus of a point the sum of whose distances from the points $(0, \pm 3)$ is 8.

15. Find the locus of the mid-points of the abscissas of the ellipse $b^2x^2 + a^2y^2 = a^2b^2$.

16. Let OC be any segment from the origin to a point on the ellipse $b^2x^2 + a^2y^2 = a^2b^2$, and let E be a point on OC such that $OE = r \cdot OC$, where r is any constant. Show that the locus of E is an ellipse and that it has the same eccentricity as the given ellipse.

17. For two ellipses $b_1^2x^2 + a_1^2y^2 = a_1^2b_1^2$ and $b_2^2x^2 + a_2^2y^2 = a_2^2b_2^2$ it is known that $a_1 : a_2 = b_1 : b_2 = r_1 : r_2$. Show that, if a line from the origin O meets these ellipses at P_1 and P_2, then $OP_1 : OP_2 = r_1 : r_2$.

18. Show that a section of the surface of a right circular cylinder made by a plane which cuts all the elements, but is not perpendicular to them, is an ellipse.

Hint. Let α be the inclination of the cutting plane to the plane of the base, let the origin be on the axis of the cylinder, and take the x-axis perpendicular to the edge of the dihedral angle α. Then, if $P(x, y)$ is any point of the section and $P'(x', y')$ is its projection on the base of the cylinder, it is easy to show that $y' = y$ and $x' = x \cos \alpha$.

19. A line of constant length moves so that its ends A and B are on the coördinate axes. Find the locus of a point P on the line at a distance a from A and b from B.

20. Find the locus of a point whose distance from the point $(0, -5)$ is one half its distance from the line $y = -20$.

21. Two circles of radii a and b have their common center at the origin O. Let C be a point on the larger circle, let OC meet the smaller circle at B, let CD be perpendicular to the x-axis, and let E be the foot of a perpendicular from B to CD. Find the locus of E.

22. The vertices of an ellipse are fixed at $(\pm a, 0)$. What curve will be traced by the end of a latus rectum if b is allowed to vary?

23. Sketch the ellipses for which

(a) the foci are $(5, 3)$ and $(-3, 3)$, the sum of the focal radii is 12;

(b) the foci are $(2, -4)$ and $(2, 4)$, the sum of the focal radii is 20.

24. Using the definition in § 64, derive the equation of each ellipse in Problem 23.

CHAPTER VII

THE HYPERBOLA

75. Definition. *The hyperbola is the locus of a point such that the difference of its distances from two fixed points is a constant.*

As in the case of the ellipse, the two fixed points are called the *foci* and the line passing through them is called the *principal axis*. Let $2c$ be the distance between the foci, and let $2a$ be the difference of the distances of any point on the hyperbola from the foci.

76. The equation of the hyperbola. Take the principal axis as the x-axis and the point midway between the foci F' and F as the origin. Then the coördinates of the foci are $(\pm c, 0)$ and any point $P(x, y)$ on the hyperbola must satisfy the relation
$$F'P - FP = \pm 2a,$$
or $\sqrt{(x + c)^2 + y^2} - \sqrt{(x - c)^2 + y^2} = \pm 2a.$

If we rationalize this equation, as we did the similar equation of the ellipse (§ 65), the result is
$$\frac{x^2}{a^2} - \frac{y^2}{c^2 - a^2} = 1.$$

It will be observed that this equation is identical in form with the equation of the ellipse (§ 65). But, in this case $F'P - FP < F'F$ or $2a < 2c$.

Hence $c > a$, and $c^2 - a^2$ has a positive value for every hyperbola. Then we can write $c^2 - a^2 = b^2$ where b is always a real number, and the equation becomes
$$\frac{x^2}{a^2} - \frac{y^2}{b^2} = 1, \tag{22}$$
or $b^2x^2 - a^2y^2 = a^2b^2.$

Exercise 1. Derive equation (22) as in § 65.

117

77. Discussion of the hyperbola. The intercepts on the x-axis are $\pm a$, the y-intercepts are imaginary. The curve is symmetrical with respect to both coördinate axes and with respect to the origin. Solving equation (22) for x, we have

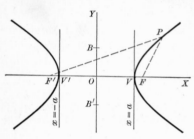

$x = \pm \dfrac{a}{b}\sqrt{y^2 + b^2}$, which shows that no value of y needs to be excluded.

Solving for y, we have $y = \pm \dfrac{b}{a}\sqrt{x^2 - a^2}$, which shows that y is imaginary for all values of x between $\pm a$, but if x is numerically greater than a, y is real and increases indefinitely as $|x|$ increases. Thus the hyperbola consists of two infinite branches, lying without the lines $x = \pm a$.

The points of the hyperbola V' and V on the principal axis are called the *vertices*. The segment $V'V$ of the principal axis is called the *transverse axis* and is of length $2a$. The segment $B'B$ of the y-axis, where $B'O = OB = b$, is called the *conjugate axis*. Since for the hyperbola we have

$$c^2 = a^2 + b^2, \qquad (23)$$

c is greater than either a or b, while there is no restriction on the relative sizes of a and b. It is for this reason that the terms major and minor axis are not used.

78. Latus rectum. The chord $L'L$ through either focus perpendicular to the principal axis is called the latus rectum and it is seen (as in the case of the ellipse) that its length is $\dfrac{2b^2}{a}$.

Exercise 2. Show that the length of the latus rectum is $\dfrac{2b^2}{a}$.

79. Hyperbola with foci on the y-axis. If we describe a hyperbola with the foci on the y-axis, with its transverse axis $2a$ and the distance between the foci $2c$, the effect on the original equation will be to interchange the variables x and y, and the equation will become

$$\frac{y^2}{a^2} - \frac{x^2}{b^2} = 1, \qquad (22a)$$

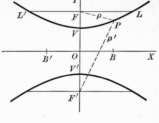

or $\quad b^2y^2 - a^2x^2 = a^2b^2$.

The vertices of this hyperbola are $(0, \pm a)$, the foci $(0, \pm c)$.

Exercise 3. Derive equation $(22a)$ as in § 76.

80. Eccentricity. The shape of the hyperbola depends on the relative values of c and a. As in the case of the ellipse, the fraction $\frac{c}{a}$ is called the *eccentricity* of the hyperbola and is denoted by e, giving the same relation

$$c = ae. \qquad (20)$$

While the value of e for the ellipse is always less than 1, for the hyperbola it is always greater than 1.

81. Focal radii and directrices. The distances of any point on a hyperbola from the foci are called the *focal radii* of the point. Proceeding as in § 71, we find that the focal radii of the point $P(x, y)$ on the hyperbola $b^2x^2 - a^2y^2 = a^2b^2$ are given by the formula
$$\rho = |ex \pm a|. \qquad (24)$$

The sign for absolute value is necessary, since even $ex + a$ is negative when x is negative, as $e > 1$ and $|x| \geqq a$. The difference of the focal radii is $2a$; this completes the demonstration in § 76.

Since $ex + a = e\left(x + \dfrac{a}{e}\right)$, the distance of any point of the hyperbola from the focus $(-c, 0)$ is e times its distance from the line $x = -\dfrac{a}{e}$. This line is called a *directrix* of the hyperbola; likewise, the line $x = \dfrac{a}{e}$ is a directrix, corresponding to the focus $(c, 0)$.

If the vertices of the hyperbola are on the y-axis, the focal radii are $|ey \pm a|$, and the equations of the directrices are $y = \pm \dfrac{a}{e}.$

Exercise 4. Write out in full the derivation of the formulas for the focal radii.

Exercise 5. Show that, if p is the distance between a focus and the corresponding directrix of a hyperbola, $c - p = \dfrac{a}{e}.$

PROBLEMS

1. Find the semitransverse and semiconjugate axes, the latus rectum, and the foci, and sketch the graphs of the following hyperbolas:

(a) $25x^2 - 9y^2 = 225$;

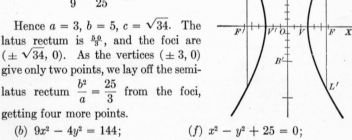

Solution. Dividing by 225, we have the standard form

$$\frac{x^2}{9} - \frac{y^2}{25} = 1.$$

Hence $a = 3$, $b = 5$, $c = \sqrt{34}$. The latus rectum is $\frac{50}{3}$, and the foci are $(\pm \sqrt{34}, 0)$. As the vertices $(\pm 3, 0)$ give only two points, we lay off the semi-latus rectum $\dfrac{b^2}{a} = \dfrac{25}{3}$ from the foci, getting four more points.

(b) $9x^2 - 4y^2 = 144$; (f) $x^2 - y^2 + 25 = 0$;
(c) $4y^2 - x^2 = 25$; (g) $3x^2 - 5y^2 = 75$;
(d) $x^2 - 2y^2 = 36$; (h) $9x^2 - 16y^2 + 144 = 0$;
(e) $3y^2 - 4x^2 = 48$; (i) $3x^2 - y^2 = 48$.

2. The same as Problem 1 for the following hyperbolas:

(a) $x^2 - 4y^2 = 36$; (e) $x^2 - 2y^2 + 18 = 0$;
(b) $4y^2 - 9x^2 = 144$; (f) $x^2 - y^2 + 49 = 0$;
(c) $9x^2 - 16y^2 = 144$; (g) $2x^2 - 3y^2 = 72$;
(d) $x^2 - 9y^2 = 36$; (h) $4x^2 - 5y^2 = 100$.

3. Find the equations of hyperbolas having the center at the origin, first taking the transverse axis along the x-axis, and then taking it along the y-axis, if:

(a) $a = 4, b = 6$;

(b) $a = 4, c = 5$;

(c) $b = 6, c = 9$;

(d) $a = 5, e = 2$;

(e) $b = 4, e = \frac{4}{3}$;

(f) $c = 6, e = \frac{3}{2}$;

(g) $a = 5$, latus rectum 10;

(h) $e = \frac{3}{2}$, latus rectum 12.

4. The same as Problem 3, if:

(a) $a = 5, b = 3$;

(b) $a = 8, c = 10$;

(c) $b = 5, c = 7$;

(d) $a = 6, e = \frac{3}{2}$;

(e) $c = 8, e = \frac{4}{3}$;

(f) $a = 6$, latus rectum 16;

(g) $b = 5$, latus rectum $\frac{25}{6}$;

(h) $c = 6$, latus rectum 10.

5. Find the eccentricity and the equations of the directrices of each hyperbola in Problem 2.

6. Find the eccentricity and the equations of the directrices of each hyperbola in Problem 1.

7. Find the equation of a hyperbola with its center at the origin and its transverse axis along the x-axis, if it passes through the points:

(a) $(4, 0)$ and $(8, -6)$;   (b) $(6, 6)$ and $(-4, 1)$.

8. The same as Problem 7, except that the transverse axis is along the y-axis and the curve passes through the points:

(a) $(5, 8)$ and $(1, -4)$;   (b) $(5, 10)$ and $(-2, 5)$.

9. An ellipse and a hyperbola both have the foci $(0, \pm 8)$ and the length of the latus rectum $\frac{36}{5}$. Find their equations and plot them.

10. An ellipse and a hyperbola both have the foci $(\pm c, 0)$ and their respective eccentricities are $\frac{1}{2}$ and 2. Find the distance between the vertices and the length of the latus rectum for each curve.

11. Find a point on the hyperbola $3x^2 - 2y^2 = 120$ such that the focal radii to this point are perpendicular to each other.

12. The point $(6, 8)$ lies on a hyperbola whose center is at the origin and whose foci are on the y-axis, and the focal radii to this point are perpendicular. Find the equation of the hyperbola.

13. Derive the formula for the length of the latus rectum by means of the formulas for the focal radii.

14. Find the locus of a point such that the difference of its distances from the points $(0, \pm 13)$ is 24.

15. Find the locus of a point whose distance from the point $(12, 0)$ is twice its distance from the line $x = 3$.

16. Find the locus of a point whose distance from the point $(0, -10)$ is one and a quarter times its distance from the line $5y + 32 = 0$.

17. Two vertices of a triangle are fixed at $(0, \pm c)$. Find the locus of the opposite vertex if the median to the fixed side is a mean proportional between the other two sides.

18. Two vertices of a triangle are at $(\pm a, 0)$. Find the locus of the opposite vertex if the product of the slopes of the variable sides is the constant $\dfrac{b^2}{a^2}$.

82. Asymptotes. If the equation $b^2x^2 - a^2y^2 = a^2b^2$ is solved for y, the result is $y = \pm \dfrac{b}{a}\sqrt{x^2 - a^2}$. It is apparent that, for large values of x, the quantity $\pm \dfrac{bx}{a}$ is an approximation to the corresponding values of y, since the value of a^2 is relatively insignificant in comparison with that of x^2. Hence it is an easy inference that this hyperbola has as asymptotes the lines whose equations are

$$y = \pm \frac{b}{a}x, \quad \text{or} \quad bx \pm ay = 0. \tag{25}$$

To prove this, let $P(x, y)$ be a point on the hyperbola in the first quadrant and let $P_1(x, y_1)$ be the point on the line $y = \dfrac{bx}{a}$ which has the same abscissa. Then

$$y_1 - y = \frac{b}{a}(x - \sqrt{x^2 - a^2}).$$

Multiplying numerator and denominator by $x + \sqrt{x^2 - a^2}$, we have

$$y_1 - y = \frac{ab}{x + \sqrt{x^2 - a^2}}.$$

When x approaches $+ \infty$, the denominator approaches $+ \infty$, but the numerator remains constant. Hence $y_1 - y$ approaches zero. This proves the theorem for this case, since the distance between P and the line is less than $y_1 - y$. The other quadrants are treated in the same way.

The above equations (25) may be combined by § 46 in the form

$$b^2x^2 - a^2y^2 = 0, \quad \text{or} \quad \frac{x^2}{a^2} - \frac{y^2}{b^2} = 0.$$

If the vertices are on the y-axis, x and y are interchanged, giving

$$y = \pm \frac{a}{b}x, \quad \text{or} \quad \frac{y^2}{a^2} - \frac{x^2}{b^2} = 0. \qquad (25a)$$

In either case, *to find the equations of the asymptotes, write the equation of the hyperbola in the standard form, replace the 1 by 0, and factor.* In drawing figures it is simpler not to use these formulas, but to employ the construction described at the end of the next section.

83. Conjugate hyperbolas. Since the relative sizes of a and b are immaterial, a hyperbola may be described having the

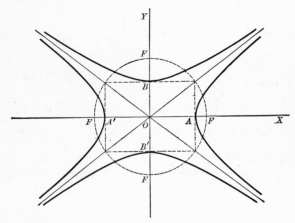

segment $2b$ for a transverse axis and the segment $2a$ for a conjugate axis. The hyperbola with transverse axis $A'A$ ($= 2a$) along the x-axis and conjugate axis $B'B$ ($= 2b$) along the y-axis has the equation $\frac{x^2}{a^2} - \frac{y^2}{b^2} = 1$. The hyperbola with transverse axis $B'B$ ($= 2b$) along the y-axis and conjugate axis $A'A$ ($= 2a$) along the x-axis has the equation $\frac{y^2}{b^2} - \frac{x^2}{a^2} = 1$. The two hyperbolas

$$(a) \ \frac{x^2}{a^2} - \frac{y^2}{b^2} = 1 \quad \text{and} \quad (b) \ \frac{y^2}{b^2} - \frac{x^2}{a^2} = 1$$

are called *conjugate hyperbolas*. The transverse axis of each is the conjugate axis of the other.

Since $c^2 = a^2 + b^2$, the foci of both hyperbolas are at the same distance from the center. Those of (a) are $(\pm c, 0)$; those of (b) are $(0, \pm c)$. If we let e_1 and e_2 be the respective eccentricities, we have $e_1 = \dfrac{c}{a}$, $e_2 = \dfrac{c}{b}$, whence $e_1 : e_2 = b : a$. From the equations it is evident that conjugate hyperbolas have the same asymptotes.

This property is useful in sketching a pair of conjugate hyperbolas. Draw the rectangle of the given axes, that is, a rectangle having its sides of length $2a$ and $2b$ and symmetrical with respect to the axes, and draw the diagonals. As these have slopes $\pm \dfrac{b}{a}$, they are the asymptotes. The circle circumscribing the rectangle has the radius $\sqrt{a^2 + b^2} = c$, and therefore intersects the axes at the foci of the required hyperbolas. With the rectangle and asymptotes as guiding lines the curves can be sketched accurately.

Exercise 6. Show that for a pair of conjugate hyperbolas
$$e_1{}^2 + e_2{}^2 = e_1{}^2 e_2{}^2.$$

84. Equilateral hyperbolas. When $b = a$ the equations of the conjugate hyperbolas reduce to the forms

$$x^2 - y^2 = \pm a^2. \tag{26}$$

In this case $e_1 = e_2 = \sqrt{2}$, and the asymptotes are the perpendicular lines

$$x - y = 0 \qquad \text{and} \qquad x + y = 0.$$

Such hyperbolas are called *equilateral* or *rectangular* hyperbolas.

If the asymptotes of the equilateral hyperbolas are taken as the coördinate axes it can be shown (see p. 133, Problem 4e) that the equations take the important form

$$xy = \pm \frac{a^2}{2}. \tag{26a}$$

From this equation we see that the distances of any point on this curve from its asymptotes have a constant product. The last statement is also true for all hyperbolas.

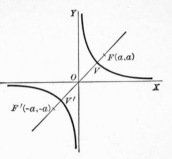

Exercise 7. Using the definition of the hyperbola, show that its equation is $xy = \dfrac{a^2}{2}$ when the foci are taken at (a, a) and $(-a, -a)$, and the difference of the focal radii to any point is $2a$.

85. Construction of a hyperbola. A hyperbola may be plotted accurately by forming a table of values from the equation or by proceeding according to methods similar to those used for the ellipse (§ 72).

1. *A construction by points.* Lay off the distance $2a$ on co-ordinate paper. Now with any radius $\rho' > 2a$ and a focus as the center describe an arc. Then with a radius $\rho = \rho' - 2a$ and with the other focus as a center describe an arc. This will intersect the former arc at two points on the hyperbola. Thus any number of points can be readily located.

2. *A mechanical construction.* Place thumb tacks in a drawing board at the foci F and F'. Let a string be tied to a pencil at

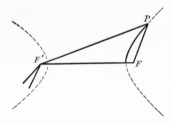

P and looped about the tacks as in the figure. If the ends are drawn in together, P will describe a hyperbola, since

$$(F'F + FP) - F'P$$

remains constant. For $F'F$ is constant; hence $F'P - FP$ is a constant.

86. Applications. The principle of the hyperbola is used in range finding. Thus if the exact time of the report of a gun is recorded at each of two listening posts, the difference in time multiplied by the velocity of sound will give the difference of the distances of the gun from these two fixed points. Hence the gun is on the hyperbola whose foci are the listening posts, and whose transverse axis is the difference of the distances of the gun from them (§ 81). By taking a third listening post another hyperbola can be found in the same way which passes through the position of the gun. Then its location is easily found at one of the intersections of the two curves.

Comets sometimes have hyperbolic orbits, as well as parabolic and elliptic ones. Certain physical quantities satisfy the relation $xy = k$, which is the equation of the equilateral hyperbola.

If the elements of a right circular cone are produced through the vertex so as to form an inverted cone, a plane which intersects both cones cuts out of the surface a section which is a hyperbola, as shown in the next section. If a standing lamp has a circular shade and one bulb, an example of this is seen in the shadow of the edge of the shade on an adjacent wall.

87. The hyperbola as a conic section. Let the cutting plane intersect the given cone so as to meet some of the elements produced. Follow the construction of § 74 and choose the axes in the same manner, viz., origin at C, and x-axis MN. Then

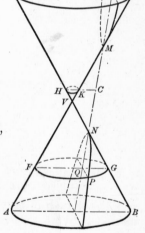

$$y^2 = \overline{QP}^2 = FQ \cdot QG.$$

Also $\dfrac{FQ}{KC} = \dfrac{MQ}{MC}$ and $\dfrac{QG}{HC} = \dfrac{NQ}{CN}.$

Substituting,

$$y^2 = \frac{MQ \cdot NQ}{MC \cdot CN}(KC \cdot HC);$$

or, if

$$MC = CN = a \quad \text{and} \quad KC \cdot HC = b^2,$$

$$y^2 = \frac{b^2}{a^2}(MQ \cdot NQ).$$

But $MQ = x + a, \quad NQ = x - a,$

whence

$$y^2 = \frac{b^2}{a^2}(x^2 - a^2) \quad \text{or} \quad \frac{x^2}{a^2} - \frac{y^2}{b^2} = 1.$$

Hence the plane cuts the surface of the cone in one branch of a hyperbola and the conical surface formed by prolonging the elements through the vertex in the other branch.

PROBLEMS

1. Find the semitransverse and semiconjugate axes, the eccentricity, the coördinates of the foci, and the equations of the asymptotes of the following hyperbolas, and sketch each curve:

(a) $25x^2 - 9y^2 + 225 = 0$;

Solution. Transposing and dividing by -225, we have

$$-\frac{x^2}{9} + \frac{y^2}{25} = 1.$$

Since the term in y is positive, this is of the form

$$\frac{y^2}{a^2} - \frac{x^2}{b^2} = 1.$$

Hence $a = 5$, $b = 3$, $c = \sqrt{34}$, and $e = \frac{1}{5}\sqrt{34}$.
The foci are $(0, \pm \sqrt{34})$ and the asymptotes are the lines $y = \pm \frac{5}{3}x$.
Drawing the asymptotes, the curve is readily sketched.

(b) $4x^2 - 5y^2 = 80$;

(c) $9x^2 - 4y^2 = -144$;

(d) $25x^2 - 16y^2 = 400$;

(e) $9y^2 - x^2 = 36$;

(f) $4x^2 - 25y^2 - 100 = 0$;

(g) $5x^2 - 3y^2 + 180 = 0$;

(h) $x^2 - 3y^2 + 192 = 0$;

(i) $4x^2 - y^2 - 100 = 0$.

2. The same as Problem 1 for the following hyperbolas:

(a) $9x^2 - 16y^2 = 144$;

(b) $16y^2 - 25x^2 = 400$;

(c) $4x^2 - y^2 = 36$;

(d) $9x^2 - 25y^2 = 900$;

(e) $16x^2 - 36y^2 = 441$;

(f) $y^2 - 3x^2 = 27$;

(g) $25x^2 - 14y^2 = 350$;

(h) $x^2 - 9y^2 + 36 = 0$.

3. Write the equations of the hyperbolas conjugate to those of Problem 1 and find the eccentricity and foci of each.

4. Write the equations of the hyperbolas conjugate to those of Problem 2 and find the eccentricity and foci of each.

5. Write the equation of the system of hyperbolas which have the center at the origin, the vertices on the x-axis, and the length of the transverse axis equal to half the distance between the foci. Sketch several of these curves.

6. Write the equation of the system of hyperbolas which have the center at the origin, the vertices on the y-axis, and the length of the conjugate axis equal to half the distance between the foci. Sketch several of these curves.

7. Plot $xy = -36$. Assuming that the locus is an equilateral hyperbola, find the vertices and the foci.

8. Show that the distance of any point on the equilateral hyperbola $x^2 - y^2 + a^2 = 0$ from the center is a mean proportional between the focal radii.

9. Find the product of the lengths of the perpendiculars from any point of the hyperbola $b^2x^2 - a^2y^2 = a^2b^2$ to its asymptotes.

10. Show that, if an ellipse and a hyperbola have the same foci and the same latera recta, their eccentricities are reciprocals.

11. In the figure of § 83 show that the directrices of the hyperbola whose vertices are on the x-axis pass through the points of intersection of the conjugate hyperbola and the circle.

12. Show that the line $y = mx$ and the hyperbola $b^2x^2 - a^2y^2 = a^2b^2$ meet in two points if $|m| < \dfrac{b}{a}$. What happens if $|m| > \dfrac{b}{a}$? if $|m| = \dfrac{b}{a}$?

13. Show that the distance between a focus of a hyperbola and an asymptote is equal to the semiconjugate axis.

14. Show that the length of a focal chord of a hyperbola equals $2e$ times the distance between the directrix and the center of the chord.

15. The center of a circle lies on the hyperbola $x^2 - y^2 = a^2$ and the circle is tangent to the y-axis. Find the length of the segment of the x-axis intercepted by the circle.

16. Find the locus of the ends of the latera recta of the hyperbolas in Problem 5.

17. Two segments AOB and COD bisect each other at right angles. Find the locus of a point P such that $(PA)(PB) = (PC)(PD)$.

18. Find the coördinates of the vertices, the eccentricity, and the equations of the asymptotes of each of the following hyperbolas, and sketch each curve:

(a) foci $(7, -4)$ and $(-3, -4)$, difference of focal radii to any point $= 8$;

(b) foci $(2, 11)$ and $(2, -9)$, length of conjugate axis $= 16$.

19. Find the foci, vertices, and eccentricity of the hyperbolas conjugate to those in Problem 18.

20. The ends of a latus rectum of a hyperbola are $(0, \pm 9)$ and another point of the curve is $(3, 0)$. Draw the asymptotes and sketch the curve.

21. Derive the equations of the hyperbolas in Problem 18 by using the definition of the hyperbola.

22. Derive the equation of the hyperbola in Problem 20 by using the definition of the hyperbola.

CHAPTER VIII

TRANSFORMATION OF COÖRDINATES AND SIMPLIFICATION OF EQUATIONS

88. Change of axes. The position of the axes of coördinates to which a given locus is referred is arbitrary. It may be changed at will and the equation of the locus altered to correspond by substituting for the former coördinates their values in terms of coördinates measured from the new axes.

The advantage to be secured by a change of axes is usually a simplification of the equation, and this is best secured by choosing a position of symmetry when possible.

When the new axes are drawn parallel to the old, the transformation of the equation is called a *transformation by translation*. When they are drawn through the same origin oblique to the axes but still perpendicular to each other, the transformation is called a *transformation by rotation*.

89. Formulas of translation. In the figure let the original

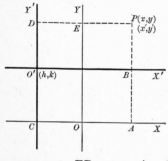

set of axes be OX and OY; the new axes $O'X'$ and $O'Y'$ with the origin at O', which has the coördinates (h, k) with reference to OX and OY. Let P be any point in the plane which has coördinates (x, y) with reference to the old axes, and (x', y') with reference to the new ones. Then

$$x = EP, \qquad x' = DP, \qquad h = OC = ED,$$
$$y = AP, \qquad y' = BP, \qquad k = CO' = AB.$$

130

From the figure

$$EP = DP - DE = DP + ED \quad \text{and} \quad AP = BP + AB.$$

Hence $\qquad\qquad x = x' + h,$

and $\qquad\qquad\qquad y = y' + k.$ $\qquad$ (27)

These are the *formulas of translation.*

By using these substitutions the equation of a given locus is transformed into a new equation in x' and y', which is the equation of the same locus referred to coördinate axes drawn through the point (h, k) parallel to the old axes.

90. Formulas of rotation. Let the original axes be OX and OY, the new axes OX' and OY', and the angle of rotation θ.

Let P be any point in the plane with coördinates (x, y) and (x', y') with reference to the old and new axes respectively. Then

$$x = OA, \qquad x' = OD,$$
$$y = AP, \qquad y' = DP.$$

Since the sides of angle CPD are perpendicular to those of θ, $CPD = \theta$. Hence we have

$$CD = y' \sin \theta, \qquad\qquad OB = x' \cos \theta,$$
$$CP = y' \cos \theta, \qquad\qquad BD = x' \sin \theta.$$

But $\quad x = OA = OB - CD \quad$ and $\quad y = AP = BD + CP.$

Substituting, we get

$$x = x' \cos \theta - y' \sin \theta,$$
$$y = x' \sin \theta + y' \cos \theta.$$ $\qquad$ (28)

These are the *formulas of rotation.*

These substitutions transform a given equation into a new equation with variables x' and y', in which the coördinate axes are drawn through the old origin but inclined at an angle θ to the old axes.

PROBLEMS

General directions. Usually the equation obtained by transformation is a known form and its locus can be identified. When this is not the case, the table of values should be computed from the new equation and the curve plotted on the new axes. Frequently the intercepts with respect to both old and new axes, together with considerations of symmetry, make an extended table of values unnecessary.

1. Translate the origin to the point indicated and transform the equation to correspond. Draw the curve and both sets of axes.

(a) $y^2 - 4y - 12x + 16 = 0$, $(1, 2)$;

(b) $25x^2 + 9y^2 - 150x + 36y + 36 = 0$, $(3, -2)$;

(c) $9x^2 - 72x - 16y^2 = 0$, $(4, 0)$;

(d) $xy - 6x - 4y = 0$, $(4, 6)$;

(e) $4y = 8x - x^2$, $(4, 4)$;

(f) $y = b + (x - a)^3$, (a, b).

2. The same as Problem 1 for the following:

(a) $x^2 + 2x + 8y = 31$, $(-1, 4)$;

(b) $x^2 + 4y^2 + 4x - 24y + 4 = 0$, $(-2, 3)$;

(c) $x^2 - y^2 - 8x - 8y + 36 = 0$, $(4, -4)$;

(d) $y = x^3 + 6x^2 + 3x - 12 = 0$, $(-2, -2)$;

(e) $9x^2 + 4y^2 + 72x = 0$, $(-4, 0)$;

(f) $x^2 + xy - 2y^2 + 2x + 19y - 35 = 0$, $(-3, 4)$.

3. Rotate the axes through the angle indicated and transform the equation to correspond. Draw the curve and both sets of axes. Identify known loci.

(a) $9x^2 - 24xy + 16y^2 - 160x - 120y = 0$, $\theta = \arcsin \frac{3}{5}$;

(b) $8x^2 - 12xy + 17y^2 = 180$, $\theta = \arctan \frac{1}{2}$;

(c) $5x^2 + 24xy - 5y^2 + 325 = 0$, $\theta = \arctan \frac{2}{3}$;

(d) $x^2 - y^2 = 36$, $\theta = \dfrac{\pi}{4}$;

(e) $2xy = \pm a^2$, $\theta = \dfrac{\pi}{4}$;

(f) $(x + y - a)^2 = 4xy$, $\theta = \dfrac{\pi}{4}$.

4. The same as Problem 3 for the following:

(a) $9x^2 + 24xy + 16y^2 - 80x + 60y = 0$, $\theta = \arcsin \frac{4}{5}$;

(b) $136x^2 + 252xy + 241y^2 = 1300$, $\theta = \arctan \frac{3}{2}$;

(c) $55x^2 - 100xy - 20y^2 + 720 = 0$, $\theta = \text{arc tan } 2$;

(d) $xy = 24$, $\theta = \dfrac{\pi}{4}$;

(e) $x^2 - y^2 = \pm a^2$, $\theta = \dfrac{\pi}{4}$;

(f) $x^3 + y^3 = 3\sqrt{2}\,axy$, $\theta = \dfrac{\pi}{4}$.

5. Find the coördinates of the point $(3, -4)$ when the origin is translated to

(a) $(5, 6)$;   (b) $(-2, 4)$;   (c) $(-4, -2)$;   (d) $(5, -4)$.

6. The same as Problem 5 for the point $(-6, 2)$.

7. Find the coördinates of

(a) $(2, 4)$;   (b) $(6, -3)$;   (c) $(-4, 0)$

when the axes are rotated through the angle arc sin $\tfrac{3}{5}$.

8. The same as Problem 7 when the angle of rotation is arc sin $\tfrac{4}{5}$.

9. In the figure of § 90 draw the segment OP, let r be its length, and let ϕ be the angle POD. Then derive the formulas of rotation from the formulas for $\cos(\theta + \phi)$ and $\sin(\theta + \phi)$.

10. Show that the equation $x^2 + y^2 = r^2$ is unchanged by rotating the axes through any angle.

11. Show that the equation $(x^2 + y^2)^2 = ay(3x^2 - y^2)$ is unchanged by rotating the axes through the angle $120°$.

12. The coördinates of a point are (x, y); after a rotation of the axes through an angle θ these become (x', y'). Derive formulas expressing x' and y' in terms of x and y.

91. Test for axes of symmetry.

To find axes of symmetry parallel to the coördinate axes, proceed as follows: Solve the equation for y in terms of x. If the solution is of the form $y = k \pm f(x)$, the line $y = k$ is an axis of symmetry. This is due to the fact that each value of x, as $x = a$, gives two values of y, and thus two points, one $f(a)$ above the line $y = k$, the other $f(a)$ below. Similarly, if the solution for x is of the form $x = h \pm g(y)$, the line $x = h$ is an axis of symmetry. Since the lines $x = h$ and $y = k$ are perpendicular to each other, a curve symmetrical with respect to both of these lines has their intersection (h, k) as a center of symmetry. (See § 25.)

92. Simplification of equations by translation. If the curve has two axes of symmetry, they can be found by the method just given and the translation made by formula. When this is not true, the second method illustrated in the following examples must be used.

EXAMPLE 1. Simplify $x^2 + 4y^2 - 2x - 24y + 21 = 0$.

Solution. First method. Solving for x and y, we have

$$x = 1 \pm f(y)^*$$

and
$$y = 3 \pm g(x).$$

Hence the axes of symmetry are

$$x = 1 \quad \text{and} \quad y = 3$$

and the center of symmetry is $(1, 3)$.
Substitute

$$x = x' + 1 \quad \text{and} \quad y = y' + 3$$

in the original equation, and we have

$$(x' + 1)^2 + 4(y' + 3)^2 - 2(x' + 1) - 24(y' + 3) + 21 = 0.$$

This reduces to $\qquad x'^2 + 4y'^2 = 16,$

or
$$\frac{x'^2}{16} + \frac{y'^2}{4} = 1.$$

Thus the curve is an ellipse with its center at $(1, 3)$ and semiaxes 4 and 2.

Second method. In the given equation substitute $x = x' + h$ and $y = y' + k$. It becomes, after collecting coefficients,

$$x'^2 + (2h - 2)x' + 4y'^2 + (8k - 24)y' + (h^2 + 4k^2 - 2h - 24k + 21) = 0.$$

If the curve is symmetrical with respect to the new axes, there can be no terms of the first degree in the new equation. This is the case if

$$2h - 2 = 0 \quad \text{and} \quad 8k - 24 = 0, \quad \text{or} \quad h = 1, k = 3.$$

Hence the center of symmetry is $(1, 3)$ and the transformed equation becomes $x'^2 + 4y'^2 - 16 = 0$ as before, on substituting $h = 1$, $k = 3$.

EXAMPLE 2. Simplify $y^2 + 8x + 4y - 20 = 0$.

---

* In solving for x, the terms not involving x may be disregarded, as we are interested only in showing that the solution is of the form $x = h \pm f(y)$.

Solution. If the equation is solved for x no axis of symmetry is revealed, and so we must use the second method. Substitute $x = x' + h$, and $y = y' + k$. Collecting coefficients, we have

$$y'^2 + 8x' + (2k + 4)y' + (k^2 + 8h + 4k - 20) = 0.$$

Evidently the terms in y'^2 and x' cannot be eliminated. But if $2k + 4 = 0$ and $k^2 + 8h + 4k - 20 = 0$, the term in y' and the constant term vanish. These equations give $k = -2$, $h = 3$. The new equation then is

$$y'^2 = -8x',$$

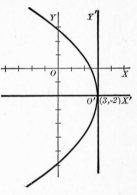

which is of the form $y^2 = -2px$. The curve is a parabola which has its vertex at $(3, -2)$ and its axis $y = -2$.

PROBLEMS

1. Find the center of symmetry by solving for x and y, and move the origin to this point. Draw the curve and both sets of axes.

(a) $4x^2 + y^2 + 16x - 6y = 39$;

(b) $16x^2 - 9y^2 - 64x - 18y - 66 = 0$;

(c) $9x^2 + 4y^2 + 54x - 32y + 1 = 0$;

(d) $4x^2 - y^2 - 8x + 4y + 36 = 0$;

(e) $x^2 + y^2 - 6x + 4y = 0$.

2. The same as Problem 1 for the following:

(a) $16x^2 + 9y^2 - 64x - 54y + 1 = 0$;

(b) $2x^2 - 3y^2 + 12x - 12y - 42 = 0$;

(c) $4x^2 + y^2 + 64x + 192 = 0$;

(d) $4x^2 - 9y^2 - 4x - 12y + 321 = 0$;

(e) $4x^2 + 9y^2 + 24x - 18y + 45 = 0$.

3. Simplify the following equations by the second method. Draw the curve and both sets of axes.

(a) $y^2 + 4x + 4y - 4 = 0$;

(b) $9x^2 - 36x + 4y^2 + 16y + 16 = 0$;

(c) $x^2 - 12x + 12y + 48 = 0$;

(d) $16x^2 - 4y^2 + 16x - 16y - 93 = 0$;

(e) $9x^2 + 25y^2 - 72x + 100y + 19 = 0$.

4. The same as Problem 3 for the following:

(a) $x^2 + 2x - 7y + 29 = 0$;

(b) $16x^2 - 25y^2 - 64x - 336 = 0$;

(c) $y^2 + 8y + 10x - 34 = 0$;

(d) $25x^2 + 9y^2 - 150x + 36y + 36 = 0$;

(e) $4x^2 - y^2 + 4x + 8y - 15 = 0$.

5. Show by the second method that the term in x^2 and the constant term can be removed from the equation $y = ax^3 + bx^2 + cx + d$ by a proper translation of the axes. What does this show regarding the symmetry of the locus?

6. Translate the axes so as to remove the term in x^2 and the constant term from the equation $y = x^3 + 6x^2 + 3x - 7$.

7. Translate the axes so as to remove the term in x and the constant term from the equation $y = x^3 - 10x^2 + 28x - 21$.

8. What relation must hold between a, b, and c in order that it be possible to remove the terms in x and x^3 from the equation $y = x^4 + ax^3 + bx^2 + cx + d$?

9. Find the equation of each of the following parabolas and translate the origin to the vertex:

(a) focus $(-6, 0)$, directrix $x = 0$;

(b) focus $(4, 6)$, directrix $y = -2$;

(c) focus $(-9, 3)$, directrix $x = -4$;

(d) focus $(4, -3)$, directrix $y = 7$.

10. Find the equation of each of the following parabolas and translate the origin to the vertex:

(a) focus $(2, 8)$, directrix $y = 0$;

(b) focus $(-3, -4)$, directrix $x = 5$;

(c) focus $(-2, 9)$, directrix $y = 2$;

(d) focus $(0, -6)$, directrix $x = -6$.

11. Find the equation of each of the following ellipses and translate the origin to the center of symmetry:

(a) foci $(-1, 4)$ and $(11, 4)$, sum of focal radii 16;

(b) foci $(2, -1)$ and $(2, 7)$, sum of focal radii 10.

12. Find the equation of each of the following hyperbolas and translate the origin to the center of symmetry:

(a) foci $(-3, 4)$ and $(9, 4)$, difference of focal radii 8;

(b) foci $(-2, -3)$ and $(-2, 7)$, difference of focal radii 6.

13. In each of the following problems on pages 30 and 31 find the equation of the locus and simplify by a translation of the axes:

(a) 6a;   (b) 6c;   (c) 8a;   (d) 10a;   (e) 15c;   (f) 16b.

In each of the following locus problems simplify the equation by a translation of the axes.

14. From one focus of the ellipse $9x^2 + 25y^2 = 900$ focal radii are drawn and bisected. Show that the locus of the points of bisection is an ellipse and find its center and foci.

15. In the ellipse $b^2x^2 + a^2y^2 = a^2b^2$ chords are drawn from one end of (a) the major axis; (b) the minor axis. In each case show that the locus of the mid-points is an ellipse.

16. Find the locus of the mid-points of chords which are drawn from the point $(-6, 4)$ of the ellipse $x^2 + 4y^2 = 100$.

17. Find the locus of the center of a circle which passes through the point $(0, b)$ and cuts out of the x-axis a segment of length c.

18. Find the locus of the center of a circle tangent to the circle $x^2 + y^2 = r^2$ and the line $y = a$.

93. Discussion of equation $Ax^2 + Cy^2 + Dx + Ey + F = 0$. This represents the general form of a quadratic in x and y with the xy term lacking. The only restriction on the coefficients is that A and C cannot both be zero. We desire to find under what conditions the locus is a parabola, an ellipse, or a hyperbola.

CASE 1. *When either A or C is zero.* Let $A = 0$. Here the equation has the form

$$Cy^2 + Dx + Ey + F = 0.$$

If $D \neq 0$, by a proper translation we can remove * the y term and the constant, and obtain an equation of the form $Cy'^2 + Dx' = 0$, of which the locus is a parabola.

* By actual substitution of $x = x' + h$ and $y = y' + k$, it can be shown that (a) translation does not affect the coefficients of the highest powers of the variables; (b) that, if neither A nor C is zero, the first degree terms can be removed; (c) that, if one variable appears only to the first degree, the first power of the other variable and the constant term can be removed; (d) that, if one variable is missing, the first power of the other can be removed.

If $D = 0$, the y term can be removed by translation, and we get $Cy'^2 + F' = 0$, of which the locus is imaginary if F' and C have the same sign; the new x-axis if $F' = 0$; and a pair of lines parallel to the x-axis if F' and C have unlike signs.

A similar discussion holds when $C = 0$.

CASE 2. *When A and C are of like sign.* Removing the first degree terms by translation, we have

$$Ax'^2 + Cy'^2 = F'.$$

This is evidently an ellipse if F' has the same sign as A and C; a point if $F' = 0$; and an imaginary locus if F' has the opposite sign to that of A and C.

CASE 3. *When A and C are of unlike sign.* Removing the first degree terms, we have

$$Ax'^2 + Cy'^2 = F'.$$

This is evidently a hyperbola unless $F' = 0$, in which case the locus is a pair of lines intersecting at the new origin.

94. Conics. Any plane section of a right circular cone is an ellipse, parabola, hyperbola, or a limiting form of one of these

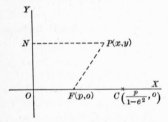

curves. Hence they are called *conic sections* or *conics.*

Although these curves were defined separately in the preceding chapters, it is evident from the discussion in §§ 71 and 81 that they are all included in the following general definition:

A conic is the locus of a point such that its distance from a fixed point has a constant ratio to its distance from a fixed line.

The fixed line is called a directrix. Let p be the distance of the fixed point F from the directrix and denote the constant ratio by e. Take the directrix as the y-axis and let F be on the x-axis. Then any point P on the conic must satisfy the relation

$$FP = e \cdot NP,$$

or $$\sqrt{(x - p)^2 + y^2} = ex.$$

Squaring and collecting terms, we have

$$(1 - e^2)x^2 - 2px + y^2 + p^2 = 0. \qquad (29)$$

If $e = 1$, the coefficient of x^2 is zero and the locus is a parabola. (See Case 1, § 93.)

If $e < 1$, the coefficients of x^2 and y^2 have like signs and the locus is an ellipse. (See Case 2, § 93.)

If $e > 1$, the coefficients of x^2 and y^2 have unlike signs and the locus is a hyperbola. (See Case 3, § 93.)

By completing the square, (29) becomes

$$\left(x - \frac{p}{1 - e^2}\right)^2 + \frac{y^2}{1 - e^2} = \left(\frac{ep}{1 - e^2}\right)^2.$$

Hence, by the first method of § 92, the point $\left(\dfrac{p}{1 - e^2}, \, 0\right)$ is a center of symmetry, and if the origin is translated to this point the new equation is

$$x^2 + \frac{y^2}{1 - e^2} = \left(\frac{ep}{1 - e^2}\right)^2 \quad \text{or} \quad \frac{x^2}{\left(\dfrac{ep}{1 - e^2}\right)^2} + \frac{y^2}{\dfrac{(ep)^2}{1 - e^2}} = 1.$$

If $e < 1$ this equation is of the type $\dfrac{x^2}{a^2} + \dfrac{y^2}{b^2} = 1$, and therefore $a = \dfrac{ep}{1 - e^2}$, and $b = \dfrac{ep}{\sqrt{1 - e^2}} = a\sqrt{1 - e^2}$. Since for the ellipse $c^2 = a^2 - b^2$ we have on substituting

$$c^2 = a^2 e^2 \quad \text{or} \quad c = ae \quad \text{and} \quad e = \frac{c}{a}.$$

Hence the constant ratio e is the eccentricity of the ellipse. Also the distance from F to the center C is seen to be

$$OC - OF = \frac{p}{1 - e^2} - p = \frac{e^2 p}{1 - e^2} = ae = c.$$

Hence the fixed point F is a focus of the ellipse and, since the ellipse is symmetrical with respect to its center, there must be a directrix corresponding to each focus.

The student should show that these same results are true for the hyperbola by taking $e > 1$ and using the relation $c^2 = a^2 + b^2$.

Exercise 1. Write the equations of the conic when the directrix is the y-axis and the focus is $(-p, 0)$, and when the directrix is the x-axis and the focus is $(0, p)$ or $(0, -p)$.

Exercise 2. From the preceding discussion show that, if $e < 1$, the focus lies between the directrix and the center of symmetry and $c + p = \dfrac{a}{e}$, and that, if $e > 1$, the directrix lies between the focus and the center of symmetry and $c - p = \dfrac{a}{e}$.

95. General statement. The preceding analysis may be summed up as follows:

A quadratic equation of the form

$$Ax^2 + Cy^2 + Dx + Ey + F = 0,$$

where the coefficients are any real numbers, zero included, always defines a conic or one of its degenerate forms.

If either A or C is zero, the conic is a parabola or in special cases two parallel straight lines distinct, coincident, or imaginary.

If A and C have the same sign, the conic is an ellipse, or in special cases a circle, point, or imaginary ellipse.

If A and C have unlike signs, the conic is a hyperbola, or in special cases two intersecting straight lines.

96. Generalized standard equations of the conics. The equations derived in Chapters V, VI, and VII we have seen to be of a special character, since they are applicable only to the case that the vertex or center is at the origin and the principal axis is the x- or y-axis. We are now in a position to generalize these equations and obtain standard forms where the only restriction is that the principal axis is parallel to one of the coördinate axes.

Consider an ellipse with the center at (h, k), semiaxes a and b, and principal axis $y = k$. It is required to find its equation.

If the origin is translated to (h, k), we know from Chapter VI that the transformed equation will be

$$\frac{x'^2}{a^2} + \frac{y'^2}{b^2} = 1.$$

The problem then is the reverse of that considered in § 92, viz., the transformed equation is given and the equation with reference to the old axes is to be found. Hence the substitutions are those of § 89 reversed, that is, $x' = x - h$, and $y' = y - k$. These give

$$\frac{(x - h)^2}{a^2} + \frac{(y - k)^2}{b^2} = 1$$

as the required equation.

In the same way we discuss the other cases and obtain the following equations:

Parabola —

Vertex (h, k), axis $y = k$: $(y - k)^2 = 2p(x - h)$;   (30)
"   "   " $x = h$: $(x - h)^2 = 2p(y - k)$;   (30a)

Ellipse —

Center (h, k), axis $y = k$: $\dfrac{(x - h)^2}{a^2} + \dfrac{(y - k)^2}{b^2} = 1$;   (31)

"   "   " $x = h$: $\dfrac{(y - k)^2}{a^2} + \dfrac{(x - h)^2}{b^2} = 1$;   (31$a$)

Hyperbola —

Center (h, k), axis $y = k$: $\dfrac{(x - h)^2}{a^2} - \dfrac{(y - k)^2}{b^2} = 1$;   (32)

"   "   " $x = h$: $\dfrac{(y - k)^2}{a^2} - \dfrac{(x - h)^2}{b^2} = 1$.   (32$a$)

These forms are easy to remember if one bears in mind that they are merely generalizations of the simple forms $y^2 = 2px$, $x^2 = 2py$, etc. To reduce an equation to one of these forms, it is necessary only to complete the squares.

EXAMPLE 1. Write the equation of the ellipse which has the center $(0, 1)$, one focus $(- 4, 1)$, and the minor axis 6.

Solution. Here the principal axis is $y = 1$. From the above data $b = 3$ and $c = 4$, whence $a = 5$. Therefore the equation is

$$\frac{(x - 0)^2}{25} + \frac{(y - 1)^2}{9} = 1.$$

EXAMPLE 2. Simplify the equation $2x^2 - 3y^2 + 8x - 6y + 11 = 0$.
Find the center, semiaxes, vertices, and foci, and draw the curve.

Solution. Completing squares, we
have

$$2(x + 2)^2 - 3(y + 1)^2 = -6,$$

or $$-\frac{(x + 2)^2}{3} + \frac{(y + 1)^2}{2} = 1.$$

The center is $(-2, -1)$ and since the
term in $(y + 1)^2$ is positive, the principal axis is $x = -2$. Hence

$$a = \sqrt{2}, \quad b = \sqrt{3}, \quad \text{and} \quad c = \sqrt{5}.$$

The vertices are

$$(-2, -1 \pm \sqrt{2}),$$

and the foci

$$(-2, -1 \pm \sqrt{5}).$$

PROBLEMS

1. Write the equations of the ellipses satisfying the following conditions:

    (a) vertices $(\pm 6, -2)$, focus $(4, -2)$;

    (b) vertices $(1, 8)$ and $(1, -2)$, focus $(1, 7)$;

    (c) vertices $(-4, 3)$ and $(8, 3)$, $e = \frac{2}{3}$;

    (d) foci $(2, -2)$ and $(2, 8)$, $e = \frac{5}{6}$.

2. Write the equations of the ellipses satisfying the following conditions, the major axis being first parallel to the x-axis, and second
parallel to the y-axis:

    (a) $a = 5$, $b = 4$, center $(-5, 4)$;

    (b) $a = 6$, $b = 3$, center $(2, -3)$;

    (c) $b = 5$, $c = \sqrt{39}$, center $(2, 1)$;

    (d) $b = 8$, $c = \sqrt{80}$, center $(-4, 0)$.

3. Write the equations of the hyperbolas satisfying the following
conditions:

    (a) vertices $(\pm 3, 4)$, focus $(-5, 4)$;

    (b) foci $(2, 8)$ and $(2, -4)$, vertex $(2, 6)$;

    (c) foci $(\pm 8, 2)$, $e = \frac{4}{3}$;

    (d) vertices $(-6, 2)$ and $(10, 2)$, $e = 2$.

4. Write the equations of the hyperbolas satisfying the data of Problem 2.

5. Write the equations of the asymptotes to the hyperbolas in Problem 3.

6. Write the equations of the parabolas satisfying the following conditions:

(a) focus $(2, 4)$, vertex $(2, -1)$;

(b) vertex $(-4, -2)$, directrix $x = -8$;

(c) focus $(3, -6)$, directrix $y = 0$;

(d) vertex $(5, 0)$, ends of latus rectum $(1, \pm 8)$;

(e) focus $(0, 0)$, vertex $(a, 0)$.

7. Write the equations of the parabolas satisfying the following conditions:

(a) focus $(-2, 3)$, vertex $(4, 3)$;

(b) vertex $(-4, -2)$, directrix $y = -6$;

(c) focus $(2, 1)$, directrix $x = 7$;

(d) focus $(0, 0)$, vertex $(0, a)$;

(e) focus $(0, 0)$, directrix $y = a$.

8. Simplify the following equations by completing the squares and draw their loci:

(a) $9x^2 + 4y^2 - 36x + 16y - 92 = 0$;

(b) $16x^2 - 25y^2 - 64x - 336 = 0$;

(c) $4x^2 - 4x - 32y - 15 = 0$;

(d) $4x^2 - y^2 + 32x + 4y + 60 = 0$;

(e) $25x^2 + 9y^2 - 150x + 36y + 36 = 0$;

(f) $6x + y^2 + 8y = 0$.

9. Simplify the following equations by completing the squares and draw their loci:

(a) $4x^2 + y^2 + 16x - 6y - 39 = 0$;

(b) $16x^2 - 4y^2 + 16x - 16y - 93 = 0$;

(c) $y^2 + 6y - 3x + 6 = 0$;

(d) $9x^2 - 16y^2 + 18x + 64y + 66 = 0$;

(e) $x^2 + 4x + 4y - 4 = 0$;

(f) $9x^2 + 4y^2 + 54x - 32y + 1 = 0$.

10. Find the foci, eccentricity, and equations of the directrices for the conics in Problem 8.

11. Find the foci, eccentricity, and equations of the directrices for the conics in Problem 9.

12. Show that the locus of $y = a + bx + cx^2$, where a, b, and c are constants and $c \neq 0$, is a parabola whose axis is parallel to the y-axis and which extends upwards from the vertex if $c > 0$, and downwards if $c < 0$.

13. Derive the equation of the conic, taking the origin as the focus and the line $x = -p$ as the directrix.

14. Derive the equation of the conic, taking the point $(c, 0)$ as the focus and the line $x = \dfrac{a}{e}$ as the directrix. Reduce the result to the standard forms for the ellipse and hyperbola when $e < 1$ and $e > 1$, respectively.

15. Verify each statement in the footnote on page 137.

16. Find the vertex and focus and draw the graph of each of the following parabolas:

(a) $6y = 12x + x^2$;

(b) $8y = 8x - x^2$;

(c) $12x = (y - 5)(y + 7)$;

(d) $y^2 + 2y - 7x + 29 = 0$;

(e) $y^2 + 12x - 36 = 0$;

(f) $x^2 + 10x - 14y + 11 = 0$.

17. The following numbers refer to curves on pages 38, 39. Reduce each equation to one of the standard forms of § 96 and make a sketch:

(a) 5;

(b) 6;

(c) 7;

(d) 8;

(e) 11;

(f) 13;

(g) 14;

(h) 15;

(i) 16.

18. For which of the equations on pages 38, 39 are the loci (a) parabolas; (b) ellipses; (c) hyperbolas?

19. The following numbers refer to problems on page 137. In each case find the equation of the locus and reduce it to a generalized standard form.

(a) 14;   (b) 16;   (c) 17;   (d) 18.

20. Let $2l$ denote the length of the latus rectum and $2a$ the distance between the vertices of an ellipse or a hyperbola. Choosing axes so that a vertex is at the origin and the nearer focus is on the positive half of the x-axis, show that (a) the equation of the ellipse is $y^2 = 2lx - \dfrac{l}{a}x^2$; and (b) that of the hyperbola is $y^2 = 2lx + \dfrac{l}{a}x^2$.

97. Simplification of equations by rotation. The process of rotation of the axes effects the removal of the xy term from the second degree equation if the proper angle θ is chosen. Let us substitute in the general equation

$$Ax^2 + Bxy + Cy^2 + Dx + Ey + F = 0$$

the rotation formulas

$$x = x' \cos \theta - y' \sin \theta,$$
$$y = x' \sin \theta + y' \cos \theta.$$

The coefficient of the $x'y'$ term will be

$$- 2A \sin \theta \cos \theta + B(\cos^2 \theta - \sin^2 \theta) + 2C \sin \theta \cos \theta,$$

or $\qquad - A \sin 2\theta + B \cos 2\theta + C \sin 2\theta.$

(The student should make the substitution in full for all terms of the general equation.)

The term in $x'y'$ will vanish if

$$(C - A) \sin 2\theta + B \cos 2\theta = 0,$$

or if $\qquad\qquad \tan 2\theta = \dfrac{B}{A - C}.$ $\qquad\qquad$ **(33)**

Thus we have the theorem:

For any second degree equation there is an angle of value less than 90° such that the substitutions for rotation through this angle will transform the equation into one containing no xy term.

For the equation $\tan 2\theta = \dfrac{B}{A - C}$, gives values of $\tan 2\theta$, positive or negative, from 0 when $B = 0$ to infinity when $A = C$. Hence for all values of A, B, and C, 2θ will have some value between 0 and 180°.

Example. Simplify $41x^2 - 24xy + 34y^2 = 25$.

Solution. Here $A = 41$, $B = - 24$, and $C = 34$.

Therefore $\qquad\qquad \tan 2\theta = - \dfrac{24}{7}.$

This gives at once $\qquad\qquad \cos 2\theta = - \dfrac{7}{25}.$

Substituting in the half-angle formulas of trigonometry,

$$\sin \theta = \sqrt{\frac{1 - \cos 2\theta}{2}} = \frac{4}{5},$$

and $$\cos \theta = \sqrt{\frac{1 + \cos 2\theta}{2}} = \frac{3}{5}.$$

Hence $x = \frac{3}{5} x' - \frac{4}{5} y'$ and $y = \frac{4}{5} x' + \frac{3}{5} y'$.
Substituting in the above equation and reducing, we have

$$x'^2 + 2y'^2 = 1,$$

an ellipse of semiaxes 1 and $\dfrac{\sqrt{2}}{2}$.

98. The general equation of the second degree.
We have seen that the equations of the conics are all special cases of the general equation

$$Ax^2 + Bxy + Cy^2 + Dx + Ey + F = 0.$$

We are now ready to prove the converse theorem; namely,

Every equation of the second degree in two variables defines a conic or one of the limiting forms of the conic.

It has been shown in § 93 that this theorem is true for every form of the second degree equation in which the product xy does not appear. Also we have just seen in the previous section that by a proper rotation of the axes the xy term can be made to disappear from the equation. Thus the proof of the theorem is complete.

99. The characteristic.
The quantity $B^2 - 4AC$ is called the characteristic of the general equation of the second degree, and is denoted by Δ. We now prove the theorem:

The characteristic of a general equation of the second degree is unaltered by a rotation of the axes through any angle θ.

In the general equation substitute the values given in the rotation formulas. The first three terms become

| $\begin{aligned}A \cos^2 \theta \\ + B \sin \theta \cos \theta \\ \\ + C \sin^2 \theta\end{aligned}$ x'^2 | $\begin{aligned}- 2A \sin \theta \cos \theta \\ - B \sin^2 \theta \\ + B \cos^2 \theta \\ + 2C \sin \theta \cos \theta\end{aligned}$ $x'y'$ | $\begin{aligned}+ A \sin^2 \theta \\ - B \sin \theta \cos \theta \\ \\ + C \cos^2 \theta\end{aligned}$ y'^2 |

Calling the coefficients of the new equation A', B', C', etc., we have:

$$A' = A \cos^2 \theta + C \sin^2 \theta + B \sin \theta \cos \theta,$$
$$C' = A \sin^2 \theta + C \cos^2 \theta - B \sin \theta \cos \theta,$$
$$B' = 2C \sin \theta \cos \theta - 2A \sin \theta \cos \theta + B \cos^2 \theta - B \sin^2 \theta.$$

The characteristic of the new equation, $B'^2 - 4A'C'$, becomes on multiplying and collecting the terms:

$$B^2 \cos^4 \theta + B^2 \sin^4 \theta - 8AC \sin^2 \theta \cos^2 \theta - 4AC \sin^4 \theta$$
$$- 4AC \cos^4 \theta + 2B^2 \sin^2 \theta \cos^2 \theta$$
$$= (B^2 - 4AC) \cos^4 \theta + (B^2 - 4AC) \sin^4 \theta$$
$$+ 2(B^2 - 4AC) \sin^2 \theta \cos^2 \theta$$
$$= (B^2 - 4AC)(\cos^4 \theta + 2 \sin^2 \theta \cos^2 \theta + \sin^4 \theta)$$
$$= (B^2 - 4AC)(\cos^2 \theta + \sin^2 \theta)^2$$
$$= B^2 - 4AC.$$

It is easy to see that Δ is also unchanged by a translation of the axes. For this reason it is called an *invariant* of the equation.

Exercise 3. Prove that $A + C$ is not changed by the substitutions for rotation or translation of the axes.

100. Test for distinguishing the conics. If in the previous section, the angle θ were chosen so that the xy term vanished, the new equation would be

$$A'x'^2 + C'y'^2 + D'x' + E'y' + F' = 0,$$

and $\Delta = B^2 - 4AC = B'^2 - 4A'C' = -4A'C',$

since $B' = 0$.

From this relation and § 95 we see that

if $\Delta < 0$, A' and C' are of like sign, and the conic is an ellipse,[*]
if $\Delta = 0$, A' or C' is zero, and the conic is a parabola,[*]
if $\Delta > 0$, A' and C' are of unlike sign, and the conic is a hyperbola.[*]

[*] Or one of the limiting forms discussed in §§ 93, 95.

101. Suggestions for simplifying the equation of a conic.
If the conic is an ellipse or hyperbola (that is, if $\Delta \neq 0$), determine the coördinates (h, k) of the center of symmetry and remove the first degree terms by translation. Then rotate the axes as in the example of § 97.

If the conic is a parabola ($\Delta = 0$), the substitutions for rotation should be made first, and then equations of condition involving h and k can be formed.

A convenient check on the accuracy of the rotation substitutions is the fact that $A + C$ is unchanged until the new equation is simplified. (See Exercise 3, § 99.)

PROBLEMS

Simplify the following equations. In each case draw the conic and the three sets of coördinate axes.*

1. $52x^2 - 72xy + 73y^2 + 8x - 294y - 1167 = 0$.
2. $17x^2 - 6xy + 9y^2 - 126x + 90y + 81 = 0$.
3. $66x^2 - 24xy + 59y^2 + 156x - 142y + 149 = 0$.
4. $32x^2 - 52xy - 7y^2 + 80x + 160y - 1120 = 0$.
5. $16x^2 + 24xy + 9y^2 + 150x - 200y - 1000 = 0$.
6. $109x^2 - 64xy + 61y^2 + 1000x - 500y + 1375 = 0$.
7. $24xy - 7y^2 - 120y - 144 = 0$.
8. $16x^2 - 24xy + 9y^2 + 120x + 160y - 800 = 0$.
9. $4x^2 + 4xy + y^2 + 8\sqrt{5}x + 4\sqrt{5}y + 25 = 0$.
10. $85x^2 + 96xy + 45y^2 + 532x + 372y + 436 = 0$.
11. $3x^2 + 8xy - 3y^2 + 54x + 22y - 77 = 0$.
12. $7x^2 - 6xy - y^2 + 58x - 2y - 9 = 0$.
13. $144x^2 + 120xy + 25y^2 - 260x + 624y + 676 = 0$.
14. $7x^2 + 6xy - y^2 - 38x - 30y - 97 = 0$.
15. $108x^2 + 300xy - 17y^2 + 1116x + 198y + 855 = 0$.
16. $x^2 + 4xy + y^2 - 10x - 2y - 11 = 0$.
17. $25x^2 + 36xy + 40y^2 - 308x - 384y - 108 = 0$.

* In certain problems the conic is degenerate or imaginary. Here one transformation is often sufficient and the locus can be determined by means of § 29 or § 46.

18. $9x^2 - 24xy + 16y^2 - 360x - 20y = 0.$

19. $64x^2 - 96xy + 36y^2 + 480x - 360y + 675 = 0.$

20. The numbers below refer to the above set of problems. In each case find the coördinates of a focus and the equation of the corresponding directrix referred to the given set of coördinate axes.

(a) 1;   (b) 5;   (c) 7;   (d) 8;   (e) 13;   (f) 18.

21. The ends of the base of a triangle are $(\pm 4, 0)$ and the difference of the base angles is 45°. Find the locus of the vertex and simplify the equation.

22. The ends of the base of a triangle are $(0, 0)$ and $(4, 0)$. Find the locus of the vertex if the sum of the slopes of the sides is (a) $\frac{7}{12}$;

(b) $-\dfrac{2}{\sqrt{3}}$. Simplify the equation found and draw the locus.

23. Solve the previous problem when the given points are $(\pm a, 0)$ and the sum of the slopes is any constant k. Then show that the locus is a hyperbola which passes through the given points and has its axis of symmetry inclined at an angle θ, where $\tan 2\theta = -\dfrac{2}{k}$.

24. Show that the locus of $\sqrt{x} + \sqrt{y} = \sqrt{a}$ is an arc of a parabola by rationalizing the equation and finding the characteristic. Then transform the equation as in the above problems and find the focus and the directrix.

25. Through the point $(2, 0)$ a line is drawn which meets the lines $2y = x$ and $y = 2x$ in the points R and S. Find the locus of the mid-point of RS and plot it. Also find the center and the asymptotes of the locus.

Hint. First express the coördinates x and y of the mid-point of RS in terms of the slope of the variable line.

102. The conic through five points. The general equation of the second degree involves six arbitrary constants. As in the case of the circle, however, one of these can be divided out; hence, if we can express five of the coefficients in terms of the sixth, the conic is completely determined. This means that the conic is completely determined by five points.

To find the equation of a conic so defined we proceed to form equations between the coefficients of the general equation and solve them. For example, suppose that the conic is to pass through the points (4, 2), (2, 4), (− 3, 1), (1, − 3), and (0, 0). Substituting these in the general equation,

$$Ax^2 + Bxy + Cy^2 + Dx + Ey + F = 0,$$

we have:
$$16A + 8B + 4C + 4D + 2E + F = 0,$$
$$4A + 8B + 16C + 2D + 4E + F = 0,$$
$$9A - 3B + C - 3D + E + F = 0,$$
$$A - 3B + 9C + D - 3E + F = 0,$$
$$F = 0.$$

Solving these, we find that $A = C = \dfrac{B}{50}$, and $D = E = -\dfrac{7B}{5}$. This makes the general equation, on dividing out B and clearing of fractions:

$$x^2 + 50xy + y^2 - 70x - 70y = 0.$$

The value of Δ shows that the conic is a hyperbola. Its center is found by the method of § 92 to be $(\frac{35}{26}, \frac{35}{26})$. The

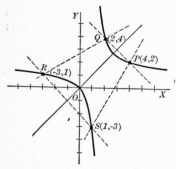

inclination of its axes is 45°, since $\tan 2\theta = \infty$. This information, together with the five points given, is sufficient for sketching the curve. The graph is shown.

A shorter method of solving the above problem is given by the theorem of § 45. Call the first four points P, Q, R, and S. The equations of the lines PQ and RS are $x + y - 6 = 0$ and $x + y + 2 = 0$. Multiplying these together, the equation of the pair of lines is

$$x^2 + 2xy + y^2 - 4x - 4y - 12 = 0,$$

by § 46. Similarly the equation of the pair of lines RQ and SP is

$$15x^2 - 34xy + 15y^2 + 28x + 28y - 196 = 0.$$

Now the intersections of the loci of these two equations are the points P, Q, R, and S. Hence by § 45

$$15x^2 - 34xy + 15y^2 + 28x + 28y - 196$$
$$+ k(x^2 + 2xy + y^2 - 4x - 4y - 12) = 0 \quad (a)$$

is the equation of a system of curves passing through these four points. As this is of the second degree for all values of k, they are all conics. To find the conic of this system passing through the fifth point $(0, 0)$, substitute its coördinates for the variables. This gives

$$- 196 - 12k = 0,$$

whence $k = -\frac{49}{3}$. Putting this value for k in (a) and collecting terms, we have the same result as before.

If special conditions are imposed on the conic, fewer than five points will usually determine it. If the conic is a parabola, $B^2 - 4AC = 0$. If the conic is symmetrical with respect to the origin, $D = E = 0$. If the axes of symmetry of the conic are parallel to the coördinate axes, $B = 0$. In the first and third cases four points are usually sufficient, in the second three points.

PROBLEMS

1. Find the equation of the conic which passes through the following points:

(a) $(-10, 5)$, $(2, -11)$, $(0, 0)$, $(6, 17)$, $(18, 1)$;

(b) $(1, 3)$, $(3, -1)$, $(5, 5)$, $(8, 4)$, $(7, 1)$.

2. The same as Problem 1 for the following points:

(a) $(2, 4)$, $(-2, -4)$, $(-4, -2)$, $(4, 2)$, $(1, 8)$;

(b) $(0, 3)$, $(4, 1)$, $(3, 9)$, $(7, 7)$, $(1, 0)$.

3. Find the equation of the parabola which passes through the following points:

(a) $(1, -1)$, $(5, -1)$, $(1, 2)$, $(-7, 7)$;

(b) $(-3, -2)$, $(1, 4)$, $(1, -2)$, $(9, 4)$.

4. Find the equation of the parabola which passes through the following points:

(a) $(0, 0)$, $(-2, 11)$, $(10, -5)$, $(4, 28)$;

(b) $(1, 0)$, $(0, 0)$, $(0, 1)$, $(6, 3)$.

5. Find the equation of a conic which is symmetrical with respect to the origin and which passes through:

(a) $(2, 4), (-2, 2), (6, 4)$;   (c) $(2, 4), (-2, 2), (4, 2)$.

(b) $(2, -6), (4, 0), (-8, -6)$;

6. Find the equation of a conic which has its axes of symmetry parallel to the coördinate axes and which passes through:

(a) $(7, 9), (2, -3), (-3, 9), (-3, 1)$;

(b) $(4, -3), (-1, 7), (-6, -3), (2, 5)$;

(c) $(2, 6), (6, 8), (2, 0), (-2, -2)$;

(d) $(6, 4), (5, 1), (6, -2), (-3, 1)$.

7. Find the equation of a parabola which passes through the following points and which has its axis parallel to the x-axis:

(a) $(-3, 3), (-1, 2), (0, 4)$;   (c) $(-1, 2), (0, 3), (2, 4)$;

(b) $(1, 3), (2, 2), (3, 4)$;   (d) $(-2, 0), (0, 2), (6, 4)$.

8. The same as Problem 7 except that the axis is parallel to the y-axis.

CHAPTER IX

POLAR COÖRDINATES

103. Preliminary note. The student who is not thoroughly familiar with trigonometry will find his work in this chapter materially lightened if he reviews the following topics:

1. The signs and variation of the trigonometric functions as the angle varies from 0° to 360°.
2. Radian measure of angles.
3. The values of the functions of the special angles 0°, 90°, 180°, 270°, and multiples of 30° and 45°.
4. The formulas expressing the functions of $-\theta$, $\pi - \theta$, $\pi + \theta$, and $2\pi - \theta$ in terms of functions of θ.

The essential information in these respects is given in the Introduction.

104. Definitions. Some topics in analytic geometry, especially those involving motion about a point, can be better investigated by the use of *polar coördinates* than by rectangular coördinates. In the polar system the position of a point is fixed by measuring a distance and a direction instead of by the measures of two distances. This is essentially the same system as that of bearing and distance used in surveying, contrasted with that of latitude and longitude used in geography.

Choose a fixed point O as the origin, called the **pole,** and a fixed line OA through it, called the **polar axis.** Then any point P is determined if we know its distance from O and the angle that OP makes with OA. The measures of the distance OP and the angle AOP are called the polar coördinates of P and are designated by ρ and θ. The distance ρ is called the **radius vector** of P, and θ is called the **vectorial angle.**

153

Polar coördinates do not obey the conventions as to direction and magnitude which we have used in the rectangular system. As in trigonometry the radius vector may be rotated indefinitely in a counter-clockwise or clockwise direction, making θ take on any positive or negative value. *Distances measured on the terminal line of θ from the pole are positive; those measured in the opposite direction, on the terminal line produced, are negative.*

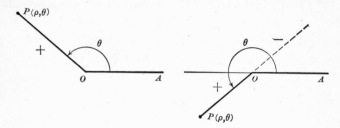

(See the right-hand diagram above.) Hence every pair of real numbers (ρ, θ) determines one point which may be located according to the following rule.

RULE FOR PLOTTING. *Taking the polar axis as an initial line, lay off the vectorial angle θ, counter-clockwise if positive, clockwise if negative. Then measure off the radius vector ρ, on the terminal line of θ if positive, on the terminal line of θ produced through the pole if negative.*

Since θ and $\theta + 2\pi$ have the same terminal line, a point may be represented by an indefinite number of pairs of coördinates. Thus in the adjoining figure we may take for the coördinates of

P, $\rho = 8$, $\theta = \dfrac{7\pi}{6}$ or $\dfrac{7\pi}{6} \pm 2n\pi$.

Since the terminal line of θ produced is the terminal line of $\theta \pm \pi$, a second set of coördinates is

$\rho = -8$, $\theta = \dfrac{\pi}{6}$ or $\dfrac{\pi}{6} \pm 2n\pi$.

If we express θ in terms of degrees, these coördinates read as follows:

$\rho = 8$, $\theta = 210°$, $570°$, $930°$, etc., and $- 150°$, $- 510°$, etc.;
or

$\rho = - 8$, $\theta = 30°$, $390°$, $750°$, etc., and $- 330°$, $- 690°$, etc.

Ordinarily we keep θ within the limits $\pm \pi$, or 0 and 2π.

105. Relations between rectangular and polar coördinates.
Take the pole at the origin of rectangular coördinates and the

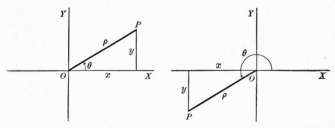

polar axis as the positive half of the x-axis. From the figures
and the definitions of the trigonometric functions it is evident
that for $P(x, y) = P(\rho, \theta)$ in any quadrant the following formulas are true:

$$x = \rho \cos \theta, \qquad y = \rho \sin \theta, \tag{34}$$

$$\rho^2 = x^2 + y^2, \qquad \tan \theta = \frac{y}{x}. \tag{35}$$

These equations enable us to transform rectangular equations
and coördinates into polar forms, and inversely.

NOTE. In transforming the rectangular coördinates of a point into
polar coördinates, care should be taken to group together the corresponding
values of ρ and θ.

106. Polar curves.
The *definitions* of equation and locus
for polar coördinates are the same as those for rectangular coördinates (§ 17), if (ρ, θ) is substituted for (x, y). Since, however, a point may be represented by different pairs of polar
coördinates, two different equations may have the same locus.
For example, the equations $\rho = 4$ and $\rho = - 4$ both have as a
locus a circle of radius 4 whose center is the pole. The equation

in polar coördinates is derived as in the rectangular system (§ 20). In a few cases the polar equation may be obtained more easily by deriving it in the rectangular form and then substituting for x and y their values in terms of ρ and θ and *vice versa*.

Plotting in polar coördinates resembles that in rectangular coördinates. The equation should usually be solved for ρ and a table of values formed, taking values of θ at intervals of 30° or less. If the equation involves functions of multiple angles, the values of θ should be taken so close together that the interval between successive values of the multiple is not more than 30°. For example, in plotting $\rho = 10 \cos 3\theta$, take θ at 10° intervals. When the curve has symmetry, it is usually unnecessary to carry the table through more than two quadrants. Polar plotting paper should always be used.

EXAMPLE. Plot the ellipse $2\rho - \rho \cos \theta = 6$.

Solving, $$\rho = \frac{6}{2 - \cos \theta}.$$

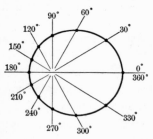

TABLE OF VALUES

$\theta°$	ρ	$\theta°$	ρ
0	6.0	210	2.1
30	5.3	240	2.4
60	4.0	270	3.0
90	3.0	300	4.0
120	2.4	330	5.3
150	2.1	360	6.0
180	2.0		

PROBLEMS

1. Plot each of the following pairs of points: (*a*) (8, ± 60°); (*b*) (± 5, 405°); (*c*) $\left(10, \frac{\pi}{3}\right)$, $\left(10, \frac{2\pi}{3}\right)$; (*d*) (6, 30°), (6, 210°). What symmetry has each pair of points?

2. Plot $\left(10, \frac{\pi}{6}\right)$. Plot points symmetrical to this with respect to the pole, the polar axis, and the 90° axis, and find two pairs of coördinates for each point.

3. The same as Problem 2 for:

(a) $\left(8, \dfrac{3\pi}{4}\right)$;   (b) $\left(-8, \dfrac{\pi}{4}\right)$;   (c) $\left(6, -\dfrac{\pi}{3}\right)$.

4. Fix $P(\rho, \theta)$ in any quadrant and find its symmetry to:

(a) $(\rho, -\theta)$;   (c) $(\rho, \pi - \theta)$;   (e) $(-\rho, \pi - \theta)$;

(b) $(-\rho, \theta)$;   (d) $(\rho, \pi + \theta)$;   (f) $(-\rho, -\theta)$.

5. Find the rectangular coördinates of the following points:

(a) $(-8, 150°)$;   (b) $(-8, 0°)$;   (c) $(10, 300°)$;

(d) $\left(12, \dfrac{\pi}{4}\right)$;   (e) $\left(-10, \dfrac{\pi}{3}\right)$;   (f) $\left(12, \dfrac{5\pi}{6}\right)$.

6. Find the rectangular coördinates of the following points:

(a) $(10, 330°)$;   (b) $(14, 120°)$;   (c) $(6, 225°)$;

(d) $\left(-16, \dfrac{\pi}{6}\right)$;   (e) $(12, \pi)$;   (f) $\left(8, \dfrac{3\pi}{4}\right)$.

7. Find two pairs of polar coördinates for each of the following points and plot the point in each case:

(a) $(5\sqrt{3}, -5)$;   (b) $(-6, 6)$;   (c) $(-8\sqrt{3}, -8)$;

(d) $(10, 10)$;   (e) $(8, -6)$;   (f) $(-8, 0)$.

8. Find two pairs of polar coördinates for each of the following points and plot the point in each case:

(a) $(5\sqrt{3}, 5)$;   (b) $(-5, -5\sqrt{3})$;   (c) $(0, 10)$;

(d) $(6\sqrt{3}, -6)$;   (e) $(-12, 5)$;   (f) $(-8, 8\sqrt{3})$.

9. Plot each of the following equations by means of polar coördinates and identify each locus by transforming its equation to rectangular coördinates:

(a) $\rho = 10$;   (d) $\rho^2 = 25$;   (g) $\rho = 2a \cos \theta$;

(b) $\tan \theta = \frac{1}{2}$;   (e) $\cot \theta = \frac{4}{3}$;   (h) $\rho = 6 \sin \theta + 8 \cos \theta$;

(c) $\rho = -10 \sin \theta$;   (f) $\rho \sin \theta = 6$;   (i) $\rho \cos \theta = a$.

10. Draw each of the following curves and transform each equation into polar coördinates:

(a) $y = -3x$;   (e) $x^2 + y^2 = r^2$;   (i) $y^2 - x^2 = 36$;

(b) $x - 2y = 0$;   (f) $x^2 + y^2 - 10y = 0$;   (j) $x^2 - y^2 = a^2$;

(c) $x + 8 = 0$;   (g) $x^2 + y^2 + 12x = 0$;   (k) $2xy = a^2$;

(d) $y = b$;   (h) $x^2 - y^2 = 36$;   (l) $2xy = -a^2$.

107. Equations of the straight line. The general equation of the straight line in polar coördinates is not as convenient

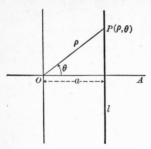

as the equation in rectangular coordinates and will not be discussed. The special cases where the line is parallel or perpendicular to the polar axis or passes through the pole lead to very simple equations.

In the figure let the line l be perpendicular to the polar axis OA and have the polar intercept a.

For any point $P(\rho, \theta)$ on the line it is evident that $\cos \theta = \dfrac{a}{\rho}$, whence the equation of the line is

$$\rho \cos \theta = a. \tag{36}$$

Similarly the equation of a line parallel to the polar axis, of 90° intercept a, is

$$\rho \sin \theta = a. \tag{36a}$$

For a line passing through the pole the equation is evidently

$$\theta = c. \tag{37}$$

Exercise 1. By transforming the normal form of the straight line equation into polar coördinates show that the equation of any line in polar coördinates is

$$\rho \cos (\theta - \omega) = p.$$

108. Equations of the circle. As in the case of the straight line the general form of the circle equation is not often used. Several common special forms are as follows:

Circle with center at pole, radius r: $\rho = r;$ (38)

Circle with center at $(r, 0)$, radius r: $\rho = 2r \cos \theta;$ (39)

Circle with center at $\left(r, \dfrac{\pi}{2}\right)$, radius r: $\rho = 2r \sin \theta;$ (39a)

Circle through pole, with polar intercept a and 90° intercept b:

$$\rho = a \cos \theta + b \sin \theta. \tag{40}$$

The first equation is obvious. The second may be readily derived from the adjoining figure, and the third from a similar figure.

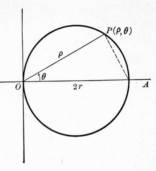

The simplest way of getting the fourth equation is to observe that the rectangular equation of this circle is

$$x^2 + y^2 - ax - by = 0.$$

Transforming this into polar coordinates, we have the desired result.

Exercise 2. Derive equation (40) directly from a figure.

Hint. Show that the radius vector is in length the sum of the projections upon it of the *x*- and *y*-intercepts of the circle.

Exercise 3. Show that a circle of radius *r* which has its center at (r, π) has the equation $\rho = -2r \cos \theta$, and that, if the center is at $\left(r, \dfrac{3\pi}{2}\right)$, it has the equation $\rho = -2r \sin \theta$.

109. Discussion of polar curves. As in the case of rectangular equations, the study of polar curves is facilitated by discussion of the equation in conjunction with plotting. The topics discussed are of much the same character.

(*a*) *Intercepts.* The intercepts on the polar and 90° axes are the values of ρ for $\theta = 0°$ and 180°, and 90° and 270°, respectively.

(*b*) *Symmetry.* It is easy to establish that in accordance with the definitions of § 25, (ρ, θ) is symmetrical to $(-\rho, \theta)$ and $(\rho, \pi + \theta)$ with respect to the pole; to $(\rho, -\theta)$ and $(-\rho, \pi - \theta)$ with respect to the polar axis; and to $(\rho, \pi - \theta)$ and $(-\rho, -\theta)$ with respect to the 90° axis. Hence we have the following tests for symmetry:

If the substitution of
$-\rho$ *for* ρ *or* $\pi + \theta$ *for* θ *does not change the equation, there is symmetry with respect to the pole;*

$- \theta$ for θ or $- \rho$ for ρ and $\pi - \theta$ for θ *does not change the equation, there is symmetry with respect to the polar axis;*

$\pi - \theta$ for θ or $- \rho$ for ρ and $- \theta$ for θ *does not change the equation, there is symmetry with respect to the* 90° *axis.*

Exercise 4. Prove that (ρ, θ) is symmetrical to:

    (a) $(- \rho, \theta)$ with respect to the pole;

    (b) $(\rho, - \theta)$ with respect to the polar axis;

    (c) $(\rho, \pi - \theta)$ with respect to the 90° axis;

    (d) $(\rho, \pi + \theta)$ with respect to the pole;

    (e) $(- \rho, \pi - \theta)$ with respect to the polar axis;

    (f) $(- \rho, - \theta)$ with respect to the 90° axis.

(c) *Extent of the curve.* If in the solution for ρ we obtain $\rho = a \pm \sqrt{f(\theta)}$, values of θ for which $f(\theta) < 0$ make ρ imaginary and must be excluded. If any values of θ make ρ infinite, these values determine the direction in which the curve extends to infinity. If ρ is never infinite, the values of θ which make ρ take on its greatest numerical value should be found. Likewise the values of θ for which $\rho = 0$, or for which ρ takes on its least numerical value, should be found.

After completing the discussion, the student should consider it as a whole and think out the way in which ρ varies as the radius vector turns about the pole.

Example 1. Discuss and plot the locus of the equation

$$\rho = \frac{2}{1 + \cos \theta}.$$

Solution.

(a) Intercepts:

θ	0°	90°	180°	270°
ρ	1	2	∞	2

(b) Symmetry: The locus is symmetrical with respect to the polar axis, since $\cos (- \theta) = \cos \theta$. Hence the table of values is unnecessary for $\theta > 180°$.

(c) Extent of the curve: ρ is infinite when $1 + \cos \theta = 0$, i.e., when $\cos \theta = - 1$, or $\theta = \pi$.

ρ is evidently never 0. Its least value occurs when $1 + \cos \theta$ is greatest, i.e., when $\cos \theta = 1$, or $\theta = 0$. Here $\rho = 1$.

TABLE OF VALUES

θ (radians)	θ (degrees)	$1 + \cos\theta$	ρ
$\pm\ 0$	0	2.00	1.0
$\pm\ \dfrac{\pi}{6}$	$\pm\ 30$	1.87	1.1
$\pm\ \dfrac{\pi}{3}$	$\pm\ 60$	1.50	1.3
$\pm\ \dfrac{\pi}{2}$	$\pm\ 90$	1.00	2.0
$\pm\ \dfrac{2\pi}{3}$	$\pm\ 120$	0.50	4.0
$\pm\ \dfrac{5\pi}{6}$	$\pm\ 150$	0.13	15.0
$\pm\ \pi$	$\pm\ 180$	0.00	∞

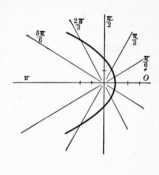

Transformation to rectangular coördinates shows that this curve is a parabola.

EXAMPLE 2. $\rho^2 = a^2 \cos 2\theta$, or $\rho = \pm a\sqrt{\cos 2\theta}$.   (Lemniscate)

Solution.   (a) The intercepts on the polar axis are $\pm a$; on the 90° axis they are imaginary.

(b) The three tests for symmetry are satisfied, for $\cos 2(-\theta)$ $= \cos 2\theta$, etc. Hence values of θ up to 90° only are needed.

(c) ρ is imaginary when $\cos 2\theta < 0$, i.e., when

$$90° < 2\theta < 270°,$$

or $$45° < \theta < 135°.$$

The greatest numerical value of ρ occurs when $\cos 2\theta = 1$, or $\theta = 0$ or 180°. This value is a.

$\rho = 0$ when $\cos 2\theta = 0$, or when $2\theta = 90°$, $270°$, etc., or $\theta = 45°$, $135°$, $225°$, and $315°$.

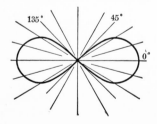

TABLE OF VALUES, $(a = 10)$

$\theta°$	2θ	$\cos 2\theta$	$\sqrt{\cos 2\theta}$	ρ
0	0	1.00	± 1.00	± 10
15	30	.87	$\pm .93$	± 9.3
30	60	.50	$\pm .71$	± 7.1
45	90	.00	.00	0.0

EXAMPLE 3. $\rho = 1 + 2 \sin \theta$. (Limaçon)

Solution. (a)

θ	0°	90°	180°	270°
ρ	1	3	1	-1

(b) Since $\sin (\pi - \theta) = \sin \theta$, the curve is symmetrical with respect to the 90° axis.

(c) ρ is never infinite; its greatest value occurs when $\sin \theta = 1$, or $\theta = 90°$.

$\rho = 0$ when $1 + 2 \sin \theta = 0$, or $\sin \theta = -\frac{1}{2}$. Hence the curve passes through the pole when $\theta = 210°$ or 330°.

TABLE OF VALUES

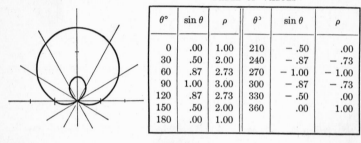

$\theta°$	$\sin \theta$	ρ	$\theta°$	$\sin \theta$	ρ
0	.00	1.00	210	$-.50$	.00
30	.50	2.00	240	$-.87$	$-.73$
60	.87	2.73	270	-1.00	-1.00
90	1.00	3.00	300	$-.87$	$-.73$
120	.87	2.73	330	$-.50$	.00
150	.50	2.00	360	.00	1.00
180	.00	1.00			

PROBLEMS

1. Using §§ 107, 108, identify and draw the locus of each of the following:

(a) $\rho \cos \theta - 7 = 0$;

(b) $\rho \cos \theta + 9 = 0$;

(c) $\rho = 8$;

(d) $\cos \theta = \frac{1}{2}$;

(e) $\rho - 10 \sin \theta = 0$;

(f) $\rho + 10 \cos \theta = 0$;

(g) $\rho^2 - 5\rho - 50 = 0$;

(h) $\tan \theta = -\sqrt{3}$;

(i) $\theta = \frac{\pi}{3}$;

(j) $\rho = -8 \sin \theta$;

(k) $\rho = 12 \cos \theta$;

(l) $\rho = 5 \cos \theta - 7 \sin \theta$;

(m) $\rho = 8 \sin \theta - 6 \cos \theta$.

2. Transform into polar coördinates:

(a) $Ax + By + C = 0$;

(b) $x^2 + y^2 + Dx + Ey + F = 0$.

Discuss * and plot the locus of each of the following:

* The arbitrary constants should be kept throughout the discussion, the intercepts, etc., being found in terms of the arbitrary constants. Substitution of numerical values should be made only in finding the table of values for plotting. Compare Example 2.

3. (a) $\rho = a(1 - \cos \theta)$;   (c) $\rho = a(1 - \sin \theta)$;

     (b) $\rho = a(1 + \cos \theta)$;   (d) $\rho = a(1 + \sin \theta)$.

                                            (Cardioids)

4. (a) $\rho = a + b \cos \theta, (a < b)$;   (e) $\rho = a + b \sin \theta, (a < b)$;

     (b) $\rho = a + b \cos \theta, (a > b)$;   (f) $\rho = a + b \sin \theta, (a > b)$;

     (c) $\rho = a - b \cos \theta, (a < b)$;   (g) $\rho = a - b \sin \theta, (a < b)$;

     (d) $\rho = a - b \cos \theta, (a > b)$;   (h) $\rho = a - b \sin \theta, (a > b)$.

     (Limaçons; the special form when $a = b$ is called a cardioid)

5. (a) $\rho = a \tan^2 \theta \sec \theta$;   (b) $\rho = a \cot^2 \theta \csc \theta$.

                                (Semicubical parabolas)

6. (a) $\rho = a \sec \theta \pm b, (a < b)$;   (d) $\rho = a \csc \theta \pm b, (a < b)$;

     (b) $\rho = a \sec \theta \pm b, (a = b)$;   (e) $\rho = a \csc \theta \pm b, (a = b)$;

     (c) $\rho = a \sec \theta \pm b, (a > b)$;   (f) $\rho = a \csc \theta \pm b, (a > b)$.

                             (Conchoids of Nicomedes)

7. (a) $\rho = 2a \tan \theta \sin \theta$;   (b) $\rho = 2a \cot \theta \cos \theta$.

                              (Cissoids of Diocles)

8. (a) $\rho = a \sin 2\theta$;   (b) $\rho = a \cos 2\theta$.   (Four-leafed roses)

9. (a) $\rho = a \sin 3\theta$;   (b) $\rho = a \cos 3\theta$.   (Three-leafed roses)

10. (a) $\rho = a \sin 5\theta$;   (b) $\rho = a \cos 5\theta$.   (Five-leafed roses)

11. $\rho^2 = a^2 \sin 2\theta$.   (Lemniscate)

12. (a) $\rho^2 = a^2 \csc 2\theta$;   (b) $\rho^2 = a^2 \sec 2\theta$.

13. (a) $\rho \sin 2\theta = a$;   (b) $\rho \cos 2\theta = a$.

14. (a) $\rho \sin 3\theta = a$;   (b) $\rho \cos 3\theta = a$.

15. (a) $\rho = a \sin \dfrac{\theta}{3}$;   (b) $\rho = a \cos \dfrac{\theta}{3}$.

16.* $\rho = a\theta$.   (Spiral of Archimedes)

17.* $\rho\theta = a$.   (Hyperbolic spiral)

18.* $\rho^2\theta = a$.   (Lituus)

19.* $(\rho - a)^2 = 2ap\theta$.   (Parabolic spiral)

---

* Since no trigonometric functions are involved in these equations, a discussion gives little or no help. The angle θ should be expressed in radians and enough of the curve plotted to show several revolutions of the radius vector. A proper choice of the arbitrary constant will save much labor in computing the table of values.

110. Rotation of axes. Rotation of the polar axis does not affect the value of ρ. The figure shows that if the coördinates

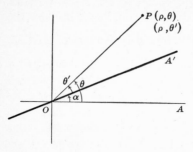

of P with reference to OA are (ρ, θ), and to OA' are (ρ, θ'), while angle $A'OA$ is α, we have as a formula of rotation

$$\theta = \theta' + \alpha. \quad (41)$$

By rotating the polar axis the standard equations of curves may be written in a variety of forms.

Translation of the pole is seldom necessary and is best performed by transforming the equation into rectangular coördinates.

111. Symmetrical Transformations. Equations may also be transformed by the substitutions for symmetry. As in the case of rectangular coördinates it can be shown that the effect of such a substitution is to transform the locus into a curve symmetrical to the given locus with respect to the center or axis involved. Thus we have the following:

If in an equation substitution is made of

$$
\left.
\begin{array}{l}
\pi + \theta \text{ for } \theta \\
- \theta \text{ for } \theta \\
\pi - \theta \text{ for } \theta
\end{array}
\right\}
\left\{
\begin{array}{c}
\text{the locus of the new equation} \\
\text{is symmetrical to that of the} \\
\text{old with respect to the}
\end{array}
\right\}
\left.
\begin{array}{l}
\text{pole;} \\
\text{polar axis;} \\
90° \text{ axis.}
\end{array}
\right.
$$

Since there are two sets of substitutions for symmetry, it is important to notice that, if we apply in succession both substitutions for symmetry with respect to the pole or an axis, we often obtain a new equation which has the same locus as the given equation. For example, if we substitute $\pi - \theta$ for θ in the equation $\rho = a(1 - \cos \theta)$, we get $\rho = a(1 + \cos \theta)$, which is the equation of a cardioid symmetrical to the given cardioid with respect to the 90° axis. If we now substitute $- \rho$ for ρ and $- \theta$ for θ, we get $\rho = - a(1 + \cos \theta)$, which has the original cardioid as its locus.

Substitution in the equation $\rho = a(1 - \cos \theta)$ shows that $\left(\dfrac{a}{2}, \dfrac{\pi}{3}\right)$ is a point of the cardioid, but these coördinates do not satisfy $\rho = -a(1 + \cos \theta)$. However, this point has also the coördinates $\left(-\dfrac{a}{2}, -\dfrac{2\pi}{3}\right)$, which do satisfy the latter equation. Difficulties of this sort due to the multiplicity of coördinates for a given point cause no trouble in plotting, but on solving two equations simultaneously to find points of intersection, some of these may not be obtained. Therefore, to find the points of intersection of two curves, it is best to plot the curves; this will indicate probable intersections. If these are not given by solving the given equations simultaneously, use equivalent equations obtained as in the above example or otherwise. Special attention must be given to the pole, since the curves meet at this point if it is possible to find for each curve some value of θ for which $\rho = 0$; these values of θ need not be the same.

PROBLEMS

1. In the following find the new equation after rotating the polar axis through the indicated angle, and draw the curve and both axes:

(a) $\rho = a \sin \theta, \alpha = 90°$;

(b) $\rho = a \sin 3\theta, \alpha = 30°$;

(c) $\rho^2 = a^2 \sin 2\theta, \alpha = 45°$;

(d) $\rho = 2a \cot \theta \cos \theta, \alpha = 90°$;

(e) $\rho = a \sec \theta \pm b, \alpha = -90°$;

(f) $\rho = a \cos \theta + b \sin \theta, \alpha = \arctan \dfrac{b}{a}$.

2. Show that the first of each of the following pairs of equations can be transformed into the second by a proper rotation of the polar axis:

(a) $\rho = a + b \sin \theta, \rho = a + b \cos \theta$;

(b) $\rho = a \sin 2\theta, \rho = a \cos 2\theta$;

(c) $\rho = a \cos 3\theta, \rho = a \sin 3\theta$;

(d) $\rho = a \sin 4\theta, \rho = a \cos 4\theta$.

3. Find the new equation when a substitution for symmetry with respect to the 90° axis is made, and draw both curves on the same axes:

(a) $\rho = a(1 + \cos \theta)$;

(b) $\rho = a \cos 3\theta$;

(c) $\rho = 2a \tan \theta \sin \theta$;

(d) $\rho = a \cos \theta$;

(e) $\rho = a \cos \theta + b \sin \theta$;

(f) $\rho^2 = a^2 \sin 2\theta$.

4. Find the new equation when a substitution for symmetry with respect to the polar axis is made and draw both curves on the same axes:

(a) $\rho = a(1 + \sin \theta)$;

(b) $\rho = a \sin \theta$;

(c) $\rho^2 = a^2 \sin 2\theta$;

(d) $\rho = a \sin 3\theta$.

5. Show that the graphs of $\rho = a\theta$ and $\rho = k + a\theta$ have the same shape, if θ is allowed to vary from $-\infty$ to $+\infty$.

6. Show by means of the symmetrical substitutions that each of the following pairs of equations have the same locus:

(a) $\rho = a + b \sin \theta$, $\rho = b \sin \theta - a$;

(b) $\rho = a\theta$, $\rho = -a(\pi + \theta)$;

(c) $\rho = \dfrac{a}{1 - \cos \theta}$, $\rho = \dfrac{-a}{1 + \cos \theta}$;

(d) $\rho = a \sec^2 \dfrac{\theta}{2}$, $\rho = -a \csc^2 \dfrac{\theta}{2}$.

7. Find the points of intersection of each of the following pairs of curves:

(a) $\rho = a \sin \theta$, $\rho = a \sin 2\theta$;

(b) $\rho = a(\cos \theta - 1)$, $\rho = 2a \sin \theta$;

(c) $\rho = \cos 2\theta$, $\rho = 1 + \cos \theta$;

(d) $\rho = a(1 - \cos \theta)$, $\rho = a(1 - \sin \theta)$;

(e) $\rho = 4(1 + \sin \theta)$, $\rho(1 - \sin \theta) = 3$.

112. Polar equation of the conics. If the pole is taken at the focus and the directrix is perpendicular to the polar axis as in the figure, we have at once from the definition of a conic (§ 94), $OP = eMP$, whence

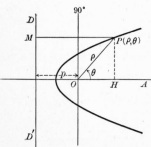

$$\rho = e(p + \rho \cos \theta),$$

which gives

$$\rho = \frac{ep}{1 - e \cos \theta}. \qquad (42)$$

If the directrix is taken parallel to the polar axis, the equation becomes

$$\rho = \frac{ep}{1 - e \sin \theta}. \tag{42a}$$

The transformations of rotation and symmetry give eight forms of the conic equation in which the focus is at the pole and the directrix is perpendicular or parallel to the polar axis. They are:

$$\rho = \frac{\pm ep}{1 \pm e \cos \theta}; \qquad \rho = \frac{\pm ep}{1 \pm e \sin \theta}.$$

In the first set the principal axis is the polar axis; in the second it is the 90° axis. To sketch a conic it is sufficient to put the equation in standard form and find the intercepts. The standard form determines the principal axis and eccentricity, and the intercepts give the vertices and the ends of the latus rectum.

By using the polar equation many of the properties of the conics may be derived more easily than by the use of the rectangular equations. Some of these are indicated in the following problems.

EXAMPLE. Identify and draw the conic whose equation is

$$\rho = \frac{15}{2 + 4 \sin \theta}.$$

Solution. To reduce the equation to the standard form divide numerator and denominator by 2. This gives us

$$\rho = \frac{\frac{15}{2}}{1 + 2 \sin \theta}$$

and shows that the curve is a hyperbola whose eccentricity is 2 and whose principal axis is the 90° axis.

The intercepts are

0°	90°	180°	270°
7.5	2.5	7.5	− 7.5

Since the pole is the focus, the latus rectum is 15.

The center is easily seen to be the point (5, 90°) and the other focus is therefore (10, 90°). Two other points are then 7.5 units to the right and left of the second focus.

Since $ep = \frac{15}{2}$, $p = \frac{15}{4}$ and the directrix is parallel to the polar axis, $\frac{15}{4}$ units above it.

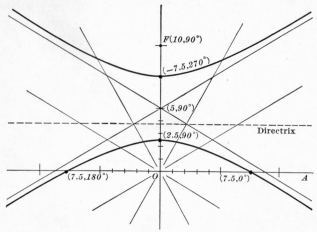

Since ρ becomes infinite when $1 + 2 \sin \theta = 0$, or $\sin \theta = -\frac{1}{2}$, the asymptotes must be parallel to the radii vectores corresponding to $\theta = 210°$ and $\theta = 330°$.

PROBLEMS

1. Transform the equation of the conic, $x^2 + y^2 = e^2(x + p)^2$, into the polar form.

2. Arrange the eight forms of the polar equation of the conic in four pairs of equivalent equations, and for each pair give the equation of the directrix.

3. Find the length of the latus rectum of the conic.

4. Reduce to the standard polar form each of the following equations of conics, find e and p, and draw the curve and its directrix:

(a) $\rho = \dfrac{12}{2 - \cos \theta}$;

(c) $\rho = \dfrac{8}{\cos \theta - 1}$;

(b) $\rho = \dfrac{9}{1 - 2 \sin \theta}$;

(d) $\rho = \dfrac{14}{4 - 3 \sin \theta}$;

(e) $\rho = \dfrac{10}{2 - 3 \cos \theta}$;

(k) $\rho = \dfrac{24}{3 + 5 \cos \theta}$;

(f) $\rho = \dfrac{10}{1 - \sin \theta}$;

(l) $\rho = \dfrac{8}{1 + \sin \theta}$;

(g) $\rho = \dfrac{20}{5 + 3 \cos \theta}$;

(m) $\rho = \dfrac{-15}{5 + 4 \cos \theta}$;

(h) $\rho = \dfrac{8}{1 + 3 \sin \theta}$;

(n) $\rho = \dfrac{12}{4 + 5 \sin \theta}$;

(i) $\rho = \dfrac{6}{1 - \cos \theta}$;

(o) $\rho = \dfrac{-6}{1 + \cos \theta}$;

(j) $\rho = \dfrac{15}{3 + 2 \sin \theta}$;

(p) $\rho = \dfrac{-12}{2 + \sin \theta}$.

5. In the ellipses of Problem 4 find the lengths of the major and minor axes.

6. Show that if $\rho = \dfrac{ep}{1 - e \cos \theta}$ is the equation of a hyperbola, the inclinations of the asymptotes are given by $\cos \theta = \pm \dfrac{1}{e}$.

7. Find the polar intercepts of the conic. From these show that

(a) the major axis of the ellipse is $\dfrac{2ep}{1 - e^2}$;

(b) the transverse axis of the hyperbola is $\dfrac{2ep}{e^2 - 1}$.

8. Derive the equation of the conic when the focus is the pole and the equation of the directrix is:

(a) $\rho \cos \theta = p$;   (b) $\rho \sin \theta = p$.

9. Transform the following equations into the polar form and reduce the results to forms containing only one trigonometric function:

(a) $b^2x^2 + a^2y^2 = a^2b^2$;   (b) $b^2x^2 - a^2y^2 = a^2b^2$.

10. Show that the locus of $\rho = a \sec^2 \dfrac{\theta}{2}$ is a parabola.

11. Show that for any focal chord of a conic the sum of the reciprocals of the lengths of the segments into which the focus divides it is $\dfrac{2}{ep}$.

12. Show that the length of any focal chord of a parabola is $2p \sec^2 \alpha$, where α is the acute angle between the chord and the latus rectum.

13. Find the length of the major axis of an ellipse in terms of e and p and show that it is greater than the length of any other chord drawn through the focus.

14. From the answer to Problem 9(a) show that the length of the major axis is greater than that of any other chord drawn through the center.

113. Equations derived in polar coördinates.

The equation of a locus may sometimes be derived more readily in polar than in rectangular coördinates. This is especially true when the locus is described by the end of a line of varying length revolving around a fixed point. The process is substantially the same as when rectangular coördinates are used. The pole should be chosen at a convenient place, usually a fixed point about which some line in the problem revolves. Then a point (ρ, θ) satisfying the conditions is chosen, and relations between ρ, θ, and the given arbitrary constants are obtained by means (usually) of trigonometric formulas.

EXAMPLE. A chord through the end of a diameter of a circle is extended the length of the diameter. Find the locus of the end of this line.

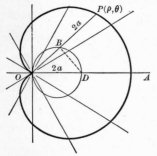

Solution. Choose one end of the given diameter as the pole, and the diameter as the polar axis. Let $2a$ be the diameter of the given circle.

Then from the figure:

$$OB = 2a \cos \theta, \quad \rho = OB + 2a.$$

Therefore the equation is

$$\rho = 2a(1 + \cos \theta),$$

and the required locus is a cardioid.

PROBLEMS

1. Find the locus under the conditions of the above example when the chord is extended a distance $2b$.

2. The radius of a circle whose center is the origin is prolonged a distance equal to the ordinate of its extremity. Find the locus of the end of this line.

$\rho = r + r \sin \theta$

3. Derive a formula for the distance between two points in terms of their polar coördinates.

Hint. Use the law of cosines.

4. Derive the polar equation of the circle having the center (ρ_1, θ_1).

5. Derive the polar equation of the ellipse when the pole is at the center.

Hint. Use the law of cosines and the fact that the sum of the focal radii is $2a$.

6. Derive the polar equation of the hyperbola when the pole is at the center.

Hint. Use the law of cosines and the fact that the difference of the focal radii is $2a$.

7. Find the locus of the vertex C of a triangle whose base OB is of length a and which has the angle C equal to one half of angle O.*

Hint. Use the law of sines and the relation $\sin 3A = 3 \sin A - 4 \sin^3 A$.

8. Let P be any point on the limaçon $\rho = a(2 \cos \theta + 1)$ for which θ is between $0°$ and $90°$. Prove that the angle between the radius vector to P and the line joining P to the point $(a, 0)$ is $\dfrac{\theta}{2}$.

$\alpha = \dfrac{\theta}{2}$

Hint. Use the law of sines.

9. What would be the equation of the limaçon $\rho = a(1 + 2 \cos \theta)$ if the pole were moved to $(a, 0)$?

10. A fixed point A is at a distance a from a fixed line BC. From A a line is drawn cutting BC in D and points P and P' are chosen on this line b units from D on either side. Find the locus of P and P' as D slides along BC.

$\rho = a \sec \theta \pm b$

11. A tangent is drawn to a circle whose center is the origin and terminated by the x- and y-axes. Find the locus of its mid-point.

12. Find the locus of the mid-points of chords drawn from the end of a fixed diameter of a circle.

$\rho = a \cos \theta$

* Since the vertical angle C is one third of the exterior angle at B, this curve can be used to trisect any angle, and so is called the trisectrix.

13. A line of length $2a$ has its extremities on two fixed perpendicular lines. Find the locus of the foot of a perpendicular from the intersection of the fixed lines to the line of constant length.

14. Given the circle $\rho = 2a \cos \theta$ and the line $\rho \cos \theta = 2a$. From the pole a chord OB is drawn, meeting the line in C. Find the locus of a point P on OC, if OP always equals BC. $\rho = 2a \tan \theta \sin \theta$

15. The base of a triangle is in length $2a$. Find the locus of the vertex if the product of the sides is equal to a^2.

Hint. Take the pole at the center of the base and use the law of cosines.

16. The point Q lies on the line $\rho \cos \theta = 2a$ and O is the pole. Find the locus of a point P on OQ such that $OP \times OQ = 4a^2$.

17. An indicator has two hands of length a, one of which rotates at twice the speed of the other. Find the locus of the mid-point of the line joining the ends of the hands.

18. Let the x-axis cut the circle $x^2 + y^2 = a^2$ at A. An arc AB is laid off on the circle equal in length to the abscissa of a point on the parabola $y^2 = 2px$, and the radius OB is prolonged a distance BP equal to the ordinate of that point. Find the locus of P. $\rho = a + y = a + \sqrt{2ap\theta}$

19. A man steps upon a swing bridge of length $2a$ just as it begins to turn and walks to the other end as the bridge turns to a position perpendicular to the line of the road. If both the man and the bridge move at constant speeds, find the equation of the path which he describes.

114. Historical notes. Review problems.

Polar coördinates came into use in the seventeenth century, being first employed in connection with spirals. Three of the curves discussed in this chapter were known to the ancients. Archimedes defined the spiral which bears his name as the locus of a point moving with uniform speed along a radius vector which turns at a uniform rate, and showed how the curve can be used to rectify a circle. The cissoid of Diocles and the conchoid of Nicomedes were invented in connection with the problems of duplicating the cube and trisecting an angle. The conchoid is easily constructed mechanically (see Problem 10, page 171) and the trisection is performed as follows. Let the angle to be trisected be AOF, where OA is the polar axis and F lies on the line $\rho = b \sec \theta$. If we take $a = 2OF$, and G is the intersection of the conchoid $\rho = a + b \sec \theta$ and a line through F parallel to OA, it is easy to show that $AOG = \frac{1}{3} AOF$.

The limaçon was discovered by Blaise Pascal (1623–62) and the lemniscate by James Bernoulli (1654–1705). The roses are one of the classes of curves described by Guido Grandi (1728) under the name *Flores geometrici*.

Although polar coördinates are not used in mathematics as frequently as are rectangular, it is desirable that the student become sufficiently familiar with the standard polar equations to be able to recognize and draw their loci without resorting to point by point plotting. The following problems are added to give practice in identifying polar curves.

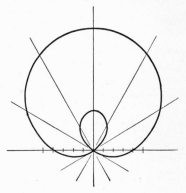

EXAMPLE. Identify and sketch the locus of $\rho = 4 + 8 \sin \theta$.

Solution. This is of the form $\rho = a + b \sin \theta$ and therefore is a limaçon symmetrical with respect to the 90° axis. The intercepts are 4, 12, 4, and -4. Plotting the corresponding points, it is apparent that this is a limaçon having a loop.

REVIEW PROBLEMS

Identify and sketch the following curves.

1. $\rho = -12 \cos \theta$.

2. $\rho = 10 \tan \theta \sin \theta$.

3. $\rho = 8 \sin \theta - 6 \cos \theta$.

4. $\rho^2 \sin 2\theta = 24$.

5. $\rho = -6 \csc \theta$.

6. $\rho = 8 \sin 2\theta$.

7. $\rho = 10 \sin 3\theta$.

8. $\rho = 4 \csc^2 \dfrac{\theta}{2}$.

9. $\rho \cos \theta = -8$.

10. $\rho = 5(\csc \theta + 1)$.

11. $\rho^2\theta = 100\pi$.

12. $\rho = 5 + 5\cos\theta$.

13. $\cos\theta = \frac{3}{5}$.

14. $\rho^2 = 25\sin 2\theta$.

15. $\rho = 8\cot^2\theta\csc\theta$.

16. $\rho = 4 - 8\sin\theta$.

17. $\rho\theta = 10\pi$.

18. $\rho = -10\cos 3\theta$.

19. $\rho = 5\sec\theta + 8$.

20. $\rho = 6 + 4\cos\theta$.

21. $\rho(2 - \cos\theta) = 12$.

22. $\rho = -8\sin 3\theta$.

23. $\rho = \dfrac{12}{1 + 2\sin\theta}$.

24. $\rho^2 = -64\cos 2\theta$.

25. $\rho(1 + \sin\theta) = 8$.

26. $\rho = 10\cos 4\theta$.

27. $\rho = 5\theta$.

28. $\rho\cos\left(\theta - \dfrac{\pi}{4}\right) = 5$.

29. $\rho^2\cos 2\theta = 16$.

30. $\rho = 10\cos 5\theta$.

31. Transform into rectangular form the standard polar equations of the following curves, as given on page 163. If several forms are given for the equation, in each case choose the first:

(a) the cardioid;

(b) the limaçon;

(c) the semicubical parabola;

(d) the conchoid of Nicomedes;

(e) the cissoid;

(f) the four-leafed rose;

(g) the three-leafed rose;

(h) the lemniscate;

(i) the spiral of Archimedes;

(j) the hyperbolic spiral;

(k) $\rho\cos 2\theta = a$;

(l) $\rho\sin 2\theta = a$;

(m) $\rho\cos 3\theta = a$.

CHAPTER X

HIGHER PLANE CURVES

115. Algebraic and transcendental equations. The equations in Cartesian coördinates which we have hitherto treated have been *algebraic* equations, i.e., have involved only integral and fractional powers of x and y.

Any equation which is not algebraic (e.g., $y + \sin x = 0$) is called *transcendental*, and functions defined by such equations are called transcendental functions. The elementary equations of this class are those in which the exponential, logarithmic, trigonometric, and inverse trigonometric functions are used.

In this chapter we shall discuss a number of curves defined by transcendental equations and algebraic equations of degree higher than the second. Such curves are called *higher plane curves*.

116. The exponential curve. This is defined by the exponential equation

$$y = b^x,$$

where b is any *positive* constant. The quantity b is called the *base*. If the exponent is fractional and involves even roots of b, only the positive value of the root is used.

Discussion. For simplicity consider the case that $b > 1$.

When $x = 0$, $y = b^0 = 1$. If $y = 0$, we would have $0 = b^x$, which is impossible for any value of x. Therefore the curve crosses the y-axis one unit above the origin and does not cross the x-axis.

For all values of x, positive and negative, y is positive, since any power of a positive number is positive. When $x > 0$, b^x increases with x, since $b > 1$. Therefore in the first

175

quadrant the curve recedes to infinity away from both the x- and y-axes. Since $b^{-x} = \dfrac{1}{b^x}$, it is evident that the value of y for any negative value of x is the reciprocal of that for the corresponding positive value of x. We have just seen that y increases indefinitely as x approaches $+ \infty$; hence y must decrease and approach 0 as x approaches $- \infty$. Thus in the second quadrant the curve approaches the x-axis as an asymptote. In the following figure the curve is plotted for two values of b.

The base e. The most important case of the exponential function is for the base e ($= 2.71828^+$), the base of the *natural* or *Naperian* system of logarithms. Values of various powers of e are given in any good set of tables.

In the figure the dotted line is the graph of $y = e^x$ and the heavy line that of $y = 2^x$.

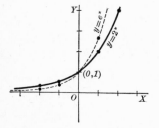

x	$y = e^x$	$y = 2^x$
-2	0.135	0.25
-1	0.368	0.5
0	1.	1.
1	2.718	2.
2	7.389	4.
3	20.086	8.

117. The logarithmic curve. This is the graph of the equation

$$y = \log_b x.$$

The base b is always positive and different from 1, and usually greater than 1.

Since in the algebra the logarithm of a number to a given base is defined as the exponent of that power of the base which is equal to the given number, the equation $y = \log_b x$ may be written in the form $x = b^y$. This is the exponential equation with the variables interchanged. Thus the logarithmic equation is obtained from the exponential equation $y = b^x$ by solving for

x and interchanging variables. Logarithmic and exponential functions are said to be the *inverse* of each other.

The discussion of the logarithmic equation $y = \log_b x$ will therefore follow from that of the exponential equation $y = b^x$ on interchanging variables. Thus the logarithmic curve crosses the x-axis at (1, 0) and does not cross the y-axis. For $x > 1$, $y > 0$, and as $x \to^* \infty$, $y \to \infty$; for $x < 1$, $y < 0$ and as $x \to 0$, $y \to -\infty$. Since $x = b^y$, the abscissa x is positive for all real values of y, whether positive or negative. This is the reason for the statement that negative numbers do not have real logarithms.

The following graph is the logarithmic curve for $b = 10$.

$y = \log_{10} x$

x	y	x	y
1.0	0	.1	-1
3.1	.5	.01	-2
10	1	.001	-3
100	2	.0001	-4
etc.	etc.	etc.	etc.

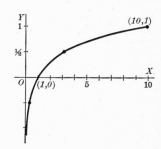

The table of values may be computed by using a table of common logarithms or by writing the equation in the form $x = 10^y$ and computing values of x corresponding to various values of y. Note that the logarithmic curve is symmetrical to the exponential curve with respect to the line $y = x$.

118. Applications. In previous chapters we have used equations to learn the properties of their graphs. Here the point of view is changed; the principal use of the graphs of the exponential and logarithmic functions is to portray the method of variation of these functions. Thus the former graph shows that, for $b > 1$, no power of b is negative or zero, positive powers are greater than 1, negative powers are less than 1, etc. An

* This symbol is used for the words "approaches as a limit."

instructive exercise for the student is to see how many distinct statements of this kind can be made by a glance at the graphs of pages 176 and 177. Similar remarks apply to the graphs of the trigonometric functions in the following sections.

Exponential and logarithmic functions of various kinds constantly appear in higher mathematics, especially in applications 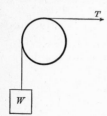 to sciences. For example, the adjoining figure represents a weight W suspended by a rope wrapped several times about a wooden beam and kept from falling by a tension T. The relation between W and T is given by the equation

$$W = Te^{\mu x},$$

where x represents the number of times the rope is wound around the beam and μ is a constant depending on the friction between the rope and the beam. For a hemp rope on smooth oak $\mu = 3.34$, nearly. (See also § 170.)

A knowledge of the properties of the simple exponential and logarithmic functions of §§ 116, 117 may be employed advantageously in plotting more complicated functions, as the following examples show.

EXAMPLE 1. Plot $y = (\tfrac{1}{2})^x$.

Solution. By the properties of exponents this equation may be written in the form $y = 2^{-x}$. The graph is therefore symmetrical to that of $y = 2^x$ with respect to the y-axis. The table of values confirms this.

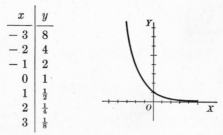

x	y
-3	8
-2	4
-1	2
0	1
1	$\tfrac{1}{2}$
2	$\tfrac{1}{4}$
3	$\tfrac{1}{8}$

EXAMPLE 2. Plot $y = \log_{10}(x^2 - 3)$.

Solution. When $x = 0$, y is not defined. When $y = 0$, $x^2 - 3 = 1$, since $0 = \log 1$. Hence the x-intercepts are ± 2. Obviously there is symmetry with respect to the y-axis.

Considering the branch where x is positive, we see that y is positive when $x^2 - 3 > 1$ or $x > 2$; and that y is negative when $x < 2$. Since the logarithm of a number approaches $-\infty$ when the number approaches 0, y approaches $-\infty$ when $x^2 - 3$ approaches 0, or when x approaches $\sqrt{3}$. Thus there is a vertical asymptote at $x = \sqrt{3}$. The other branch can be drawn by symmetry.

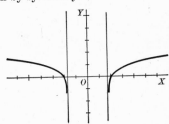

x	y
± 1.8	$-.62$
$\pm 2.$	0.00
$\pm 3.$	0.78
$\pm 4.$	1.11
$\pm 6.$	1.52

PROBLEMS

1. Plot on the same coördinate axes the graphs of $y = b^x$ for $b = 1$, 3, and 5.

2. Plot on the same coördinate axes the graphs of $y = b^x$ for $b = 1, \frac{1}{2}$, and $\frac{1}{4}$.

3. Plot on the same coördinate axes the logarithmic curve for the bases 10 and e.

4. Sketch the graphs of the following, plotting the points where the values of the exponent are 0 and ± 1:

(a) $y = 3^{-x}$;   (d) $y = 2^{x-4}$;   (g) $y = 5e^{-.2x}$;

(b) $y = 4^{-x}$;   (e) $y = 3^{1-x}$;   (h) $y = -e^{-x}$.

(c) $y = (\frac{1}{3})^x$;   (f) $y = e^{-x}$;

5. By using logarithms solve each of the equations in Problem 4 for x in terms of y.

6. Draw the graphs and asymptotes of the following:

(a) $y = \log_2 x$;   (e) $y = \log_{10} (5 - x)$;

(b) $y = \log_{10} x^2$;   (f) $y = 2 \log_e x$;

(c) $y = \log_{10} (x - 5)$;   (g) $y = \log_e (1 + x^2)$;

(d) $y = \log_{10} (x + 5)$;   (h) $y = \log_{10} (10 - x^2)$.

7. By using the definition of a logarithm solve each of the equations in Problem 6 for x in terms of y.

8. Plot the graphs of the following:

(a) $y = \dfrac{e^x + e^{-x}}{2}$; (The hyperbolic cosine curve *)

(b) $y = \dfrac{e^x - e^{-x}}{2}$; (The hyperbolic sine curve *)

(c) $y = \dfrac{a}{2}\left(e^{\frac{x}{a}} + e^{-\frac{x}{a}}\right)$; (The catenary *)

(d) $y = e^{-\frac{x^2}{2}}$; (The probability curve *)

(e) $y = e^{\frac{1}{x}}$; (i) $y = \dfrac{xe^x}{10}$; (k) $y = \dfrac{e^x}{x}$;

(f) $y = x^x$;

(g) $y = xe^{-x^2}$; (j) $y = e^x - x$; (l) $y = e^{\sqrt{x}}$.

(h) $y = xe^{-x}$;

9. Solve the equations in Problem 8 (a), (b), and (c) for x in terms of y. In (a) and (c) find the smallest possible value of y; and in (b) show that there is exactly one real value of x for each value of y.

10. Plot the equiangular spiral $\rho = e^{a\theta}$.

Hint. Choose a so that $e^{\frac{a}{\pi}}$ is a small integer.

11. Plot the curve $y = 3^x$ and estimate the logarithms to the base 3 of the integers from 2 to 10.

12. Plot the graph of the function $W = Te^{\mu x}$, where $T = 100$ lb. and $\mu = 1.1$. Estimate from the graph how many turns of the rope would be required for this tension to support 1 ton; 2 tons; 10 tons.

Hint. This value of μ makes $e^\mu = 3$, nearly.

119. Periodic functions. A function whose values are repeated in the same order after the independent variable has passed through a certain range of values is called periodic. A more precise definition is the following: *The function $f(x)$ is periodic if there is a constant k such that $f(x + k) = f(x)$ for all values of x.* An example is $\cos x$; this function passes suc-

---

* The hyperbolic sine and cosine are often written as sinh x and cosh x. These functions satisfy formulas analogous to those of trigonometry; e.g., sinh $2x = 2$ sinh x cosh x. The catenary is the form assumed by a perfectly flexible cord or chain suspended between two points. The probability curve is of fundamental importance in statistics.

cessively through all values from $+1$ to -1 and back to $+1$ as x increases from 0 to 2π, and repeats these values in the same order as often as the angle x increases by 2π; or n times for a change of $2n\pi$ in the angle.

$f(x)$	PERIOD	AMPLITUDE
Sin x	2π	1
Cos x	2π	1
Tan x	π	∞
Sin $2x$	π	1
Cos $\dfrac{x}{n}$	$2n\pi$	1

The smallest value of k satisfying the above definition is called the *period* of the function. The maximum numerical value of the function is called the *amplitude*. The table illustrates these definitions for several functions.

120. The sine curve. This is plotted from the equation $y = \sin x$, where the values of x are expressed in radians.

x (radians)	x (deg.)	sin x	cos x
0	0	.00	1.00
$\dfrac{\pi}{6} = .52$	30	.50	.87
$\dfrac{\pi}{3} = 1.05$	60	.87	.50
$\dfrac{\pi}{2} = 1.57$	90	1.00	.00
$\dfrac{2\pi}{3} = 2.09$	120	.87	$-.50$
$\dfrac{5\pi}{6} = 2.62$	150	.50	$-.87$
$\pi = 3.14$	180	.00	-1.00
3.66	210	$-.50$	$-.87$
4.19	240	$-.87$	$-.50$
4.71	270	-1.00	.00
5.24	300	$-.87$	.50
5.76	330	$-.50$	.87
$2\pi = 6.28$	360	.00	1.00
6.81	390	.50	.87
7.33	420	.87	.50
etc.	etc.	etc.	etc.

We may assume values for x at any small interval, as $\dfrac{\pi}{6}$, and take the corresponding values of sin x from a table of natural sines.

In the accompanying table the values of x in degrees are found in column 2 and their circular measures to be used in plotting are in column 1. The circular measure of x is the abscissa and the value of its sine is the ordinate.

After the values from the table up to 2π have been plotted the curve is constructed through one period, and the same values of y may be used to construct it through successive periods.

Since the angle x may be taken negative as well as positive, the curve may be extended indefinitely in the negative direction.

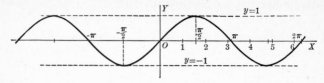

If we substitute $(-x, -y)$ for (x, y) in the equation $y = \sin x$, we have

$$- y = \sin(-x) = -\sin x,$$

which may be reduced to the given equation by multiplying through by -1. Hence the curve is symmetrical with respect to the origin.

121. Circular measure. In plotting $y = \sin x$ we could measure x in degrees and use any convenient unit along the x-axis for a degree. If this is done, however, certain advantages attached to measuring angles in radians are lost.

Among these is the fact that when x is measured in radians, both x and $y = \sin x$ can be expressed as linear magnitudes on the same scale. For, if a central angle is measured in radians, we learn from trigonometry that

$$\text{angle} = \frac{\text{arc}}{\text{radius}},$$

or

$$x = \frac{AB}{r}.$$

But

$$y = \sin x = \frac{AC}{r}.$$

Hence, as the angle x is generated by rotating the side OA from the initial position OB, the lengths of AB and AC *in terms of the radius as a unit* are the values of x and $\sin x$ given in columns 1 and 3 of the table of values in § 120. This is only true when x is expressed in circular measure.

122. The cosine curve. The cosine function has the same period and amplitude as the sine function, and the graph of $y = \cos x$ has the same shape as that of $y = \sin x$; but the curve passes through (0, 1) instead of the origin.

This is true because the cosine of any angle is equal to the sine of an angle 90° greater, or $\cos x = \sin (90° + x)$. Hence the table of sines can be used for plotting the cosine curve by moving the whole column of sine values up 90°, so that the sine curve becomes the cosine curve when the origin is advanced to the point $\left(\dfrac{\pi}{2}, 0\right)$.

123. Multiple angles. Consider $y = \sin nx$. *The multiple n divides the period of the function by n, but does not alter the amplitude.* To prove this, let us recall from § 119 that k is a period of $f(x)$ if $f(x + k) = f(x)$. We must show then that, if $f(x) = \sin nx, f\left(x + \dfrac{2\pi}{n}\right) = f(x)$. Substituting, we have

$$\sin n\left(x + \frac{2\pi}{n}\right) = \sin (nx + 2\pi) = \sin nx.$$

Hence $\dfrac{2\pi}{n}$ is the period of $\sin nx$. That the amplitude is unaltered is obvious.

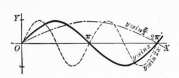 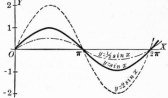

Compare this with $y = n \sin x$, where the period is unaltered but the amplitude is multiplied by n. All of this appears clearly in the figures. Thus we have

for $y = \sin x$, the period is 2π, and $y = 1$ when $x = \pi/2$;

for $y = \sin 2x$, the period is π, and $y = 1$ when $x = \pi/4$;

for $y = 2 \sin x$, the period is 2π, and $y = 2$ when $x = \pi/2$;

for $y = 3 \sin \pi x$, the period is 2, and $y = 3$ when $x = \frac{1}{2}$.

By investigating the period we can quickly sketch the graphs of equations of the type $y = a \sin nx$, $y = a \cos nx$, etc. For we need only to determine the period and mark the points at the quarter periods, since the general shape of the curve is the same as that of the simple trigonometric curves.

EXAMPLE. Sketch the graph of $y = \frac{1}{2} \cos \pi x$ through two periods.

Solution. The period is $\dfrac{2\pi}{\pi} = 2$. The values at the quarter periods include the x-intercepts and the largest and smallest values of y. They are

x	0	$\frac{1}{2}$	1	$\frac{3}{2}$	2	$\frac{5}{2}$
y	$\frac{1}{2}$	0	$-\frac{1}{2}$	0	$\frac{1}{2}$	0

, etc.

The graph of $y = \cos x$ is also shown in the figure as a dotted line for comparison.

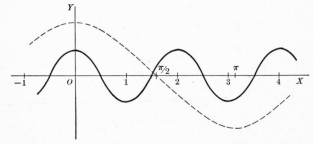

124. Sums of functions. Sometimes it is necessary to plot functions which are the sum of two or more trigonometric functions. In calculating the table of values the interval between successive values of x should not be greater than $\frac{1}{12}$ of the smallest period involved, although a fair sketch is possible if $\frac{1}{4}$ of the smallest period is used.* Time is saved by writing the values of the various terms in parallel columns and adding corresponding values to get the various ordinates. Thus in plotting $y = \sin 2x + 2 \cos x$, we observe that the period of

* This will not, however, give the largest and smallest values of y, as might be inferred from the example in the previous section. In general these values cannot be found without the aid of the differential calculus.

sin $2x$ is π and take our values of x at intervals of $\dfrac{\pi}{12} = 15°$, obtaining the following table:

x (degrees)	x (radians)	sin $2x$	2 cos x	y
0	0	0.0000	2.0000	2.0000
15	.2618	0.5000	1.9318	2.4318
30	.5236	0.8660	1.7320	2.5980
45	.7854	1.0000	1.4142	2.4142
etc.	etc.	etc.	etc.	etc.

Another method, which in some ways is a better one, is to plot the curves $y' = \sin 2x$ and $y'' = 2 \cos x$ on the same axes and obtain the sum of y' and y'' by measurement. With a pair of compasses as many points of the required curve as are desired can be easily obtained. The figure illustrates this method.

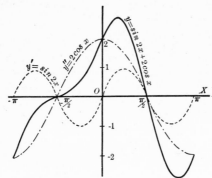

125. The tangent curve. The graph of $y = \tan x$ passes through the origin and the function has the period π. The value becomes infinite when x is an odd multiple of $\dfrac{\pi}{2}$ and passes through all values from $-\infty$ to $+\infty$ as x increases from $-\dfrac{\pi}{2}$ to $\dfrac{\pi}{2}$, and so on in each interval of length π, the period.

The table of values follows.

x	$\tan x$
$-\dfrac{\pi}{2}$	$-\infty$
$-\dfrac{\pi}{3}$	-1.73
$-\dfrac{\pi}{6}$	$-.58$
0	0
$\dfrac{\pi}{6}$	$.58$
$\dfrac{\pi}{3}$	1.73
$\dfrac{\pi}{2}$	∞

126. Inverse trigonometric functions. The relation expressed in the inverse notation by $y = \sin^{-1} x$ reads in direct notation $x = \sin y$.

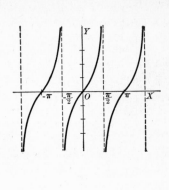

$$y = \cos^{-1} x = \text{arc cos } x.$$
$$y = \sin^{-1} x = \text{arc sin } x.$$

The curve of inverse sines is therefore the same as the curve of sines in shape, period, and amplitude, but the axes are interchanged.

The notation arc sin x is preferable to $\sin^{-1} x$.

PROBLEMS

1. Plot the graphs of the following, letting x range from -2π to 2π:

(a) $y = \cos x$;   (b) $y = \cot x$;   (c) $y = \sec x$;   (d) $y = \csc x$.

2. In the following find the period, make a table of values extending through two periods, taking x at intervals of a quarter period, and draw the graph:

(a) $y = \sin 3x$;

(b) $y = \cos \dfrac{x}{2}$;

(c) $y = \tan \tfrac{3}{2} x$;

(d) $y = \tfrac{1}{2} \sec 2x$;

(e) $y = .2 \cos \pi x$;

(f) $y = \tfrac{1}{2} \cot \pi x$;

(g) $y = .1 \sin 10\pi x$;

(h) $y = \tfrac{2}{3} \cos \tfrac{3}{2} x$.

3. Plot the graph of:

(a) $y = \text{arc } \tan x$;

(b) $y = \text{arc } \sec x$;

(c) $y = \text{arc } \cot x$;

(d) $y = \text{arc } \csc x$;

(e) $y = 2 \text{ arc } \cos 2x$;

(f) $y = 3 \text{ arc } \sin \dfrac{x}{3}$;

(g) $y = \dfrac{2}{\pi} \text{ arc } \cos x$.

4. Draw on the same axes the graphs of:

(a) $\begin{cases} y = \sin x, \\ y = \csc x; \end{cases}$ (b) $\begin{cases} y = \cos x, \\ y = \sec x; \end{cases}$ (c) $\begin{cases} y = \tan x, \\ y = \cot x. \end{cases}$

What relation holds between corresponding ordinates of each pair of curves?

5. Draw each of the following curves. For any value of x, draw ordinates at $\pm x$, $\pi \pm x$, $2\pi \pm x$, and then write the trigonometric formulas suggested by the figure.

(a) $y = \sin x$;   (c) $y = \tan x$;   (e) $y = \sec x$;

(b) $y = \cos x$;   (d) $y = \cot x$;   (f) $y = \csc x$.

6. Plot the graphs of the following equations for the range of values indicated:

(a) $y = \sin x + \cos x$, (0 to 2π);

(b) $y = \cos x - \sin x$, (0 to 2π);

(c) $y = \cos 2x + \sin x$, (0 to 2π);

(d) $y = 2 \sin x - \cos \dfrac{x}{2}$, (0 to 4π);

(e) $y = \cos x - \sin 2x$, (0 to 2π);

(f) $y = \sin 2\pi x + \cos \pi x$, (0 to 2);

(g) $y = \sin^2 x$, (0 to π);

(h) $y = \cos^2 x$, (0 to π);

(i) $y = x + 2 \sin x$, (0 to 3π);

(j) $y = x - \sin \pi x$, (0 to 3);

(k) $y = e^{\sin x}$, (0 to 2π);

(l) $y = x - \cos 2x$, ($-\pi$ to $+\pi$).

7.* Each of the following curves oscillates between two boundary curves; e.g., the boundary curves in (a) are the lines $y = \pm x$. In each case plot both the curve and its boundary curves. A sketch can be made by marking the points where the sine or cosine has the values 0 and ± 1.

(a) $y = x \sin x$, (0 to 4π);

(b) $y = x^2 \sin x$, ($- 2\pi$ to 2π);

(c) $y = x \cos \dfrac{x}{2}$, ($- \pi$ to 2π);

(d) $y = x \sin^2 x$, ($- 2\pi$ to 2π);

(e) $y = e^x \cos x$, (0 to 2π);

(f) $y = e^x \sin x$, (0 to 2π);

(g) $y = e^{-x} \sin x$, (0 to 2π);

(h) $y = e^{-x} \cos x$, (0 to 2π);

(i) $y = \dfrac{\sin x}{x}$, (0† to 4π);

(j) $y = x \sin \dfrac{\pi}{x}$, (0† to 2).

127. Parametric equations.

In the case of some curves the coördinates are functions of a third variable such that the conditions determining the curve can be conveniently expressed by two equations in these three variables instead of by a single equation in x and y. This third variable is called a *parameter*, and the two equations *parametric equations* of the curve. If t is the parameter, the parametric equations of the curve are usually of the form $x = f(t)$, $y = g(t)$.

To plot the graph of such equations we take various values of the parameter and compute the corresponding values of x and y. Then plot the points (x, y) as usual. The values of the parameter appear only in the table of values, and not in locating the point.

The parameter often represents some geometric magnitude, or the time during which the point tracing the curve has been in motion; but it may be chosen in any manner that is convenient. For example, consider the equation $y^3 - y^2 = x^2 y - x^3$. To calculate a table of values for this by ordinary means would

---

* In some of these problems considerable labor is saved by using a table giving the trigonometric functions of the angle expressed in radians. When such a table is not available it is often convenient to choose values of the angle at intervals of 0.2 or 0.5 radians and find the various functions involved by converting the radians into degrees.

† In (i) and (j) the functions are not defined for $x = 0$; in the first case the limit is 1 and in the second case the limit is 0 as x approaches 0.

be very laborious. But, if we substitute $y = tx$ and solve for x, we obtain

$$x = \frac{t^2}{1 - t + t^3} \quad \text{and} \quad y = \frac{t^3}{1 - t + t^3}.$$

It is now comparatively easy to find as many points as are desired.

128. Parametric equations of the circle. Let us take the origin at the center of the circle. Then the circle is generated by rotating OP. Taking θ as the parameter, we have at once from the figure and the definitions of the sine and cosine:

$$x = r \cos \theta, \qquad y = r \sin \theta.$$

These are the parametric equations of the circle.* From the table of values below points on the curve are $(10, 0)$, $(8.66, 5)$, $(5, 8.66)$, $(0, 10)$, $(- 5, 8.66)$, $(- 8.66, 5)$, $(- 10, 0)$, $(- 8.66, - 5)$, etc.

TABLE OF VALUES FOR $r = 10$

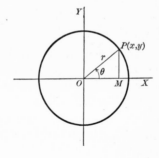

$\theta°$	x	y
0	10.	0
30	8.66	5.
60	5.	8.66
90	0	10.
120	− 5.	8.66
150	− 8.66	5.
180	− 10.	0
210	− 8.66	− 5.

Note that if we eliminate θ between the parametric equations, we get the standard form $x^2 + y^2 = r^2$.

129. Parametric equations of the ellipse. Suppose that we have a circle of radius a and center O, in which OA is any radius and AM is a perpendicular from A upon a fixed diameter.

* I.e., corresponding to this choice of a parameter. A different choice of the parameter would in general yield a different equation.

B is a point on the radius at a distance b from O and P is the projection of B on AM. It is required to find the locus of P.

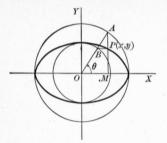

Take the fixed diameter as the x-axis and the center as the origin. Let (x, y) be the coördinates of P and $\theta = \angle MOA$ be the parameter. Then we have at once from the figure,

$$x = OM = OA \cos \theta = a \cos \theta,$$
$$y = MP = OB \sin \theta = b \sin \theta.$$

These are the parametric equations of the locus. It remains to show that the curve is an ellipse. Solving the equations for $\cos \theta$ and $\sin \theta$ respectively, squaring, and adding, we get

$$\frac{x^2}{a^2} + \frac{y^2}{b^2} = \cos^2 \theta + \sin^2 \theta = 1,$$

the equation of the ellipse.

The circles described by B and A are called the *auxiliary circles* of the ellipse. By drawing them on coördinate paper, the various positions of P can readily be found and any ellipse of given semiaxes plotted with accuracy.

It is apparent from inspection of the standard equation of the ellipse that the substitutions $x = a \cos \theta$ and $y = b \sin \theta$ verify the equation for all values of θ. Hence these parametric equations could have been obtained without considering any possible relation between the angle θ and the curve.

130. Path of a projectile. If an object moves with a velocity of v feet per second along a line inclined to the x-axis at an angle α, it is clear from the figure following that at the end of each second its distance from the y-axis has been increased by $v_x = v \cos \alpha$ feet, likewise from the x-axis by $v_y = v \sin \alpha$ feet. These quantities v_x and v_y are called the x- and y-*components*, respectively, of the velocity, and when multiplied by the time give the total displacement parallel to the x- and y-axes.

When the motion is in a vertical plane, the vertical velocity does not remain constant, but is affected by the force of gravity.

In this case we learn from mechanics that the height is given by the formula $h = v_y t - \frac{1}{2}gt^2$, where h is the height, t the time, v_y the vertical component of the initial velocity, and g the constant acceleration due to gravity.* If the units are feet and seconds, the value of g is very near to 32, and this value will be used in numerical problems.

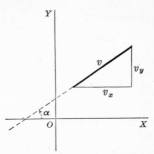

Using these principles, let us solve the problem: Find the path of a projectile discharged at an angle $\alpha = \text{arc cos } \frac{3}{5}$ with an initial velocity of 80 feet per second.

Taking the point of projection as the origin, the y-axis vertical to the earth's surface and the x-axis horizontal in the direction of projection, let $P(x, y)$ be the position of the projectile after t seconds.

The horizontal component of the initial velocity is

$$v_x = 80 \cos \alpha = 80 \cdot \tfrac{3}{5} = 48;$$

the vertical component is

$$v_y = 80 \sin \alpha = 80 \cdot \tfrac{4}{5} = 64.$$

As the horizontal velocity remains constant,

$$x = v_x t = 48t. \qquad (a)$$

Using the above formula for vertical motion, we have

$$y = v_y t - 16t^2 = 64t - 16t^2. \qquad (b)$$

Equations (a) and (b) are the parametric equations of the locus, and the graph can now be plotted from these equations. To identify the curve, eliminate t and we have

$$y = \tfrac{4}{3}x - \tfrac{1}{144}x^2.$$

Hence the locus is a parabola with a vertical axis of symmetry.

* In this and all that follows, we disregard air resistance. The results are therefore first approximations to the true ones.

If we set $y = 0$ in equation (b) we get $t = 0$ or 4. Hence the *time of flight* is 4 seconds. Setting $t = 4$ in equation (a) gives the *range* $x = 192$ feet. The abscissa of the vertex of the parabola is then $\frac{1}{2} \cdot 192 = 96$. For this value of x, $t = 2$ and $y = 128 - 64 = 64$. Thus the *greatest height* reached by the projectile is 64 feet.

PROBLEMS

1. The equations of the *folium of Descartes* are $x = \dfrac{3at}{1+t^3}$, $y = \dfrac{3at^2}{1+t^3}$. Make a table of values and plot the graph.

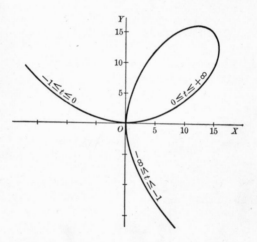

Solution. The parameter t ranges in value from $-\infty$ to $+\infty$. In general, spacing the values of the parameter evenly will not give enough points to plot the curve unless a very large number of points are taken.

In this particular example we find by trial that we need a large number of values between -1 and $+1$. After making the table of values for $a = 10$ we plot the points and join them in the order of the values of t. The range of values of t for the parts of the curve in the various quadrants is indicated on the graph.

Since $y = tx$ for all values of t, each point in the following table of values is the intersection of the curve and the line which passes through the origin and has the corresponding value of t as its slope.

TABLE OF VALUES

t	x	y	t	x	y
$\pm \infty$	0	0	0	0	0
-10	0.30	-3.00	0.1	3.00	0.30
-5	1.21	-6.05	0.2	5.95	1.19
-2	8.57	-17.14	0.5	13.33	6.67
-1.5	18.95	-28.42	1	15	15
-1	$\pm \infty$	$\mp \infty$	1.5	10.29	15.43
-0.5	-17.14	8.57	2	6.67	13.33
-0.2	-6.05	1.21	5	1.19	5.95
-0.1	-3.00	0.30	10	0.30	3.00

2. Make tables of values and plot the graphs of the following parametric equations:

(a) $x = 1 - t, y = t^2$;

(b) $x = t^2, y = t^3$;

(c) $x = 3t, y = 6t - t^2$;

(d) $x = 4t^2, y = 4t - t^3$;

(e) $x = t + \dfrac{1}{t}, y = t - \dfrac{1}{t}$;

(f) $x = \dfrac{2t^2 - 2}{1 + t^2}, y = \dfrac{2t^3 - 2t}{1 + t^2}$;

(g) $x = \dfrac{2at^2}{1 + t^2}, y = \dfrac{2at^3}{1 + t^2}$;

(h) $x = t^2 + 2t, y = t^3$;

(i) $x = 20 \cos \theta, y = 10 \sin \theta$;

(j) $x = \sin \theta, y = \cos 2\theta$;

(k) $x = 3 + 5 \cos \theta,$
  $y = 5 \sin \theta - 4$;

(l) $x = a \sec \theta, y = a \tan \theta$;

(m) $x = 5 \cos \theta, y = 3 \sin 2\theta$;

(n) $x = a \sin \theta, y = b \sin 2\theta$;

(o) $x = a \cos^4 t, y = a \sin^4 t$;

(p) $x = \tan t, y = \sin 2t$;

(q) $x = 2a \cot \theta, y = 2a \sin^2 \theta$;

(r) $x = a \cos^3 \theta, y = b \sin^3 \theta$;

(s) $x = a \cos \theta, y = b \sin^3 \theta$;

(t) $x = a \sec t, y = a \sec t \tan t$;

(u) $x = a(2 \cos t - \cos 2t), y = a(2 \sin t - \sin 2t)$.

3. Eliminate the parameter in each pair of equations in Problem 2.

4. The equation of the folium of Descartes is $x^3 + y^3 - 3axy = 0$. By substituting $y = tx$ obtain the parametric equations of Problem 1.

5. A straight line passes through the point (6, 4) and has the slope $\frac{3}{4}$. Find its parametric equations if the parameter t is taken as the distance of the tracing point from the given point.

6. Find parametric equations of the circle whose center is the point $(-4, 5)$ and whose radius is 10.

7. Find the parametric equations of the path of a projectile, its range, and the highest point reached, from the following data:

(a) initial velocity 128 feet per second, angle of projection 45°;

(b) initial velocity 80 feet per second, angle of projection 60°;

(c) initial velocity 100 feet per second, angle of projection arc sin $\frac{3}{5}$.

(d) initial velocity 200 feet per second, angle of projection arc sin $\frac{4}{5}$.

8. Eliminate the parameter from the results in Problem 7.

9. In Problem 7(b) the ground is level and the point of projection is 16 feet above the ground. Find the range.

10. Find the parametric equations of the path of a projectile if the initial velocity is u and the angle of projection is α. Show that the range is $\dfrac{u^2 \sin 2\alpha}{g}$ and that the coördinates of the highest point are $\left(\dfrac{u^2 \sin 2\alpha}{2g}, \dfrac{u^2 \sin^2 \alpha}{2g}\right).$

11. Eliminate the parameter from the equations found in Problem 10.

12. In Problem 7(a) assume that the point of projection is on the ground and find the range: first, when the ground is level; second, when it slopes down at an angle of 45°.

13. If the point of projection is the origin, the initial velocity is a constant u, and the angle of projection is allowed to vary, show that the locus of the highest point reached is an arc of an ellipse which has the major axis $\dfrac{u^2}{g}$ and the center $\left(0, \dfrac{u^2}{4g}\right).$

14. A point moves on a spoke of a wheel from the hub toward the rim at the rate of 20 feet per minute. The wheel makes two revolutions per minute. Find the equation in polar coördinates of the path described by the point and name the locus.

15. The parametric equations of the path of a point are

$$x = a \cos kt,$$
$$y = 0,$$

where x is measured in feet, t is measured in seconds, and a and k are constants. Plot the locus. How often does the point pass through the origin?

16. A point moves around a circle of radius 2 feet 20 times per minute. Write the parametric equations of the circle, using the time during which the point has been in motion as the parameter.

17. Find parametric equations for each of the following in forms such that the calculation of a table of values will not involve the extraction of roots, and plot the curves:

(a) $y^2 = ax^3$;

(b) $b^2x^2 - a^2y^2 = a^2b^2$;

(c) $y^2(2a - x) = x^3$;

(d) $x^{\frac{2}{3}} - y^{\frac{2}{3}} = a^{\frac{2}{3}}$;

(e) $y^2(a - x) = (a + x)^3$;

(f) $x^3 + xy^2 + ay^2 - 3ax^2 = 0$;

(g) $(a - x)y^2 = x^2(a + x)$;

(h) $(x^2 + y^2)^2 = ax^2y$;

(i) $x^3 + y^3 = ax^2$;

(j) $x^5 + y^3 = xy^2$.

131. The cycloid. If a circle rolls along a straight line the curve traced by a point on the circumference is called a *cycloid*. The straight line is called the base.

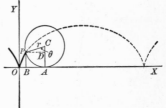

As the circle rolls it describes the length of the circumference on the base at each revolution, and a proportional distance for any part of a revolution. Hence the point of the circle touching the base is always at a distance from the starting point equal to the length of the arc subtending θ.

In the figure the tracing point P starts from the point O, which is taken as the origin, and the base is the x-axis.

Call the angle which the radius to the tracing point makes with the vertical, θ. Then $OA = $ arc $PA = r\theta$, since

$$\text{arc} = \text{angle} \times \text{radius}.$$

This gives

$$x = OA - BA = r\theta - r\sin\theta,$$
$$y = AC - DC = r - r\cos\theta,$$

which are the parametric equations of the cycloid.

The prolate and curtate cycloids. If the tracing point is taken anywhere on the radius of the rolling circle or the radius produced, the curve is called the *prolate cycloid* when P is without the circle and the *curtate cycloid* when P is within. The term *trochoid* is also used for both prolate and curtate cycloids.

Let a be the distance from the center to the tracing point. The parametric equations of both prolate and curtate cycloids are

$$x = r\theta - a \sin \theta,$$
$$y = r - a \cos \theta.$$

They are derived in the same manner as those of the ordinary cycloid.

PROBLEMS

1. A wheel of radius 10 inches rolls along a straight line. Sketch the paths for two revolutions of a point on the rim and of a point midway between the first point and the center of the wheel. Find the coördinates of these points when the wheel has made one third, one half, and two thirds of a revolution.

2. Can you find the coördinates of the points of intersection of the curves in Problem 1? Explain your answer.

3. Eliminate θ between the parametric equations of the cycloid.

Hint. $\cos \theta = \dfrac{r - y}{r}$ and vers* $\theta = 1 - \cos \theta$.

4. Write out in full the derivation of the parametric equations of (*a*) the curtate cycloid; (*b*) the prolate cycloid.

5. Make a table of values and plot each of the following:

(*a*) the cycloid for $r = 10$;

(*b*) the prolate cycloid for $r = 8$ and $a = 10$;

(*c*) the curtate cycloid for $r = 10$ and $a = 8$.

6. Show from the equations of the cycloid that y is a periodic function of x, of period $2\pi r$.

7. In the prolate cycloid of Problem 5(*b*) find as accurately as you can the values of the y-intercepts and of two x-intercepts.

8. Show that $x = a(\theta + \sin \theta)$, $y = a(1 - \cos \theta)$ are equations of a cycloid and draw the curve.

9. Show that the first arch of the cycloid is symmetrical with respect to the line $x = \pi r$.

Hint. Show that for any value of y, as y_1, $\theta = \theta_1$, or $2\pi - \theta_1$. From this get two values of x, x_1, and x_2, and show that $x_2 - \pi r = \pi r - x_1$. Then apply the definition of symmetry.

* This abbreviation is used for the *versine*, a trigonometric function defined as here indicated and seldom used except in this connection.

10. The curve $x = r\theta$, $y = r(1 - \cos \theta)$ is called the *companion to the cycloid*. Draw this curve and the cycloid on the same axes for the case that $r = 10$. Of what point in the figure on page 195 is the companion the locus?

11. A bicycle has wheels of diameter 28 inches and is moving along a level road at a speed of 10 miles per hour. Find the parametric equations of the cycloid described by a point on the tread of the tire, using as a parameter t, the time elapsed since the tracing point was at the origin. Let the units be feet and seconds.

132. The epicycloid and hypocycloid. If a circle rolls upon the circumference of a fixed circle, the path described by a given point on the circumference of the generating circle is called an *epicycloid* if the generating circle rolls on the outside of the fixed circle, and a *hypocycloid* if it rolls inside.

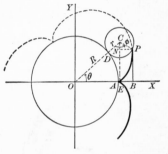

Let the tracing point start from A and the generating circle move on the outside until its contact with the base is at D. Thus the arc AP of an epicycloid is described and the arc PD has rolled over the arc AD of the base.

Let the angle which the radius CP of the generating circle makes with the line of centers be ϕ, and the angle of this line CO with the x-axis be θ.

Using circular measure, since arc AD = arc PD,
$$R\theta = r\phi. \tag{a}$$

Since CPN is the supplement of $\theta + \phi$,
$$\sin CPN = \sin (\theta + \phi),$$
and $\quad\quad \cos CPN = -\cos (\theta + \phi)$.

But $\quad\quad\quad x = OB = OE + NP$
$$= (R + r) \cos \theta + r \cos CPN$$
$$= (R + r) \cos \theta - r \cos (\theta + \phi),$$
and $\quad\quad\quad y = BP = EC - NC$
$$= (R + r) \sin \theta - r \sin (\theta + \phi).$$

These equations contain two parameters, θ and ϕ. The parameter ϕ may be eliminated by substituting its value from (*a*), which gives

$$x = (R + r) \cos \theta - r \cos \frac{R + r}{r} \theta,$$

$$y = (R + r) \sin \theta - r \sin \frac{R + r}{r} \theta.$$

If r is replaced by $- r$ we have the equations of the hypocycloid:

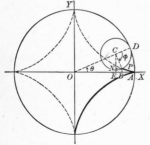

$$x = (R - r) \cos \theta + r \cos \frac{R - r}{r} \theta,$$

$$y = (R - r) \sin \theta - r \sin \frac{R - r}{r} \theta.$$

These equations can also be derived directly from the adjoining figure.

The astroid. In the hypocycloid for which $r = \frac{1}{4}R$, the rolling circle makes four revolutions in passing around the base, forming the astroid, or hypocycloid of four cusps.

133. The involute of the circle. A string is wound about the circumference of a circle. One end is fastened to the circumference and the string is unwound. If the string is kept stretched, the curve traced by the free end is called the *involute* of the circle.

If it begins to unwind at A, the arc AP of the involute is traced when the string has unwound as far as B, and the part unwound is BP.

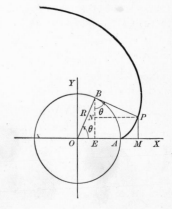

BP is tangent to the circle at B, and

$$BP = \text{arc } BA = R\theta.$$

The equations are

$$x = R \cos \theta + R\theta \sin \theta,$$
$$y = R \sin \theta - R\theta \cos \theta.$$

NOTE. The cycloidal curves have many interesting properties, but most of them cannot be derived without the aid of the calculus. The length of one arch of a cycloid is exactly four times the diameter of the generating circle. If a wire is bent into the form of the cycloid of page 195 inverted and a bead slides on the wire without friction, the time of descent to the bottom is independent of the starting point. If a pendulum is suspended from a cusp of the same cycloid and swings between adjacent arches, the involute described by the pendulum bob is itself a cycloid and the time of a swing is independent of the amplitude.

A point tracing an epicycloid or a hypocycloid will never return to its starting point if r and R are incommensurable. If their ratio is a fraction whose numerator and denominator are relatively prime, but large, the design is quite intricate. The student may find it of interest to investigate what happens if the notion of prolate and curtate cycloids is applied to the epicycloid and hypocycloid. The solution of Problem 6 on page 200 shows a method of converting circular into alternating linear motion.

The teeth of large geared wheels are sometimes cut in the shape of epicycloids or hypocycloids to avoid the binding and friction that occur between straight teeth. Others are cut in the shape of involutes of a circle. In the latter type the parts having contact do not wear so rapidly, since the direction of motion at the point of contact is always perpendicular to the surface at that point.

The cycloid does not appear in the works of the ancients. It seems to have been invented by Charles Bouvelles (1470–1553); the name is due to Galileo (1564–1642). Many properties of the cycloidal curves were found by the mathematicians of the seventeenth century.

PROBLEMS

1. Write the equations of the epicycloid in which $r = \dfrac{R}{3}$, make a table of values taking θ at intervals of 30°, and plot the curve.

2. Same as Problem 1, for the hypocycloid.

3. Make a table of values and plot the involute of the circle.

4. Show that the equations of the hypocycloid of four cusps can be reduced to $x = R \cos^3 \theta$, $y = R \sin^3 \theta$, which give the equation $x^{\frac{2}{3}} + y^{\frac{2}{3}} = R^{\frac{2}{3}}$.

5. Simplify the equations of the epicycloid and draw the curve when (a) $r = R$; (b) $r = \dfrac{R}{2}$.

6. Simplify the equations of the hypocycloid in which $r = \dfrac{R}{2}$ and draw the locus.

7. Derive the equations of the hypocycloid from a figure.

8. By using the definition of the curve draw the epicycloid for which

(a) $r = \dfrac{R}{5}$;   (b) $r = \dfrac{2R}{3}$;   (c) $r = \dfrac{R}{3}$;   (d) $r = \dfrac{3R}{4}$.

9. Same as Problem 8 for the hypocycloid.

10. Show that if the origin is translated to the point $(R, 0)$ the equations of the epicycloid for which $r = R$ become $x' = 2R \cos \theta\,(1 - \cos \theta)$, $y' = 2R \sin \theta\,(1 - \cos \theta)$. Then transform these to polar coördinates and show that this particular epicycloid is a cardioid.

11. Show by rotating the axes through an angle of 45° that

$$(x + y)^{\frac{2}{3}} + (x - y)^{\frac{2}{3}} = 2R^{\frac{2}{3}}$$

is the equation of a hypocycloid of four cusps.

134. Algebraic curves. Algebraic curves of degree higher than the second have a great variety of forms and are best studied with the aid of the calculus. Two simple examples of these curves which we have encountered are the cubical parabola $y = ax^3$ and the semicubical parabola $y^2 = ax^3$. The majority of the curves in Chapter IX are found to be algebraic curves if their equations are transformed into rectangular form. Many of these curves are of historical importance, as the limaçon, the conchoid, the cissoid, and the lemniscate, given in Chapter IX, and the witch, the strophoid, and the ovals of Cassini, which will be discussed in the following sections.

135. The witch. A circle of radius a is drawn tangent to the x-axis through the origin, meeting the y-axis in A. The tangent to the circle at A is drawn, and from O a secant is drawn meeting the circle in B and the tangent in C. The locus of the projection of B upon the ordinate of C is called the *witch*, or *witch of Agnesi*.

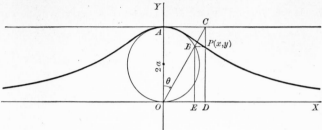

To find its equation take the angle $\theta = AOC$ as a parameter. Then we have at once

$$x = OD = AC = 2a \tan \theta,$$

and $$y = DP = EB = OB \cos \theta = 2a \cos^2 \theta.$$

Eliminating the parameter θ, we obtain the equation,

$$y = \frac{8a^3}{x^2 + 4a^2}.$$

The form of the equation shows that the curve is symmetrical with respect to the y-axis and has the x-axis as an asymptote.

Although the witch and its properties were described by the Italian mathematician Maria Agnesi (1718–1799), who called it the *versiera*, the curve was known earlier.

136. The strophoid. The distance from a fixed point A to a fixed line BC is a. From A the perpendicular AO is drawn to BC and any other line AE is drawn meeting BC at E. On AE points P and P' are taken such that $P'E = EP = OE$. The locus of the points P and P' is a curve called the *strophoid*.

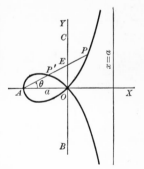

To find its equation take the fixed line as the y-axis and the x-axis through the fixed point. Let the coördinates of P and P' be (x, y) and (x', y'). Taking the angle OAE as a parameter θ, we have at once that

$$P'E = EP = OE = a \tan \theta.$$

Hence $\qquad x = EP \cos \theta = a \sin \theta,$

and $\qquad y = OE + EP \sin \theta = a \tan \theta(1 + \sin \theta).$

By eliminating the parameter and squaring both sides, we have the equation,

$$y^2 = x^2 \frac{a + x}{a - x}.$$

To show that P' is on the same locus, we have

$$x' = -a \sin \theta,$$

and $\qquad y' = a \tan \theta(1 - \sin \theta).$

Eliminating θ and rationalizing, we find that the coördinates of P' satisfy the given equation.

The curve is evidently symmetrical with respect to the x-axis and has the line $x = a$ as an asymptote.

The strophoid was invented by Isaac Barrow (1630–1677), the teacher of Newton.

137. The ovals of Cassini. The locus of the vertex of a triangle which has a constant base and has the product of its

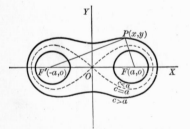

other two sides equal to a given constant is called the *ovals of Cassini.*

Call the length of the base $2a$, take the origin at its midpoint, and let the x-axis lie along the base. Then the conditions of the problem make $F'P \cdot FP$ equal to a constant, which we call c^2 since it is essentially positive.

Using the distance formula, we have

$$\sqrt{(x + a)^2 + y^2} \cdot \sqrt{(x - a)^2 + y^2} = c^2.$$

Simplifying this gives

$$(x^2 + y^2 + a^2)^2 - 4a^2x^2 = c^4.$$

Three types are possible, according to the relative values of c and a. If $c = a$, this last equation may easily be reduced to the form

$$(x^2 + y^2)^2 = 2a^2(x^2 - y^2),$$

which becomes, on transformation to polar coördinates,

$$\rho^2 = 2a^2 \cos 2\theta,$$

showing that in this case the curve is a lemniscate. (See page 161.)

The astronomer Jean-Dominique Cassini (1625–1712) invented these curves in connection with a problem in astronomy. An interesting property is that the section of a torus or anchorring (see Problem 11, page 276) made by a plane which is parallel to its axis and is at a distance equal to the radius of the generating circle is a Cassinian curve.

PROBLEMS

NOTE. In Problems 8–15 below a suitable parameter should first be chosen and x and y expressed in terms of the parameter. Then eliminate the parameter between the equations.

1. Transform into rectangular form the polar equations of the following curves:

(a) the limaçon;
(b) the cardioid;
(c) the conchoid;
(d) the cissoid;
(e) the four-leafed rose;
(f) the three-leafed rose.

2. Show that the following curves are not algebraic:

(a) the spiral of Archimedes;   (b) the lituus.

3. Plot the witch from its parametric equations.

Hint. $2 \cos^2 \theta = 1 + \cos 2\theta$.

4. Plot the following:

(a) $x^3 + xy^2 + ay^2 - 3ax^2 = 0$;   (Trisectrix of MacLaurin)
(b) $x^3 + xy^2 - 2ay^2 = 0$;   (Cissoid)
(c) $y^4 - 2ay^3 + a^2x^2 = 0$;   (Top)
(d) $(x^2 + y^2)^2 = ax^2y$;   (Bifolium)
(e) $(x^2 + 2ay - a^2)^2 - y^2(a^2 - x^2) = 0$.   (Cocked hat)

5. Plot the ovals of Cassini for

(a) $a = 5, c = 3$;   (b) $a = 3, c = 5$.

6. Transform the rectangular equation of the ovals of Cassini into polar form.

7. Derive from the figures polar equations for

(a) the strophoid;   (b) the ovals of Cassini.

8. Without using polar coördinates obtain equations in rectangular coördinates for the following problems on pages 171 and 172:

(a) No. 1;   (c) No. 11;   (e) No. 14;
(b) No. 10;   (d) No. 13;   (f) No. 16.

9. A right triangle of fixed size has an acute angle of 30° and the side opposite this angle has the length a. The triangle slides around in its plane so that the vertices of the acute angles remain on the x-axis and the y-axis respectively. Find the equation of the locus of the vertex of the right angle.

10. A point B on the circumference of the circle $x^2 + y^2 = r^2$ is joined to a variable point A on the x-axis by a segment of length r. Find the locus of a point P on AB as B moves around the circumference if the length of BP is c.

11. Find the locus in Problem 10 if the length of AB is a and P is the mid-point of AB.

12. From the point $(0, -4)$ lines are drawn to intersect the parabola $y^2 = 8x$. Find the locus of the mid-points of the chords thus formed.

13. Find the locus of the mid-points of chords of the parabola $y^2 = 2px$ drawn from the point $\left(\dfrac{p}{2}, -p\right)$.

14. A fixed circle has a radius of length r and a fixed point A is at a distance a from the center. Find the locus of the foot of a perpendicular from A to a tangent to the circle.

15. At a fixed point A on a circle of diameter a a tangent is drawn. The foot of a perpendicular from a point B on the circle to this tangent is C. Find the locus of the foot of a perpendicular from C to AB.

Hint. Take the origin at A and the tangent as the x-axis.

16. Join any point which is in the first quadrant and on the tri-sectrix of MacLaurin (see Problem 4) to the origin and the point $(2a, 0)$. Show that the inclination of one of these segments is three times that of the other.

17. A fixed line l is at a distance a from a fixed point O. If C is the foot of a perpendicular from O to l and D is the intersection of any other line through O with l, find the locus of a point P on OD such that the lengths of OP and CD are equal.

CHAPTER XI

TANGENTS AND NORMALS

138. Definitions. A line cutting a curve in more than one point is called a *secant*. In the figure PQ is a secant. If Q is

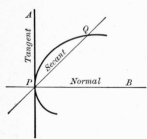

made to move along the curve towards P, it is clear that in general PQ will turn about P and approach as a limit the line PA. We therefore adopt the following definition:

The tangent to a curve at a given point is the line which is the limit of a secant through the point P and another point Q on the curve when Q approaches P. The normal to a curve at a given point is the line which is perpendicular to the tangent at that point.

In plane geometry a line is said to be tangent to a circle if it meets the circle in one and only one point. In the next section we shall see that the new definition adopted yields precisely the same tangent as the old one. This is true for all the conics, but for more general curves (e.g., $y^2 = x^3$) the old definition is not applicable.

139. Slope of tangent and normal to a circle at a given point. To find the slope of a tangent to a curve at a given point $P_1(x_1, y_1)$, we first find the slope of the secant through P_1 and a neighboring point $P_2(x_1 + h, y_1 + k)$ on the curve. This will be $\dfrac{k}{h}$. As P_2 is made to approach P_1 as a limit, the secant approaches the tangent and the slope of the tangent is the limiting value of $\dfrac{k}{h}$, which we write $\lim \dfrac{k}{h}$. Since both k and h approach the limit zero, special methods must be employed to find the value of the limit of their quotient.

In the case of the circle we proceed as follows. Since P_1 and P_2 are both on the circle, their coördinates satisfy the equation of the circle. Hence

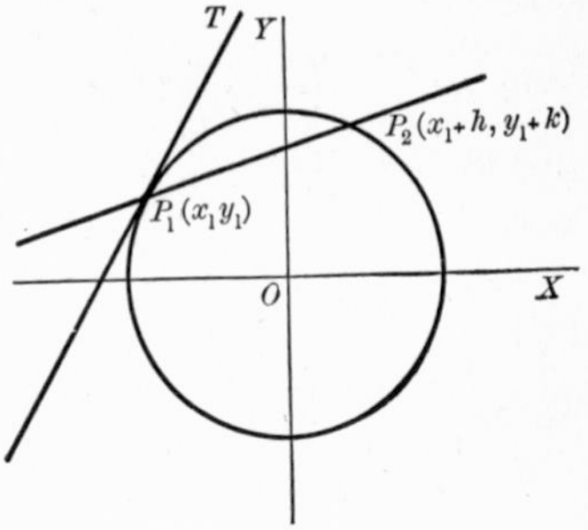

$$x_1{}^2 + y_1{}^2 = r^2,$$
$$(x_1 + h)^2 + (y_1 + k)^2 = r^2.$$

Expanding and subtracting,

$$2hx_1 + h^2 + 2ky_1 + k^2 = 0,$$
$$h(2x_1 + h) = - k(2y_1 + k),$$

and

$$\frac{k}{h} = - \frac{2x_1 + h}{2y_1 + k}.$$

From this last relation, we have

$$\lim \frac{k}{h} = - \lim \frac{2x_1 + h}{2y_1 + k} = - \frac{x_1}{y_1}.$$

Therefore for the tangent to the circle $x^2 + y^2 = r^2$,

$$m = - \frac{x_1}{y_1}. \tag{43}$$

As the normal is perpendicular to the tangent, its slope is the negative reciprocal of this expression, or $\dfrac{y_1}{x_1}$. Since this is the slope of the radius to the point (x_1, y_1), the tangent as here defined is perpendicular to the radius to the point of contact. As this property is proved in plane geometry for the definition there used, it follows that both the old and the new definitions give the same line as a tangent.

140. Slope of tangent and normal to an ellipse at a given point. The method of procedure is the same as that for the circle. Let the equation of the ellipse be

$$b^2x^2 + a^2y^2 = a^2b^2,$$

and the point of tangency be $P_1(x_1, y_1)$. A secant joining P_1 and a neighboring point $P_2(x_1 + h, y_1 + k)$ on the curve will have the slope $\dfrac{k}{h}$. Substituting the coördinates of P_1 and P_2 in the given equation,

$$b^2x_1{}^2 + a^2y_1{}^2 = a^2b^2,$$

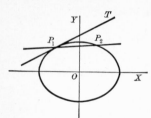

$$b^2(x_1 + h)^2 + a^2(y_1 + k)^2 = a^2b^2.$$

Expanding and subtracting,

$$2b^2x_1h + b^2h^2 + 2a^2y_1k + a^2k^2 = 0,$$

$$h(2b^2x_1 + b^2h) = -k(2a^2y_1 + a^2k),$$

$$\frac{k}{h} = -\frac{2b^2x_1 + b^2h}{2a^2y_1 + a^2k}.$$

Hence

$$\lim \frac{k}{h} = -\lim \frac{2b^2x_1 + b^2h}{2a^2y_1 + a^2k}$$

$$= -\frac{b^2x_1}{a^2y_1}.$$

Thus for the tangent to the ellipse the slope is

$$m = -\frac{b^2x_1}{a^2y_1}. \tag{44}$$

The slope of the normal is $\dfrac{a^2y_1}{b^2x_1}$.

141. Slope of tangent and normal to the parabola and hyperbola at a given point. By applying the method of §§ 139, 140 to the equations of the parabola and hyperbola, $y^2 = 2px$ and $b^2x^2 - a^2y^2 = a^2b^2$, we obtain the following results:

Tangent to parabola: $m = \dfrac{p}{y_1}.$ (45)

Tangent to hyperbola: $m = \dfrac{b^2x_1}{a^2y_1}.$ (46)

The slopes of the normals are: for the parabola, $-\dfrac{y_1}{p}$;

for the hyperbola, $-\dfrac{a^2y_1}{b^2x_1}.$

Exercise 1. Prove Formula 45.

Exercise 2. Prove Formula 46.

142. Equations of the tangent and normal at a given point. To find the equation of the tangent or normal to a curve at a given point, it is necessary only to find the slope and then use the point-slope equation of the straight line,

$$y - y_1 = m(x - x_1).$$

To learn whether or not a tangent to a curve meets the curve at the point of contact only, solve the equations of the tangent and the curve simultaneously.

Exercise 3. Show that the equation of the tangent to the circle $x^2 + y^2 = r^2$ at any point $P_1(x_1, y_1)$ is $x_1x + y_1y = r^2$.

Hint. Since P_1 is on the circle, simplify by using $x_1{}^2 + y_1{}^2 = r^2$.

Exercise 4. Show that the equation of the tangent at any point $P_1(x_1, y_1)$ is:

(a) for the ellipse $\dfrac{x^2}{a^2} + \dfrac{y^2}{b^2} = 1$, $\dfrac{x_1x}{a^2} + \dfrac{y_1y}{b^2} = 1$;

(b) for the hyperbola $\dfrac{x^2}{a^2} - \dfrac{y^2}{b^2} = 1$, $\dfrac{x_1x}{a^2} - \dfrac{y_1y}{b^2} = 1$;

(c) for the parabola $y^2 = 2px$, $y_1y = p(x + x_1)$.

PROBLEMS

1. Find the slope of the tangent to each of the following curves for any point (x_1, y_1) on the curve:

(a) $2xy = a^2$;

(b) $y = ax^3$;

(c) $(x - h)^2 = 2p(y - k)$;

(d) $y^2 = -2px$;

(e) $(x - h)^2 + (y - k)^2 = r^2$;

(f) $b^2y^2 + a^2x^2 = a^2b^2$;

(g) $b^2y^2 - a^2x^2 = a^2b^2$.

2. The same as Problem 1 for the following curves:

(a) $y^2 = ax^3$;

(b) $x^2 = 2py$;

(c) $x^2 - y^2 = a^2$;

(d) $(y - k)^2 = 2p(x - h)$;

(e) $\dfrac{(x - h)^2}{a^2} + \dfrac{(y - k)^2}{b^2} = 1$.

3.* For each of the following curves find the slopes of the tangent and the normal at the point indicated:

* The student is advised to follow the methods of §§ 139–141 in finding the slopes of the tangents in this problem, even in the cases where the formulas derived in these sections are applicable.

(a) $x^2 + 9y^2 = 52$, $(4, -2)$;

(b) $9x^2 + 25y^2 = 225$, $(-4, \frac{9}{5})$;

(c) $4x^2 - y^2 = 20$, $(3, -4)$;

(d) $x^2 = 8y$, $(-4, 2)$;

(e) $x^2 + y^2 = 100$, $(-6, 8)$;

(f) $xy = -24$, $(4, -6)$;

(g) $8y = x^3$, $(4, 8)$;

(h) $x^2 - 4y^2 + 60 = 0$, $(2, 4)$;

(i) $y(a^2 + x^2) = x$, $(0, 0)$;

(j) $y(x^2 + 4a^2) = 8a^3$, $\left(a, \dfrac{8a}{5}\right)$.

4.* For each of the following curves find the slopes of the tangent and the normal at the point indicated:

(a) $x^2 + 4y^2 = 52$, $(-6, 2)$;

(b) $16x^2 - 9y^2 = 144$, $(5, \frac{16}{3})$;

(c) $2y^2 + 5x = 0$, $(-10, 5)$;

(d) $y^2 = 12x$, $(3, -6)$;

(e) $4x^2 + 9y^2 = 72$, $(3, -2)$;

(f) $xy = 18$, $(6, 3)$;

(g) $2y^2 = x^3$, $(2, 2)$;

(h) $x^2 - 4y^2 = 20$, $(6, 2)$.

5. Write the equations of the tangent and the normal to each of the curves in Problem 4 at the point indicated.

6. Write the equations of the tangent and the normal to each of the curves in Problem 3 at the point indicated.

7. Using the results of Exercise 4 show that a tangent to a conic meets the curve in only one point.

8. Prove that the tangents at the ends of the latus rectum of a parabola are perpendicular to each other.

9. Find the angles between each of the following pairs of curves. (By the angle between two curves is meant the angle between their tangents at the points of intersection.)

(a) $y^2 = 12x$,

   $2x - y = 12$;

(b) $x^2 + y^2 = 48$,

   $y^2 = 8x$;

(c) $x^2 + 4y^2 = 16$,

   $x + 2y = 4$;

(d) $9x^2 - y^2 = 80$,

   $y^2 = 16x$.

10. Prove that the tangents at the ends of any chord through the focus of a parabola are perpendicular to each other.

11. If m and $-\dfrac{1}{m}$ are the slopes of the tangents in Problem 10, find the slope of the focal chord joining the points of contact.

12. Show that the tangents at the ends of a focal chord of a parabola meet on the directrix.

* The student is advised to follow the methods of §§ 139–141 in finding the slopes of the tangents in this problem, even in the cases where the formulas derived in these sections are applicable.

13. Show that the equilateral hyperbolas $x^2 - y^2 = a^2$ and $2xy = a^2$ meet at right angles.

14. Through what point of the ellipse $b^2x^2 + a^2y^2 = a^2b^2$ must a tangent and a normal be drawn so as to form with the principal axis an isosceles triangle?

15. An ellipse and a hyperbola have the same foci. Prove that the tangents at their points of intersection are perpendicular to each other.

Hint. The value of c is common to the curves.

16. Find the angle between the tangents at the ends of a latus rectum of

(a) the ellipse; (b) the hyperbola.

17. Show that the product of the perpendicular distances from the foci to any tangent to an ellipse is a constant.

18. The same as Problem 17 for a hyperbola.

19. Show that the point of contact of a tangent to a hyperbola is midway between the points where the tangent meets the asymptotes.

143. Tangent and normal. Subtangent and subnormal. Let P_1T be the tangent and P_1N the normal to the curve in

the figure at P_1. By the *length of the tangent* is meant the distance from the point of tangency to the point where the tangent meets the x-axis, i.e., the length of P_1T. Similarly the length of the normal is the length of P_1N.

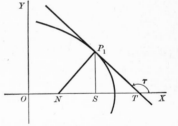

The *subtangent* is the projection of the tangent on the x-axis, i.e., TS. The *subnormal* is the projection of the normal on the x-axis, i.e., SN. The direction of reading the subtangent and subnormal is away from the intersection of the tangent with the x-axis; hence they are positive if they lie at the right of this point; negative if at the left.

To find the length of the subtangent, let m be the slope and τ the inclination of the tangent. Then

$$m = \tan \tau = \frac{SP_1}{TS} = \frac{y_1}{TS}.$$

Hence $$TS = \frac{y_1}{m}. \qquad (47)$$

To find the length of the subnormal, observe that the slope of the normal is $-\dfrac{1}{m}.$ Then

$$-\frac{1}{m} = \tan P_1 NS = \frac{SP_1}{NS} = -\frac{SP_1}{SN}.$$

Therefore $$SN = my_1. \qquad (48)$$

To find the lengths of the tangent and normal apply the Pythagorean theorem to the triangles SP_1T and NP_1S.

144. Tangent having a given slope. Suppose that we desire to find the tangent to the curve $x^2 + 4y^2 = 8$ having the slope $\frac{1}{2}$.

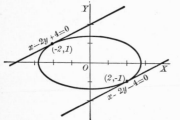

Here the slope is given and it is necessary to find the point of contact, which we call $P_1(x_1, y_1)$. Since P_1 is on the curve,

$$x_1^2 + 4y_1^2 = 8. \qquad (a)$$

Now $x^2 + 4y^2 = 8$ is an ellipse, for which $a^2 = 8$ and $b^2 = 2$.

Hence by (44) the slope of the tangent at P_1 is $-\dfrac{x_1}{4y_1}.$ But by the conditions of the problem the slope is to be $\frac{1}{2}$. Hence

$$-\frac{x_1}{4y_1} = \frac{1}{2}. \qquad (b)$$

Solving (a) and (b) simultaneously, the result is $x_1 = \pm 2$, $y_1 = \mp 1$. Thus there are two tangents with points of contact $(2, -1)$ and $(-2, 1)$ and equations

$$y \pm 1 = \tfrac{1}{2}(x \mp 2),$$

which reduce to

$$x - 2y \mp 4 = 0.$$

The method illustrated in the above problem is typical and may be applied to any problem of the same character.

Another method which is convenient is the following. The system of lines which have the slope $\frac{1}{2}$ has the equation $y = \frac{1}{2}x + k$. Substituting this in the equation of the curve and simplifying, we obtain

$$x^2 + 2kx + 2k^2 - 4 = 0.$$

The line will be a tangent if there is a single point of contact; i.e., if the discriminant of this quadratic is zero. This gives

$$4k^2 - 4(2k^2 - 4) = 0,$$

or $$k = \pm 2.$$

Hence we have the same result as before.

145. Tangent from a given external point. To find the equation of a tangent to a curve from a given external point we proceed as in the following problem.

Let the curve be $x^2 + 4y^2 = 8$ and the point $(1, \frac{3}{2})$. As before, let the point of contact be $P_1(x_1, y_1)$. Then we have

$$x_1^2 + 4y_1^2 = 8. \tag{a}$$

The slope of the tangent is, by (44), $-\dfrac{x_1}{4y_1}$. Hence the equation of the tangent is

$$y - y_1 = -\frac{x_1}{4y_1}(x - x_1).$$

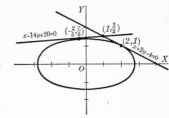

Since this is to pass through $(1, \frac{3}{2})$ we have

$$\frac{3}{2} - y_1 = -\frac{x_1}{4y_1}(1 - x_1). \tag{b}$$

Solving equations (a) and (b) simultaneously, we get $x_1 = 2$ or $-\frac{2}{5}$, $y_1 = 1$ or $\frac{7}{5}$.

Thus there are two tangents with points of contact $(2, 1)$, and $(-\frac{2}{5}, \frac{7}{5})$. For the first of these the slope is $-\frac{1}{2}$ and the equation is

$$y - 1 = -\tfrac{1}{2}(x - 2),$$

or $$x + 2y - 4 = 0.$$

For the second the slope is $\frac{1}{14}$ and the equation is

$$y - \tfrac{7}{5} = \tfrac{1}{14}(x + \tfrac{2}{5}),$$

or

$$x - 14y + 20 = 0.$$

PROBLEMS

1. Find the lengths of the subtangent and the subnormal for each of the following curves at the point indicated:

(a) $x^2 + y^2 = 52$, $(6, -4)$; (e) $x^2 = 8y$, $(4, 2)$;
(b) $x^2 + 2y^2 = 72$, $(8, -2)$; (f) $x^2 - 4y^2 + 60 = 0$, $(2, 4)$;
(c) $8y = x^3$, $(4, 8)$; (g) $16x^2 - 9y^2 = 112$, $(-4, 4)$;
(d) $xy = 12$, $(4, 3)$; (h) $x^2 + 4y^2 = 100$, $(8, 3)$.

2. Find the lengths of the subtangent and the subnormal for each of the following curves at the point indicated:

(a) $x^2 + y^2 = 100$, $(-6, 8)$; (e) $xy = 18$, $(6, 3)$;
(b) $y^2 = 24x$, $(6, 12)$; (f) $2y = x^3$, $(2, 4)$;
(c) $x^2 + 9y^2 = 52$, $(4, -2)$; (g) $y^2 = -8x$, $(-2, -4)$;
(d) $4x^2 - y^2 = 80$, $(6, -8)$; (h) $9x^2 + 4y^2 = 72$, $(-2, -3)$.

3. The letters below refer to curves in Problem 2. In each case find the equation of a tangent which has the indicated slope.

(a) $\frac{4}{3}$; (c) $\frac{2}{9}$; (e) $-\frac{1}{2}$; (g) $-\frac{1}{2}$;
(b) -1; (d) 3; (f) 6; (h) $\frac{3}{2}$.

4. The letters below refer to curves in Problem 1. In each case find the equation of a tangent which has the indicated slope.

(a) $\frac{3}{2}$; (c) $\frac{3}{2}$; (e) $\frac{1}{2}$; (g) $-\frac{16}{9}$;
(b) 2; (d) -3; (f) $-\frac{1}{8}$; (h) $\frac{2}{3}$.

5. The letters below refer to curves in Problem 2. In each case find the equation of a tangent from the given point.

(a) $(14, 2)$; (c) $(5, 4)$; (e) $(0, 6)$; (g) $(4, 2)$;
(b) $(2, -8)$; (d) $(2, -4)$; (f) $(1, -2)$; (h) $(8, 6)$.

6. The letters below refer to curves in Problem 1. In each case find the equation of a tangent from the given point.

(a) $(-4, 7)$; (c) $(4, 4)$; (e) $(7, 3)$; (g) $(-5, 12)$;
(b) $(12, 6)$; (d) $(5, -3)$; (f) $(-6, 3)$; (h) $(2, -7)$.

7. Find the lengths of the subtangent, subnormal, tangent, and normal at any point (x_1, y_1) of

(a) $y^2 = 2px$; (c) $b^2x^2 - a^2y^2 = a^2b^2$;
(b) $b^2x^2 + a^2y^2 = a^2b^2$; (d) $x^2 + y^2 = r^2$.

8. Show that a line from the focus of the parabola $y^2 = 2px$ to the point where any tangent cuts the y-axis is perpendicular to the tangent.

9. Write and simplify the equation of the normal to each of the curves of Problem 7 at any point (x_1, y_1).

10. Show that the equation of a tangent of slope m is

(a) $y = mx + \dfrac{p}{2m}$ for the parabola $y^2 = 2px$;

(b) $y = mx \pm \sqrt{a^2m^2 + b^2}$ for the ellipse $b^2x^2 + a^2y^2 = a^2b^2$;

(c) $y = mx \pm \sqrt{a^2m^2 - b^2}$ for the hyperbola $b^2x^2 - a^2y^2 = a^2b^2$.

11. Prove that the tangents to the ellipse $b^2x^2 + a^2y^2 = a^2b^2$ and the circle $x^2 + y^2 = b^2$ at points having the same ordinate meet on the y-axis.

12. Prove that the point of contact of a tangent to the hyperbola $2xy = a^2$ bisects the segment of the tangent intercepted between the coördinate axes.

13. Find the area of the triangle formed by the tangent to the curve $2xy = a^2$ at any point and the coördinate axes.

14. If a tangent to a parabola meets the latus rectum produced at A and the directrix at B, prove that $FA = FB$, F being the focus.

15. Show that a tangent to a hyperbola bisects the angle between the focal radii.

16. Show that the locus of the foot of a perpendicular from the vertex of the parabola $y^2 = 2px$ to a tangent is the cissoid
$$y^2(2x + p) = -2x^3.$$

Hint. Use Problem 10(a) and express the coördinates of the foot of the perpendicular in terms of m as a parameter.

17. Find the locus of a point P such that the tangents from P to the ellipse $b^2x^2 + a^2y^2 = a^2b^2$ are perpendicular to each other.

Hint. Let the slopes of the tangents be m and $-\dfrac{1}{m}$ and use Problem 10(b).

146. The parabolic reflector. Let TP be tangent to the parabola $y^2 = 2px$ at $P(x, y)$, and let TM be the subtangent.

Applying the subtangent formula, $TM = 2x$; hence,
$$TO = OM = x.$$

Now if F is the focus, this gives

$$TF = x + \frac{p}{2}.$$

But $$FP = NP = x + \frac{p}{2}.$$

Hence TPF is isosceles, i.e., *the tangent to a parabola makes equal angles with the focal radius and the principal axis.*

This principle is used in the construction of parabolic reflectors. These are reflectors whose surfaces are generated by

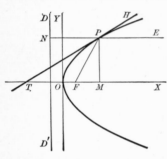

revolving a parabola about its principal axis. The lamp is placed at the focus. Then by the laws of optics a ray of light from F to any point on the surface P is reflected along PE so that angle TPF = angle HPE. But this makes angle HPE equal to angle PTF by the above proof. Therefore PE is parallel to OX.

Thus all the rays of light from a lamp placed at F are reflected along lines parallel to the axis.

Exercise 5. Use the above property of the tangent to devise a method of constructing a tangent to a given parabola at any point by ruler and compasses.

147. Angle between the focal radii and the tangent to an ellipse at any point. Let PT be a tangent and PN a normal to the ellipse at any point $P(x, y)$ on the ellipse, whose foci are F and F'. We desire to show that these lines make equal angles with the focal radii to P.

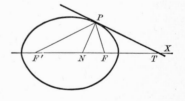

The slope of $F'P$ is $\dfrac{y}{x + c}$; of FP, $\dfrac{y}{x - c}$; and of NP, $\dfrac{a^2y}{b^2x}$, by § 140. Hence

$$\tan F'PN = \frac{\dfrac{a^2y}{b^2x} - \dfrac{y}{x+c}}{1 + \dfrac{a^2y^2}{b^2x(x+c)}} = \frac{a^2xy + a^2cy - b^2xy}{b^2x^2 + b^2cx + a^2y^2}$$

$$= \frac{c^2xy + a^2cy}{a^2b^2 + b^2cx} = \frac{cy}{b^2};$$

and $\quad \tan FPN = \dfrac{\dfrac{y}{x-c} - \dfrac{a^2y}{b^2x}}{1 + \dfrac{a^2y^2}{b^2x(x-c)}} = \dfrac{b^2xy - a^2xy + a^2cy}{b^2x^2 - b^2cx + a^2y^2}$

$$= \frac{a^2cy - c^2xy}{a^2b^2 - b^2cx} = \frac{cy}{b^2}.$$

Therefore $F'PN = FPN$; and the angles which the focal radii make with the tangent, being complementary to these, are also equal. (See § 73.)

Exercise 6. Show how to draw a tangent to an ellipse at any point.

148. Diameters of a conic. The locus of the middle points of a system of parallel chords of any conic is called a *diameter* of the conic.

Let a chord with slope m meet the ellipse

$$\frac{x^2}{a^2} + \frac{y^2}{b^2} = 1$$

in the points $P_1(x_1, y_1)$ and

$\quad P_2(x_1 + h, y_1 + k)$.

Then by § 140 the slope of the chord is

$$m = \frac{k}{h} = -\frac{b^2(2x_1 + h)}{a^2(2y_1 + k)}.$$

Now let $P(x, y)$ be the mid-point of the chord; then

$$2x = 2x_1 + h$$

and $\qquad 2y = 2y_1 + k$

by the mid-point formulas.

Substituting, we have, $m = -\dfrac{b^2 x}{a^2 y}$

or $$y = -\frac{b^2}{a^2 m} x, \tag{49}$$

which is the equation of a straight line. This line is called a *diametral line*. The equation shows that the diameter is a chord through the center of the ellipse of slope $m' = -\dfrac{b^2}{a^2 m}$. Transferring the m to the other side, we have an important relation between the slopes of a diameter and the chords which it bisects, namely,

$$mm' = -\frac{b^2}{a^2}. \tag{50}$$

In similar manner, we may show that the equation of the diametral line of the parabola $y^2 = 2px$ is

$$y = \frac{p}{m}, \tag{51}$$

where m is the slope of the system of chords.

For the hyperbola we obtain as the equation of the diametral line of a set of chords of slope m,

$$y = \frac{b^2}{a^2 m} x. \tag{52}$$

The relation between the slopes of the chords and their diameter is

$$mm' = \frac{b^2}{a^2}. \tag{53}$$

The diameter of a parabola is a part of the diametral line extending to infinity. In the case of the hyperbola the diameter consists of two parts of the diametral line extending to infinity if the chords which it bisects are terminated by the same branch of the hyperbola, and of the whole diametral line if the chords which it bisects are terminated by different branches of the hyperbola.

Exercise 7. Prove Formula 51.

Exercise 8. Prove Formula 52.

149. Conjugate diameters of an ellipse. The relation

$$mm' = -\frac{b^2}{a^2}$$

states the condition satisfied by m and m' if the line $y = m'x$ is the diametral line of a set of chords of slope m. But as m and m' can be interchanged in Formula 50 without altering the relation, we see that $y = mx$ is the diametral line of the set of chords of slope m', parallel to the first diameter.

Two diameters which have slopes m and m' such that

$$mm' = -\frac{b^2}{a^2}$$

are called *conjugate diameters.* Each diameter is one of the chords bisected by its conjugate.

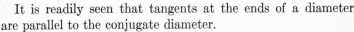

It is readily seen that tangents at the ends of a diameter are parallel to the conjugate diameter.

For, let $P_1(x_1, y_1)$ be the end of the diameter $y = mx$. The slope of the tangent at P_1 is $-\dfrac{b^2 x_1}{a^2 y_1}$ by § 140. But $\dfrac{x_1}{y_1} = \dfrac{1}{m}$, since P_1 lies on $y = mx$. Hence the slope of the tangent is $-\dfrac{b^2}{a^2 m}$, which is also the slope of the conjugate diameter.

This property, together with Exercise 6, supplies a method of constructing a diameter conjugate to a given diameter with ruler and compasses. It is easy to show that, if a circle is projected onto a plane, the projections of two mutually perpendicular diameters of the circle will be conjugate diameters of the ellipse which is the projection of the circle. (See Problem 18, page 116.)

150. Conjugate diameters of the hyperbola. The relation between the slope of a diameter of the hyperbola

$$b^2 x^2 - a^2 y^2 = a^2 b^2$$

and the slope of the corresponding chords has been found to be

$$mm' = \frac{b^2}{a^2}.$$

As the equation, $- b^2x^2 + a^2y^2 = a^2b^2$, of the conjugate hyperbola is obtained by substituting $- b^2$ for b^2 and a^2 for $- a^2$, it is easy to see that the corresponding relation for the diameter and chords of the conjugate hyperbola is $mm' = \dfrac{- b^2}{- a^2} = \dfrac{b^2}{a^2}.$ That is, it is the same in both the hyperbola and its conjugate. As in the case of the ellipse, two diameters of slopes m and m' such that $mm' = \dfrac{b^2}{a^2}$ are called *conjugate diameters*.

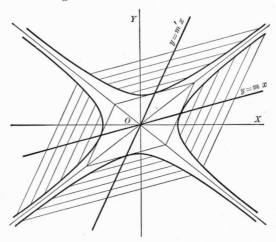

Similarly, the chords bisected by the diametral line $y = mx$ are parallel to the conjugate diametral line $y = m'x$. Also the tangents to a hyperbola at the ends of a diameter are parallel to the conjugate diameter.

Exercise 9. Show that, if in the above figure the chords parallel to the line $y = mx$ are extended to the asymptotes of the hyperbolas, the resulting segments are bisected by the line $y = m'x$.

PROBLEMS

1. For each of the following conics find the slope of the diameter bisecting the system of chords of slope 2 and draw the conic, the diameter, and several chords of the system:

(a) $x^2 + 4y^2 = 64$;

(b) $9x^2 - y^2 = 36$;

(c) $x^2 = -12y$;

(d) $y^2 = 16x$;

(e) $25x^2 + 9y^2 = 225$;

(f) $9x^2 - 16y^2 = 144$.

2. The same as Problem 1 for the slope $\frac{1}{2}$. Also draw the conjugate diameter if there is one.

3. What is the relation between the slopes of conjugate diameters of the ellipse $b^2y^2 + a^2x^2 = a^2b^2$?

4. Show that conjugate diameters of an ellipse lie in different quadrants.

5. What is the locus of the mid-points of a system of parallel chords with slope m, drawn in the parabola $x^2 = 2py$?

6. Show that conjugate diameters of a hyperbola lie in the same quadrant.

7. What relation must exist between a and b when two conjugate diameters meet the ellipse in the extremities of the latus rectum?

8. Prove that the major axis of an ellipse is greater than any other diameter.

Hint. Show that $4a^2$ is greater than the square of any diameter.

9. Lines are drawn joining the ends of the major and minor axes of an ellipse. Show that the diameters parallel to these are conjugate.

10. Prove that the tangents to an ellipse at the ends of a diameter make equal angles with the lines joining these points to a focus.

11. Tangents at the extremities of two conjugate diameters of the ellipse $\dfrac{x^2}{a^2} + \dfrac{y^2}{b^2} = 1$ form a circumscribed parallelogram. Find its area.

Hint. One conjugate diameter may be taken as a base, and the altitude may be found by using the normal form of the straight line equation.

12. Prove that the tangents to two conjugate hyperbolas at the ends of a pair of conjugate diameters meet on an asymptote.

13. Prove that chords from any point of an ellipse to the ends of any fixed diameter are parallel to a pair of conjugate diameters.

14. Prove that in an equilateral hyperbola the asymptotes bisect the angle between any pair of conjugate diameters.

CHAPTER XII

GRAPHS OF FUNCTIONS AND EMPIRICAL EQUATIONS

151. Functions in general. In Chapter II, § 21, the term *function* was defined as follows: *If one of two variables has one or more definite values corresponding to each value assigned to the other variable, the first variable is said to be a function of the second.* Various illustrations of this definition were given, but, in using this notion, we have hitherto dealt solely with the case that $y = f(x)$ represents the equation of some curve and $f(x)$ represents some mathematical expression involving the variable x. It is clear, however, from the definition, that the notion of a function is capable of much wider applications and we shall now discuss such applications. The discussion will be limited to one-valued functions, i.e., functions in which there is but one value of the dependent variable for each value of the independent variable.

The symbol $f(x)$ may represent some mathematical expression, but this is not necessary. For example, the student of elementary physics knows that if an object is dropped in a vacuum the formula $s = \frac{1}{2}gt^2$, where $g = 32.2$ approximately, expresses the distance (s feet) fallen in terms of the time (t sec.) since it was dropped. If the object falls in air, this formula no longer holds, but it is no less clear that s is a function of t. In like manner the horsepower (P) of a given type of gasoline motor is a function of the cubical contents (v) of its cylinders and we may write $P = f(v)$ without knowing any formula connecting P and v.

In the future, then, we shall regard y as a function of x, provided that to each value of x there corresponds a value of y, whether or not any formula is given.

222

152. General problems. Although the problems regarding functions are not primarily of a geometrical character, their study by means of the methods of analytic geometry is one of the important applications of this subject. The problems to be considered are:

1. To study functions by means of their graphs;

2. To discover, if possible, analytic expressions for functional relations.

153. Plotting from tabulated data. When one variable is a function of another, frequently the only information regarding this functional relation is a table of corresponding values of the variables, obtained by collecting statistics, by measurements, or by similar means. In plotting such a function the values of the variable which is regarded as independent are usually taken as abscissas and those of the dependent variable as ordinates.

The scales used should be as large as convenience permits. In general they will not be the same and they should be clearly marked on the axes. In choosing the scales the best practice is to have one space on the coördinate paper represent 1, 2, 5, 10, 20, 50, 100, etc., units of the variable concerned if its values are greater than 1; or 0.5, 0.2, 0.1, 0.05, 0.02, 0.01, 0.005, etc., units if the values are less than 1. The reason for this is that with such scales it is usually possible to estimate an additional digit from the graph.

If the values of either variable are large, but their range is relatively small, we do not attempt to show the origin on the paper, but start from a value near the smallest to be exhibited. For example, if we had $y = f(x)$ and the values of y ranged from 102 to 116, it would be advisable to choose as the base line not the x-axis, but the line $y = 100$. Then the point whose ordinate is 102 would be located two of the units chosen above this base line.

EXAMPLE 1. The amount of shipping entering New York in various years is given in the table following. Illustrate by a graph.

Solution. If we let T represent the tonnage and y the number of the year, we have to draw the graph of T regarded as a function of y.

Values of y will then be laid off on the horizontal axis. Since our paper is about 20 spaces wide, it is convenient to let 2 horizontal spaces represent 1 year and to start with $y = 1910$ at the intersection of the base lines.

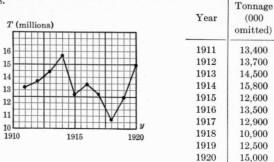

T (millions)

Year	Tonnage (000 omitted)
1911	13,400
1912	13,700
1913	14,500
1914	15,800
1915	12,600
1916	13,500
1917	12,900
1918	10,900
1919	12,500
1920	15,000

The range of values of T is $15,800,000 - 10,900,000 =$ about $5,000,000$. Letting 1 vertical space represent 500,000 tons, or 2 vertical spaces represent 1,000,000 tons, will require 10 spaces, slightly less than those available. We therefore use this scale and choose as the horizontal base line the line $T = 10,000,000$.

We now proceed to mark the scales and to plot the points. Values of y between those given evidently have no meaning, but adjacent points are joined by straight lines to aid in carrying the eye from one point to another.

EXAMPLE 2. The following table gives the expectation of life at various ages. Illustrate by a graph.

Age	Expecta-tion
20	42.20
30	35.33
40	28.18
50	20.91
60	14.10
70	8.48
80	4.39
90	1.42

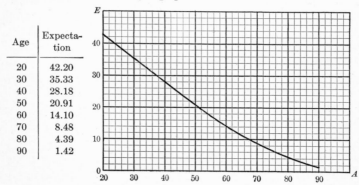

Solution. Let *A* represent age and *E* expectation; *E* is a function of *A*. If 1 space on the *A*-axis represents 2 years we need 35 spaces to cover the range of values of *A*. The same scale on the *E*-axis requires 21 spaces.

Proceeding as before, we plot the points. In this example values of *A* between those given have a meaning and there are corresponding values of *E*. We therefore join the points by as smooth a curve as possible, since it is reasonable to assume that the variation of *E* is regular.

154. Plotting from formulas. When a functional relation between two variables is given by a formula, the method of procedure in plotting is the same as in the previous case except that the table of values must be calculated. If the variables are *x* and *y* and we wish to represent *y* as a function of *x*, we solve the equation for *y* in terms of *x* and proceed as in ordinary curve plotting with two exceptions. One is that we restrict the range of values of *x* to cover only those values which we wish to exhibit. The other is that values which have no concrete meaning in the problem are not plotted, even though they may happen to satisfy the equation.

EXAMPLE. The formula $t = 10.6 + 0.0415x - 0.0000193x^2$ gives the mean temperature *t* (°C.) of a certain artesian well at various depths *x* (meters). Illustrate by a graph, letting *x* range up to 500 meters.

Solution. Negative values of *x* naturally have no meaning. Let us calculate our table of values for *x* at intervals of 50. We let $t = 10$

x	t
0	10.60
50	12.63
100	14.56
150	16.39
200	18.13
250	19.77
300	21.31
350	22.76
400	24.11
450	25.37
500	26.53

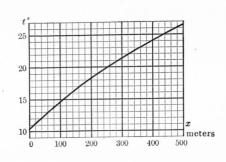

be our horizontal base line and choose for our scales: 1 space = 20 meters; 1 space = 1°. We can then plot our values of t correct to 0.2°. The graph is a curve which is concave down. By inspection of the equation it is seen to be an arc of a parabola.

155. The graph as an aid in computing. One of the important uses of the graph of a function is the finding of additional pairs of values of the variables concerned. To illustrate this consider the following graph, which shows the distance (d miles) to the horizon at sea for various heights (h feet) above sea level. From the graph we can read off at once the value of h corresponding to a given value of d, and vice versa: e.g., when $d = 20$, $h = 230$; when $d = 25$, $h = 360$; when $h = 120$, $d = 14.5$, etc.

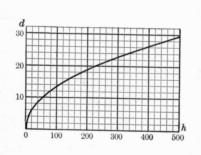

h	d
0	0
50	9.3
100	13.2
150	16.2
200	18.7
250	20.9
300	22.9
350	24.7
400	26.4
450	28.0
500	29.5

This method is of practical value only when the graph is carefully drawn on a fairly large scale. It is most useful when a very great degree of accuracy in the results is not required and when the same graph can be used often enough to justify the labor of drawing it.

If a formula is given and the value of one variable corresponding to only one value of the other is desired, it is usually easier to calculate the desired value than to plot the graph. But when many values are required, the graphical method is often superior. If in the formula plotted in the preceding section we consider the problem of calculating the value of x

for which $t = 15$, we can see how laborious such calculations can be even when the formulas are relatively simple.

When no formula is available the only alternative to using the graph is to interpolate by proportional parts. This is not only more troublesome, but frequently less accurate than using the graph. The reason is that when we interpolate by proportional parts we assume that the portion of the graph between two adjacent plotted points is a straight line. That this is often far from being the case is easily seen from the graph on page 226. For example, the graph shows that when $h = 20$, $d = 5.9$. If we interpolate to find d when $h = 20$, we have:

$$\frac{20}{50} = \frac{d}{9.3},$$

or
$$d = \tfrac{2}{5} \times 9.3 = 3.72.$$

In this case the interpolated result is too small.

PROBLEMS

1. Illustrate the following tables of statistics graphically:

(a) U. S. CORPORATION DIVIDENDS		(b) U. S. AUTOMOBILE ACCIDENTS		(c) ANNUAL RAINFALL AT NEW YORK	
Year	Amount in billions	Year	Death rate per 100,000	Year	Inches
1924	1.01	1924	15.5	1923	36.72
1925	1.07	1925	17.1	1924	37.72
1926	1.17	1926	18.0	1925	36.52
1927	2.10	1927	19.6	1926	49.68
1928	2.19	1928	20.8	1927	49.90
1929	2.98	1929	23.3	1928	40.73
1930	3.83	1930	24.5	1929	39.13
1931	3.52	1931	25.2	1930	35.33
1932	2.42	1932	21.9	1931	35.50
1933	1.69	1933	23.3	1932	38.85
1934	2.13				

2. The premium (P) on a certain $1000 life insurance policy for various ages (x yr.) is given in the following table. Draw a graph exhibiting P as a function of x. Estimate from the graph the premium at age 32 and at age 43; also the age at which the premium is $50.

x	20	25	30	35	40	45	50	55	60
P	16.86	18.88	21.49	24.89	29.38	35.43	43.73	55.17	71.03

3. The following table gives the age (x yr.) and corresponding diameter (y in.) of a certain tree. Draw a graph showing y as a function of x, and from the graph make out a table showing the approximate diameter of the tree for ages that are multiples of 50 years.

x	19	58	114	140	181	229
y	3.0	7.0	13.2	17.9	24.5	33.0

4. The following table gives the pressure per square inch (p lb.) of saturated steam corresponding to the volume (v cu. ft.) per pound. Draw a graph showing p as a function of v. Estimate from the graph the values of p corresponding to $v = 20$ and $v = 10$; also the values of v corresponding to $p = 20$ and $p = 40$.

v	53.9	26.4	14.0	7.0	4.3	2.7
p	6.9	14.7	28.8	60.4	101.9	163.3

5. An object is projected up an inclined plane with an initial velocity of 16 feet per second. Its velocity after t seconds is given by the formula $v = 16 - 4t$. Draw the graph of this function. Do negative values of v have any meaning?

6. For a certain type of motion the velocity (v ft. per sec.) after any time (t sec.) is given by the formula $v = 32(1 - e^{-t})$. Plot the graph of this function.

7. The volume V of a spherical segment of one base is given by the formula $V = \pi(rh^2 - \frac{1}{3}h^3)$, where r is the radius of the sphere and h is the height of the segment. Plot V as a function of h when (a) $r = 10$; (b) $r = 5$. Estimate from the graph the value of h for which the volume of the segment is one third that of the sphere.

8. The center of a sphere of radius r is on the surface of a sphere of radius R. The portion of the surface of the first sphere which lies within the second has an area given by the formula

$$A = \pi r^2 \left(2 - \frac{r}{R}\right).$$

Plot A as a function of r when (a) $R = 5$; (b) $R = 10$. Estimate from the graph the value of r for which A is greatest.

9. The melting point ($\theta°$ C.) of an alloy of lead and zinc containing $x\%$ of lead is given by the formula $\theta = 141.4 + 0.620x + 0.0130x^2$.

Draw the graph, letting x vary from 40% to 90%. For what percentage is the melting point 200°?

10. The temperature of a certain body cooling in moving air is given by the formula $T = 40e^{-.00144t}$, where t is the time elapsed in seconds and T is the excess of the temperature of the object over that of the air in degrees Centigrade. Plot the graph. Estimate the time required for the excess temperature to drop from 40° to 20°.

11. The amount ($\$s$) of an annuity of $1 per annum accumulated for n years at the interest rate i is given by the formula $s = \frac{1}{i}\big[(1+i)^n - 1\big]$. Plot this for the case that $i = .05$ and estimate the time required for s to equal $10, $20, etc., up to $50.

12. Two burners are 10 feet apart. At a point on the line joining them the amount of heat (H calories per second) received from the burners is given by the formula $H = \dfrac{60}{x^2} + \dfrac{480}{(10-x)^2}$, where x is the distance of the point from one of the burners. Plot the graph of this function and determine from the graph the value of x which makes H least.

13. In a circle of radius R the area of a segment cut off by a chord subtending an angle of x radians at the center is given by the formula $A = \dfrac{R^2}{2}(x - \sin x)$. Plot the graph of this function when (a) $R = 10$; (b) $R = 20$. From the graph find the value of the angle when the area of the segment is one third the area of the circle.

156. Derivation of equations. No general rules can be given for deriving the equation expressing a functional relation, since the procedure depends upon the laws of the subject from which the problem is taken. In order to express y as a function of x we must obtain from the conditions of the problem an equation of the form $y = f(x)$, in which $f(x)$ contains no variable other than x. We shall illustrate by giving three important types of problems which are commonly met in applications of mathematics.

157. A geometrical problem. A rectangle is inscribed in a semicircle of fixed radius r. It is required to express the area of the rectangle as a function of the base.

Solution. Let A be the area and let $x = EB$ be the base. If we denote the altitude BC by y, we have at once

$$A = xy.$$

But A is to be expressed as a function of x. Hence we must find a relation connecting x and y so that y can be expressed in terms of x.

Let O be the center of the circle and draw the radius OC.

Then $$r^2 = \overline{OB}^2 + \overline{BC}^2,$$

that is $$r^2 = \frac{x^2}{4} + y^2,$$

or $$y = \tfrac{1}{2}\sqrt{4r^2 - x^2}.$$

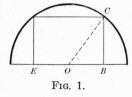

FIG. 1.

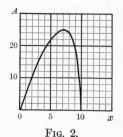

FIG. 2.

Substituting this above gives the result

$$A = \frac{x}{2}\sqrt{4r^2 - x^2}.$$

The graph of this function for the case that $r = 5$ is plotted in Fig. 2. It appears from the graph that the largest rectangle is obtained when x is approximately 7, or $1.4r$. This is within 1% of the correct value, $r\sqrt{2}$, obtainable by the calculus.

158. Linear functions. These occur when one variable changes with respect to the other at a constant rate. By the rate of change of y with respect to x is meant the change in y per unit change in x; that is, if x_1, y_1 and x_2, y_2 are two pairs of values, the rate of change is $\dfrac{y_2 - y_1}{x_2 - x_1}$.

We now proceed to prove two theorems analogous to those of § 36.

Theorem I. *If $y = f(x)$ is linear, the rate of change of y with respect to x is constant.*

Proof. By hypothesis, $y = f(x)$ is of the form $y = b + mx$, where b and m are constants. If x_1, y_1 and x_2, y_2 are any two pairs of values of x and y,

$$y_1 = b + mx_1,$$

and
$$y_2 = b + mx_2.$$

Subtracting, we have

$$y_1 - y_2 = m(x_1 - x_2),$$

whence
$$\frac{y_1 - y_2}{x_1 - x_2} = m.$$

The left member of this is the rate of change of y with respect to x. As it equals m, a constant, the theorem is proved.

Theorem II. *If y changes at a constant rate with respect to x, $y = f(x)$ is linear.*

Proof. Let m denote the rate of change and x_1, y_1 be a fixed pair of values of the variables. Since the rate of change is constant, we have for *any* other pair of values x, y:

$$\frac{y - y_1}{x - x_1} = m,$$

whence
$$y - y_1 = m(x - x_1).$$

This is a linear equation.

Corollary. *If the rate of change of y with respect to x is m and $y = b$ when $x = 0$, $y = b + mx$.*

From the above it is apparent that the graph of a function changing at a constant rate is a straight line whose slope is the rate of change (due allowance being made for the use of different scales in plotting). Hence we need but two pairs of values to plot the graph and we can use any of the forms of Chapter III in writing the equation.

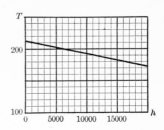

EXAMPLE. If T is the boiling point of water and h is the height above sea level, T is a linear function of h. $T = 212°$ F. when $h = 0$, and $T = 202°$ F. when $h = 5000$ ft. Express T as a function of h, find the rate of change of T, and draw the graph.

Solution. As we have two pairs of values, we use the two-point form of the linear equation, obtaining

$$\frac{T - 212}{h - 0} = \frac{212 - 202}{0 - 5000} = -0.002,$$

or

$$T = 212 - 0.002h.$$

By inspection the rate of change is $-0.002°$ per foot, the minus sign showing that the boiling point falls as h increases.

The graph is the straight line containing the two given points.

159. Variation, direct and inverse. The phrases *varies as* and *varies inversely as* frequently occur in stating certain laws. The statement "y varies as x" (or "y is proportional to x") means simply that $y = kx$, where k is a constant. The statement "y varies inversely as x" (or "y is inversely proportional to x") means that $y = \dfrac{k}{x}$, where k is a constant. Obviously the value of k can be determined if one pair of values of the variables is given.

EXAMPLE. The square of the time of revolution (T) of a planet about the sun varies as the cube of its distance (x) from the sun. The distance of the earth from the sun is 92.9 millions of miles. Express T as a function of x.

Solution. The statement of the problem gives

$$T^2 = kx^3.$$

But when $x = 92.9$, $T = 1$ year.
Hence

$$1 = (92.9)^3 k, \quad \text{or} \quad k = \frac{1}{(92.9)^3}.$$

Substitution of this gives

$$T = \frac{x^{\frac{3}{2}}}{(92.9)^{\frac{3}{2}}},$$

whence

$$T = 0.001117 x^{\frac{3}{2}}.$$

The graph is evidently a semicubical parabola.

160. Several common algebraic functions. Besides linear functions we frequently have functions of the form $y = kx^n$ and

$y = a + bx + cx^2$. In the first quadrant, if k is positive, the graph of $y = kx^n$ always assumes one of the forms given in the figure. If n is a fraction $\pm \dfrac{p}{q}$, where p and q have no common factor, it is easy to see by considerations of symmetry that the remainder of the graph is in the second quadrant when p is even, in the fourth quadrant when q is even, and in the third quadrant when p and q are both odd.

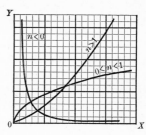

The graph of $y = a + bx + cx^2$ is a parabola with its axis perpendicular to the x-axis. For this function the greatest or the least value of y can be found by completing the square in x. For example, if $y = 2 + 8x - 3x^2$, we obtain $y = \frac{22}{3} - 3(x - \frac{4}{3})^2$. In this case the squared term has a negative sign and so y has its largest value, $\frac{22}{3}$, when $x = \frac{4}{3}$. The student will note that this is merely the method of finding the vertex of a parabola, given in Chapter VIII. The method can be used also in the case of functions which are of the quadratic form. Thus, in the example of § 157, $A^2 = \frac{1}{4}(4r^2x^2 - x^4) = r^4 - \frac{1}{4}(x^2 - 2r^2)^2$. Hence A has its largest numerical value when $x = r\sqrt{2}$.

PROBLEMS

1. Express the area of an equilateral triangle as a function of the length of a side and plot the graph.

2. Express the area of a regular hexagon as a function of the length of a side and plot the graph.

3. A plane distant a units from the center of a sphere of radius r cuts off a segment of volume $V = \dfrac{\pi}{3}(a^3 - 3ar^2 + 2r^3)$. If x denotes the greatest thickness of the segment, express V as a function of x.

4. If the perimeter of a rectangle is 100, express the area as a function of the length. Find the length for which the area is greatest.

5. If the area of a rectangle is 100, express the perimeter as a function of the length. Plot the graph and estimate the length which gives the least perimeter.

6. It is desired to fence off a rectangular piece of ground and to divide it into two pieces by another fence parallel to the ends of the rectangle. If 240 yards of fence material are available, express the area of the rectangle as a function of its length. Find the dimensions which give the largest area.

7. A linear segment passing through the point (5, 10) has its ends on the coördinate axes. Express the area of the right triangle bounded by the segment and the coördinate axes as a function of the base of the triangle, plot the graph, and estimate the length of the base for which the area is least.

8. For the data of Problem 7 express the length of the segment as a function of one of the angles of the triangle and plot the graph.

9. A rectangular box of constant volume k has a square base. Express the total surface of the box as a function of the length of one side of the base. Plot the graph of this function.

10. In a triangle ABC the length of the base AB is 100 ft. and the length of the corresponding altitude is 60 ft. A rectangle is drawn having one side lying along AB and the ends of the opposite side on AC and BC. Express the area of the rectangle as a function of its length, draw the graph, and find the area of the largest possible rectangle of this kind.

11. A right circular cone is inscribed in a sphere of radius R. Express the volume of the cone as a function of the distance from the center of the sphere to the base of the cone. Plot the graph for the case that $R = 5$, and estimate the volume of the largest such inscribed cone.

12. A long strip of tin 12 inches wide is to be made into a gutter by bending up a strip 4 inches wide on each side, so that the cross section of the gutter will be an isosceles trapezoid. Express the area of the cross section as a function of the depth, plot the graph, and estimate the depth which will give the greatest area.

13. Express the distance D from the point (10, 0) to any point P on the hyperbola $x^2 - y^2 = 16$ as a function of the abscissa of P. Plot $D = f(x)$ and estimate from the graph the value of x which makes D least.

14. The perimeter (P) of a regular polygon of n sides inscribed in a circle of radius r is given by the formula $P = 2nr \sin \dfrac{\pi}{n}$. Plot the graph of this function.

15. The formula $V = V_0\left(1 + \dfrac{T}{273}\right)$ gives the volume of expanding gas as a function of the temperature T, where the pressure remains constant and V_0 denotes the volume when $T = 0°$. Plot the graph of this function for the case that $V_0 = 100$ cu. ft. What is the rate of change in the volume?

16. The express rate over a certain distance is 40¢ for 5 lb. or less, and 1.1¢ for each additional pound or fraction thereof. Write a formula expressing this and state the meaning of the variables used.

17. A steel rail expands at a constant rate with respect to the temperature. If its length is 30 ft. at a temperature of $0°$ C., and 30.00163 at a temperature of $50°$ C., express the length as a function of the temperature. Draw a graph on such scales as will make it possible to read off the length for any temperature between $0°$ and $50°$.

18. The length (l in.) of a wire stretched by a force (p lb.) increases at a constant rate as the tension increases. If $l = 34.5$ when $p = 100$ and $l = 35.1$ when $p = 400$, at what rate does the length increase? Express l as a function of p.

19. A moving object is subject to a constant acceleration. If the velocity $v = 80$ ft. per sec. when the time $t = 5$ sec., and $v = 60$ ft. per sec. when $t = 10$ sec., express v as a function of t. What is the acceleration?

20. Express the amount ($\$A$) of a note for \$100 at simple interest 6% per annum as a function of the time (t months).

21. Plot the graphs of the following:

(a) $y = \frac{1}{4}x^{\frac{4}{3}}$; (c) $y = x^{\frac{5}{3}}$; (e) $y = 12x^{-2}$;

(b) $y = \frac{1}{2}x^{\frac{3}{2}}$; (d) $y = x^{\frac{3}{5}}$; (f) $y = 10x^{-\frac{1}{3}}$.

22. Sketch the graphs of the following, for positive integral values of the arbitrary constants:

(a) $y = kx^n$;

(b) $y = kx^{-n}$;

(c) $y = kx^{\frac{p}{q}}$, p odd, q even;

(d) $y = kx^{-\frac{p}{q}}$, p odd, q even;

(e) $y = kx^{\frac{p}{q}}$, p even, q odd;

(f) $y = kx^{-\frac{p}{q}}$, p even, q odd;

(g) $y = kx^{\frac{p}{q}}$, p odd, q odd;

(h) $y = kx^{-\frac{p}{q}}$, p odd, q odd.

23. The number (n) of vibrations per second of a string varies inversely as the length (l in.). Express n as a function of l. Sketch the graph. How could the value of the arbitrary constant be found?

24. The time of vibration (t sec.) of a pendulum varies as the square root of its length (l ft.). If $t = 1.11$ when $l = 4$, express t as a function of l. What is the graph?

25. The acceleration due to gravity (g ft. per sec. per sec.) varies inversely as the square of the distance (d miles) from the center of the earth. If $g = 32$ on the surface of the earth and the radius of the earth is taken as 4000 miles write the formula expressing g as a function of d. Sketch the graph.

26. The cost per hour for fuel to run a steamer varies as the cube of its speed, and is \$50 per hour for a speed of 10 miles per hour. Write a formula which gives the cost per hour for fuel corresponding to any speed.

27. If other expenses of the steamer in Problem 26 amount to \$200 per hour, write the formula for the cost of a trip of 400 miles in terms of the speed.

28. The pressure (p lb.) of a gas varies inversely as the volume (v cu. ft.). If $p = 50$ when $v = 3$, express p as a function of v and plot the graph.

29. The intensity of heat at a point varies inversely as the square of its distance from the source of heat. Two sources of heat are at A and B, their respective intensities at unit distance are a and b, and the length of AB is c. Write the formula for the combined intensity of heat (I) at a point P on the segment AB as a function of the distance (x) between A and P, and sketch the graph of the function.

161. Empirical formulas. Suppose that n pairs of values of the variables x and y are known and it is desired to express y in the form $y = f(x)$. The problem as stated clearly has no definite solution. For, if we take *any* equation involving n arbitrary constants and substitute the values of x and y, we get n simultaneous equations which can in general be solved. Thus we seem to have an infinite number of possible solutions of the above problem. On the other hand there is no reason to believe that any one of these possible equations would be satisfied by any pair of values of the variables other than those given.

However, the given values of x and y usually represent measurements of some kind and are themselves not exact. If then we can find a simple formula *nearly* satisfied by the measured values, this may be regarded as a solution of the problem stated above. It will serve as a practical means of calculating approximations to other values of the variables. Its form may suggest hitherto unknown laws connecting the variables, which can be established by later investigations.

Such formulas are called *empirical*, in contradistinction to *rational* formulas or formulas derived by reasoning. The formulas of pure mathematics are rational. Those of science are usually empirical in their application. The discovery of empirical formulas is sometimes called *curve fitting*. The aim in each case is to get a formula such that the calculated values of the dependent variable differ from the measured or observed values by less than the errors due to unavoidable imperfections in measurement.

162. General procedure. In finding an empirical formula the work falls into three parts: 1, choosing the type of equation; 2, finding the best values of the arbitrary constants; 3, calculating the deviations between the observed values of the dependent variable and those given by the formula.

The choice of the type of equation is sometimes dictated by theoretical considerations. If there is no reason for preferring a particular type, the choice is a matter of intelligent guesswork and experiment. The first thing to do is always to plot the data and draw a graph. Its shape will often indicate the proper equation. Other methods will be indicated later.

The second step must always be carried out even if we know the form of the equation in advance. For example, if we know that the equation is of the form $y = mx$, we cannot find m by substituting any pair of values, since different pairs will give different values. This is due to the impossibility of measuring

x and y exactly. As an experiment draw a straight line joining the origin to the point (16, 13), read off from the graph the values of y for integral values of x, and see how many exactly satisfy the equation $y = \frac{13}{16}x$.

The purpose of the last step is to check the work. As stated before the desired formula should be such that the differences between the calculated and observed values of y will be less than the errors made in measuring the latter. If this is not attainable, the formula must give results accurate enough at least for the purposes for which it is used.

In the following the discussion is confined to problems where the formulas are of the common types

$$y = b + mx, \ y = a + bx + cx^2, \ y = kx^n, \text{ and } y = ke^{nx}.$$

163. The type $y = b + mx$. Since a large number of functions change at a constant rate, we shall first consider fitting linear graphs. The method is best explained by an example.

In the following table T is a function of x and the values of T have been measured to the nearest 0.5 unit. Plotting the points, we see that they lie nearly in a straight line and therefore conclude that a linear function will give a "good fit."

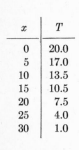

x	T
0	20.0
5	17.0
10	13.5
15	10.5
20	7.5
25	4.0
30	1.0

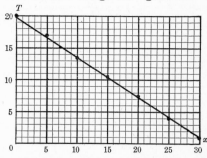

Setting $T = b + mx$, we now have to determine the proper values of the arbitrary constants b and m. There are several ways of doing this, of which three will be discussed in this and following sections. First of all, we can draw the line which seems to come nearest to all the plotted points and read off the values of b and m from the graph. In the figure shown $b = 19.8$ apparently. To get the slope take two points on the graph near the ends and use the slope formula. Thus, when $x = 6$, $T = 16$, and when $x = 27$, $T = 3$. Hence $m = -\frac{13}{21} = -0.62$. The required formula is

$$T = 19.8 - 0.62x.$$

To get good results by this method we need a large sheet of plotting paper.

The second method is what is called the "method of averages." If we substitute the values of x and T in the equation $T = b + mx$, we obtain the following equations:

$$20.0 = b \qquad\qquad 7.5 = b + 20m$$
$$17.0 = b + 5m \qquad 4.0 = b + 25m$$
$$13.5 = b + 10m \qquad 1.0 = b + 30m$$
$$10.5 = b + 15m$$

We divide these equations into two nearly equal groups, say the first four in one group and the last three in the other, and add. This gives two equations

$$4b + 30m = 61$$
$$3b + 75m = 12.5$$

which can be solved simultaneously. Solving, we find $b = 20$ and $m = -0.633$. Hence the required formula is

$$T = 20.0 - 0.633x.$$

The values of T as calculated by this formula are given in the adjoining table under the heading T_c. Subtracting these from the observed values T_0, we find the residuals or deviations $T_0 - T_c$. As none of the latter are greater than 0.2 and the observed values all had a possible error of 0.25 (since they were measured only to the nearest $\frac{1}{2}$ unit)

x	T_0	T_c	$T_0 - T_c$
0	20.0	20.0	0
5	17.0	16.8	+ 0.2
10	13.5	13.7	− 0.2
15	10.5	10.5	0
20	7.5	7.3	+ 0.2
25	4.0	4.2	− 0.2
30	1.0	1.0	0

we therefore conclude that our formula is a satisfactory one.

164. Principle involved in the method of averages. If we assume a formula of the type $T = b + mx$ and calculate values for b and m as in the previous section, we find that the substitution of a particular value for x in $b + mx$ will not give the observed value T_0 of T in general. Thus for any value of x we have $T_0 - (b + mx)$ not equal to zero but equal to the residual $T_0 - T_c$. In the example referred to $20 - b$, $17 - (b + 5m)$, $13.5 - (b + 10m)$, and $10.5 - (b + 15m)$ are the residuals for $x = 0, 5, 10$, and 15. If we set the sum of these equal to zero, we have

$$61 - (4b + 30m) = 0,$$

which is the same as the first simultaneous equation of the previous section,

$$4b + 30m = 61.$$

Thus the method of averages is merely a calculation of values of the arbitrary constants of the assumed formula which will make the algebraic sum of the residuals equal to zero for each of two groups of values of the variables. This makes the average residual zero, and we assume that the values of the constants thus obtained give a satisfactory formula.

The reason for using *two* groups is that we have two arbitrary constants. If we had only one, we would sum all the equations; if we had three, we would divide the data into three groups.

165. Method of moments. Considering again the example of § 163, we note that the expressions b, $b + 5m$, $b + 10m$, etc., are the calculated or theoretical values of T. If, then, we add the seven equations at the middle of page 239, the result, $73.5 = 7b + 105m$, equates the values of the sums of the observed and calculated values of T. Values of b and m which satisfy this equation will then give a formula for which the sums of the observed and calculated values of T are equal.

Since there are two arbitrary constants, we need another equation. This is obtained by multiplying each of the seven equations by the value of x from which it was found and adding the results, thus:

$$
\begin{aligned}
0 &= 0 \\
85.0 &= 5b + 25m \\
135.0 &= 10b + 100m \\
157.5 &= 15b + 225m \\
150.0 &= 20b + 400m \\
100.0 &= 25b + 625m \\
30.0 &= 30b + 900m \\
\hline
657.5 &= 105b + 2275m
\end{aligned}
$$

This equation and the one obtained before are called *normal equations.* By solving them simultaneously we get $b = 20.036$ and $m = -0.6357$. This gives the formula

$$T = 20.036 - 0.636x.$$

The second normal equation equates the sums of the products of the observed and calculated values of T by the corresponding values of x. These sums are called the *first moments* of x, for the observed and calculated values respectively. By analogy the sum of the values of T is called the *zeroth moment*, since $x^0 = 1$. The term "moment" comes from mechanics. If we imagine the x-axis to be a horizontal light rod hinged at the origin and each value of T to be a weight suspended at the point of abscissa x, the first moment measures the combined turning effect of these forces about the origin. In statistics ordinates are often drawn to represent the frequencies of various values of a variable x. In this case the zeroth moment is the total frequency and the quotient of the first moment by the zeroth moment is the mean value of x.

It can be shown by the calculus that for equations of the form $y = a_0 + a_1x + a_2x^2 + \cdots + a_nx^n$ the method of moments is the same as the method of least squares; i.e., the values of the arbitrary constants are those for which the sum of the squares of the deviations of the observed from the calculated values is a minimum. Another advantage is that the result obtained in a given problem is unique, whereas by the method of averages a change in the grouping of the equations will alter the result. On the other hand the numerical work involved in the method of moments is often tedious, since the coefficients in the normal equations are apt to be large and in their solution it is necessary to keep a large number of decimal places in order to secure much accuracy in the final results. Sometimes the size of the numbers involved can be diminished by a proper change of variable; e.g., the substitution $x = 5x'$ in the above problem would have given as normal equations

$$73.5 = 7b + 21m,$$
and
$$131.5 = 21b + 91m.$$

166. First differences. If in a table we subtract a value of one variable from the next following, we call the result a *first difference*. First differences are indicated by prefixing Δ to the letter representing the variable. In the adjoining table every value of Δx is $+ 5$, and the values of ΔT are tabulated opposite the corresponding values of x and T. There is of course no ΔT for the last value of x in the table.

x	T	ΔT
0	20.0	− 3.0
5	17.0	− 3.5
10	13.5	− 3.0
15	10.5	− 3.0
20	7.5	− 3.5
25	4.0	− 3.0
30	1.0	

In general, if y is a linear function of x, and therefore changes at a constant rate, it is clear that for equal values of Δx the corresponding values of Δy must be equal, and conversely. For Δy is the change in y due to a change of Δx units in x, and therefore equals Δx times the rate of change of y with respect to x.

This fact affords a method for deciding upon the availability of a linear formula without plotting the data. If the values of the independent variable are given at equal intervals, calculate the first differences for the dependent variable. If these are approximately equal, a linear relation may be assumed. In the given example the values of x are given at intervals of 5 units and ΔT is approximately constant; hence it is reasonable to assume a linear relation.

PROBLEMS

1. In each of the following find a linear formula representing the second variable as a function of the first by graphical means.

(a) x	y	(b) x	y	(c) t	d	(d) x	y
15	1.64	20	110.35	25	.00793	15	66.30
30	1.79	40	110.75	37	.00807	20	67.80
40	1.90	60	111.14	49	.00820	25	69.35
50	1.98	75	111.45	61	.00835	30	70.80
65	2.11	90	111.74	67	.00842	35	72.35
70	2.14			73	.00850	40	73.80
80	2.21					45	75.30

(e) u	v	(f) t	s	(g) x	y	(h) x	y
2.0	4.04	15	22.3	3.6	18.7	3	100.53
3.0	4.38	20	20.1	5.4	21.5	6	100.97
4.0	4.73	25	17.9	6.0	22.5	10	101.53
4.5	4.91	30	15.6	6.6	23.3	12	101.83
5.0	5.10	35	13.4	9.6	28.0	15	102.25
5.5	5.27	40	11.3	12.0	31.8		
6.0	5.45	45	9.0				
6.5	5.64	50	6.8				

2. The same as Problem 1 by the method of averages.

3. The same as Problem 1 by the method of moments.

4. In Problem 2 calculate the values of the dependent variable from the empirical formula and find the residuals.

5. In Problem 3 calculate the values of the dependent variable from the empirical formula and find the residuals.

6. In one of the sets of data of Problem 1 show the availability of a linear formula by finding the first differences.

7. The specific gravity (y) of dilute sulphuric acid at different concentrations ($x\%$) is given as follows. Find an empirical formula.

x	5	10	15	20	25	30	35
y	1.033	1.068	1.101	1.139	1.178	1.218	1.257

8. The force (F lb.) which would just lift a weight (w lb.) was found in experiments with a crane to be as follows. Find an empirical formula.

w	200	300	400	500	600	700	800	900
F	16.3	22.1	27.7	33.5	39.1	44.9	50.6	56.1

9. A barometer at various heights (*h* ft.) registered pressures (*p* in.) as follows. Find an empirical formula.

h	0	2000	4000	6000	8000	10000
p	29.90	28.65	27.35	26.15	24.95	23.80

167. Equations of the forms $y = a + bx^2$ and $y = a + \dfrac{b}{x}$. These forms involve two arbitrary constants and can therefore be obtained in the same way as linear equations. Since the first is the equation of a parabola symmetrical with respect to the *y*-axis, it is not applicable unless *y* has its least (greatest) value when $x = 0$ and increases (decreases) indefinitely with *x*. The graph of $y = a + \dfrac{b}{x}$ is an equilateral hyperbola with the asymptote $y = a$ and will sometimes fit a set of values in which the value of the dependent variable appears to approach a constant.

If in the first case we set $x' = x^2$, the equation $y = a + bx^2$ becomes $y = a + bx'$, which is linear. Hence, if we plot (x', y) and the plotted points lie nearly in a straight line, we may assume that $y = a + bx^2$ is the proper type. The values of *a* and *b* can then be approximated from the figure or obtained by the method of averages. Similar remarks apply to the type $y = a + \dfrac{b}{x}$.

EXAMPLE. Find an empirical formula fitting the data in the following table.

Solution. Inspection of the table shows that as *x* increases *y* decreases, and indicates that *y* approaches a definite limit. It seems

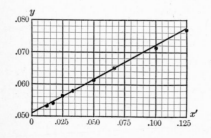

x	*y*	$x' = \dfrac{1}{x}$
8	.0770	.1250
10	.0715	.1000
15	.0650	.0667
20	.0614	.0500
30	.0582	.0333
40	.0563	.0250
60	.0540	.0167
80	.0532	.0125

reasonable therefore to try a formula of the type $y = a + \dfrac{b}{x}$. We set

$x' = \dfrac{1}{x}$ and calculate the values of x'. Plotting the points (x', y), we find that they lie nearly in a straight line,* whose equation is found from the graph to be $y = 0.051 + 0.21x'$. Hence an approximate formula is $y = 0.051 + \dfrac{0.21}{x}$.

To obtain better values of a and b we divide the data into two equal groups and use the method of averages. Substituting the values of x' and y in the equation $y = a + bx'$, we have:

$.0770 = a + .1250b$	$.0582 = a + .0333b$
$.0715 = a + .1000b$	$.0563 = a + .0250b$
$.0650 = a + .0667b$	$.0540 = a + .0167b$
$.0614 = a + .0500b$	$.0532 = a + .0125b$
$\overline{.2749 = 4a + .3417b}$ (1)	$\overline{.2217 = 4a + .0875b}$ (2)

Solving equations (1) and (2) simultaneously, we find that $b = 0.209$ and $a = 0.0509$. Hence $y = 0.0509 + 0.209x'$, or $y = 0.0509 + \dfrac{0.209}{x}$.

If we calculate the values of y by this formula, we find that the greatest residual is numerically 0.0004. However, we can obtain nearly as good results by using the simpler formula $y = 0.051 + \dfrac{0.21}{x}$. The same result is obtained if the method of moments is used, but it must be noted that in problems of this kind the first moment for the pairs of values (x', y) is not the same as that for the pairs of values (x, y).

168. The parabola $y = a + bx + cx^2$. If it is thought that the values of x and y may satisfy an equation of this type, the coefficients a, b, and c can be obtained by the method of averages or the method of moments as in the case of linear formulas. If the method of averages is used, the given values must be divided into three groups, since there are three arbitrary constants. For the same reason, if the method of moments is used, we must calculate the second moment as well as the zeroth

* An equally good test is to see whether the points (x, xy) lie on a straight line.

and first moments. The second moment is the sum of the products of the values of x^2 by the corresponding values of y.

As the work of finding these constants is much longer than in the linear case, it is desirable to have some quick method of determining the suitability of this type in advance. If the values of x are given at equal intervals, this is easily found. In fact, we have the following theorem.

If $y = a + bx + cx^2$ and Δx is a constant, Δy is a linear function of x.

Proof. Let $\Delta x = h$. Then for any value of x:

$$y = a + bx + cx^2$$
$$y + \Delta y = a + b(x + h) + c(x + h)^2$$
$$= a + bx + bh + cx^2 + 2chx + ch^2.$$

Hence
$$\Delta y = bh + 2chx + ch^2$$
$$= (bh + ch^2) + 2chx,$$

which is a linear function of x.

The converse of this is readily established. To determine whether or not Δy is linear we apply § 166. The difference between two successive first differences is called a *second difference* and is denoted by $\Delta^2 y$. If Δy is linear, § 166 tells us that $\Delta^2 y$, the first difference of Δy, must be constant. Hence we have the corollary:

t	T	ΔT	$\Delta^2 T$	T_c
0	15.1	4.9	− 0.5	15.2
5	20.0	4.4	− 0.4	20.0
10	24.4	4.0	− 0.4	24.4
15	28.4	3.6	− 0.4	28.4
20	32.0	3.2	− 0.3	32.0
25	35.2	2.9		35.3
30	38.1			38.1

If $y = a + bx + cx^2$ and Δx is constant, $\Delta^2 y$ is constant, and conversely.

From these results we conclude that if the values of x are given at equal intervals, and those of $\Delta^2 y$ are approximately equal, the proper formula is of the type $y = a + bx + cx^2$.

EXAMPLE. Find an empirical equation for the above table of values of t and T, regarding the former as the independent variable.

Solution. Here $\Delta t = 5$. Calculating ΔT and $\Delta^2 T$, we find that the latter is nearly constant and therefore assume a relation of the type

$$T = a + bt + ct^2.$$

(i) *Method of averages.* Dividing the data into three groups and substituting for t and T, we obtain the following equations:

$$
\begin{aligned}
15.1 &= a \\
20.0 &= a + 5b + 25c \\
24.4 &= a + 10b + 100c \\
\hline
59.5 &= 3a + 15b + 125c
\end{aligned}
\tag{1}
$$

$$
\begin{aligned}
28.4 &= a + 15b + 225c \\
32.0 &= a + 20b + 400c \\
\hline
60.4 &= 2a + 35b + 625c
\end{aligned}
\tag{2}
$$

$$
\begin{aligned}
35.2 &= a + 25b + 625c \\
38.1 &= a + 30b + 900c \\
\hline
73.3 &= 2a + 55b + 1525c
\end{aligned}
\tag{3}
$$

Subtracting equation (2) from equation (3) and dividing by 20, we get

$$b + 45c = 0.645. \tag{4}$$

Multiplying equation (1) by 2 and equation (2) by 3, subtracting, and dividing the result by 25, we get

$$3b + 65c = 2.488. \tag{5}$$

Now eliminate b from equations (4) and (5). This gives

$$c = -0.0079.$$

Hence $b = 1.00^{+}$. Substituting $b = 1$ and $c = -0.0079$ in equation (1) gives finally $a = 15.2$.

Our formula is then

$$T = 15.2 + t - 0.0079t^2.$$

The calculated values of $T(T_c)$ are seen to agree almost exactly with the given values.

(ii) *Method of moments.* In order to avoid large numbers we first substitute $t = 5u$. It is convenient to arrange the work as follows. Then we have for the observed values:

u	T	uT	u^2T
0	15.1	0	0
1	20.0	20.0	20.0
2	24.4	48.8	97.6
3	28.4	85.2	255.6
4	32.0	128.0	512.0
5	35.2	176.0	880.0
6	38.1	228.6	1371.6
	193.2	686.6	3136.8

0th moment = 193.2

1st moment = 686.6

2d moment = 3136.8

For the calculated values we have:

u	T_c	uT_c	u^2T_c
0	a	0	0
1	$a + b + c$	$a + b + c$	$a + b + c$
2	$a + 2b + 4c$	$2a + 4b + 8c$	$4a + 8b + 16c$
3	$a + 3b + 9c$	$3a + 9b + 27c$	$9a + 27b + 81c$
4	$a + 4b + 16c$	$4a + 16b + 64c$	$16a + 64b + 256c$
5	$a + 5b + 25c$	$5a + 25b + 125c$	$25a + 125b + 625c$
6	$a + 6b + 36c$	$6a + 36b + 216c$	$36a + 216b + 1296c$
	$7a + 21b + 91c$	$21a + 91b + 441c$	$91a + 441b + 2275c$

Equating the corresponding moments for the observed and calculated values, we obtain the normal equations:

$$7a + 21b + 91c = 193.2$$
$$21a + 91b + 441c = 686.6$$
$$91a + 441b + 2275c = 3136.8.$$

Solving these simultaneously, we find that $a = 15.14$, $b = 5.02$, and $c = -0.2$. This gives

$$T = 15.14 + 5.02u - 0.2u^2.$$

As $u = \dfrac{t}{5}$, the desired formula is

$$T = 15.14 + 1.004t - 0.008t^2,$$

a result differing little from that obtained by the method of averages.

PROBLEMS

1. Find a formula of the type $y = a + bx^2$ approximately satisfied by the following sets of values.

(a) x	y	(b) x	y	(c) x	y	(d) x	y
0.1	2.80	5	0.244	4.5	4.26	4.4	16.0
0.2	2.79	7	0.284	6.2	5.14	5.0	17.8
0.3	2.77	9	0.335	7.0	5.71	5.5	19.4
0.4	2.75	10	0.367	8.6	6.93	6.0	21.1
0.5	2.72	11	0.402	9.6	7.86	6.3	22.3
0.6	2.69	12	0.440			6.7	23.7
0.7	2.65	13	0.481				
0.8	2.60	14	0.525				

2. Find a formula of the type $y = a + \dfrac{b}{x}$ approximately satisfied by the following sets of values.

(a)

x	y
2	5.0
4	10.8
6	12.6
8	13.5
10	14.1
12	14.4

(b)

x	y
1	7.95
2	5.75
3	5.00
4	4.65
5	4.40
6	4.25
7	4.15
8	4.10

(c)

x	y
80	0.0156
60	0.0153
45	0.0148
35	0.0144
30	0.0140
25	0.0136
20	0.0127
15	0.0115

(d)

x	y
12.3	11.9
10.5	12.4
8.8	12.6
7.0	12.9
5.3	13.8
4.2	14.4

3. Find a formula of the type $y = a + bx + cx^2$ approximately satisfied by the following sets of values.

(a)

x	y
0	370
2	333
4	295
6	256
8	216
10	174

(b)

x	y
0	0.027
1	0.066
2	0.108
3	0.153
4	0.202
5	0.254
6	0.309
7	0.368
8	0.431

(c)

x	y
15	26
20	36
25	48
30	61
35	76
40	93
45	112
50	133
60	179

4. The time (n yr.) required for money to double itself at compound interest is given in the following table for various rates (i %). Express n as a function of i.

i	2	3	4	5	6	7	8	9	10
n	35.0	23.4	17.7	14.2	11.9	10.2	9.0	8.0	7.3

5. The following table gives the melting point ($T°$ C.) of an alloy of zinc and lead containing x% of lead. Express T as a function of x.

x	40	50	60	70	80	90
T	186	205	226	250	276	304

6. The following table gives the average weight (W lb.) for men aged 32 of various heights (h in.). Express W as a function of h.

h	64	65	66	67	68	69	70	71	72	73	74
W	137	141	145	149	154	158	163	168	174	180	186

7. The following table gives the time of flight (t sec.) of a certain projectile for various ranges (R thousand yards). Express t as a function of R.

R	1	2	3	4	5	6
t	2.1	4.7	7.8	11.2	15.1	19.4

8. The following table gives the mean temperature ($T°$ C.) at various depths (x meters) in a certain artesian well. Express T as a function of x.

x	200	400	600	800	1000	1200
T	16.2	19.5	22.6	25.4	27.9	30.2

9. The following table shows the velocity (v mi./hr.) of a stream at various depths (x tenths of the total depth). Express v as a function of x.

x	0	1	2	3	4	5	6	7	8
v	2.91	3.31	3.50	3.51	3.31	2.89	2.29	1.47	0.46

169. Equations of the form $y = kx^n$. Here k and n are unknown constants, whose values are to be determined. This type of equation can be reduced at once to the linear form by taking the logarithm of both members. This reduction gives $\log y = \log k + n \log x$. Setting $y' = \log y$, $k' = \log k$, and $x' = \log x$, we have $y' = k' + nx'$, an ordinary linear equation.

Hence, to fit a formula of this type to a set of values of x and y, we first tabulate the values of $x' = \log x$ and $y' = \log y$. We then plot the points (x', y') and, if these appear to lie on a line, we can then determine k' and n by any of the methods previously given.

EXAMPLE. Find a formula approximately satisfied by the table of values at the right.

x	y	$x' = \log x$	$y' = \log y$	y_c
10	1.06	1.0000	0.0253	1.06
20	1.33	1.3010	0.1239	1.33
30	1.52	1.4771	0.1818	1.52
40	1.68	1.6021	0.2253	1.67
50	1.81	1.6990	0.2577	1.80
60	1.91	1.7782	0.2810	1.92
70	2.01	1.8451	0.3032	2.02
80	2.11	1.9031	0.3243	2.11

Solution. Since the values of x are evenly spaced, we can easily show by calculating Δy and $\Delta^2 y$ that the desired formula is neither linear nor parabolic. Nor do the values of y appear to approach a definite limit.

We therefore look up the logarithms of x and y and tabulate them. Plotting the points (x', y'), we find that they lie nearly in a line. Hence the formula $y = kx^n$ is applicable and we begin with the linear relation $y' = k' + nx'$.

Proceeding by the method of averages, we have the following equations.

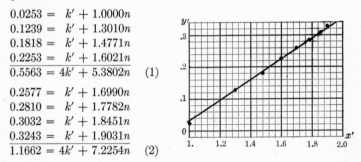

$$0.0253 = k' + 1.0000n$$
$$0.1239 = k' + 1.3010n$$
$$0.1818 = k' + 1.4771n$$
$$\underline{0.2253 = k' + 1.6021n}$$
$$0.5563 = 4k' + 5.3802n \quad (1)$$

$$0.2577 = k' + 1.6990n$$
$$0.2810 = k' + 1.7782n$$
$$0.3032 = k' + 1.8451n$$
$$\underline{0.3243 = k' + 1.9031n}$$
$$1.1662 = 4k' + 7.2254n \quad (2)$$

Solving equations (1) and (2) simultaneously, we obtain $k' = -0.3055$ and $n = 0.3305$. Thus $y' = -0.3055 + 0.3305x'$.

Since $k' = -0.3055$, $\log k = -0.3055 = 9.6945 - 10$, and so $k = 0.4949$. Hence $y = 0.4949x^{0.3305}$. The calculated values of y are given in the table.

170. Equations of the form $y = ke^{nx}$. As stated in § 118 many variables are connected by an exponential law of this kind. Since $\log_{10} e = 0.4343$ or $e = 10^{0.4343}$, the equation $y = ke^{nx}$ is equivalent to $y = k(10)^{n'x}$, where $n' = 0.4343n$. Taking logarithms of both sides, we have $\log y = \log k + n'x$. Setting $y' = \log y$ and $k' = \log k$, we have $y' = k' + n'x$.

Hence a formula of this type is indicated if the points (x, y'), where $y' = \log y$, lie approximately in a straight line. The method of finding k' and n' is the same as that used in the previous section.

EXAMPLE. Find a formula approximately satisfied by the following table of values.

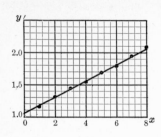

x	y	$y' = \log y$	y_c
1	15.3	1.1847	15.3
2	20.5	1.3118	20.5
3	27.4	1.4378	27.4
4	36.6	1.5635	36.7
5	49.1	1.6911	49.1
6	65.6	1.8169	65.6
7	87.8	1.9435	87.8
8	117.6	2.0704	117.5

Solution. It is easy to show that the proper formula is neither linear nor parabolic. Tabulating the values of $y' = \log y$ and plotting the points (x, y'), we find that these points lie nearly in a straight line. Hence the desired formula is of the form $y = ke^{nx}$, or $y = k(10)^{n'x}$.

Substituting the values of x and y' in the corresponding linear relation, $y' = k' + n'x$, we have

$$
\begin{aligned}
1.1847 &= k' + n' \\
1.3118 &= k' + 2n' \\
1.4378 &= k' + 3n' \\
1.5635 &= k' + 4n' \\
\hline
5.4978 &= 4k' + 10n' \quad (1)
\end{aligned}
\qquad
\begin{aligned}
1.6911 &= k' + 5n' \\
1.8169 &= k' + 6n' \\
1.9435 &= k' + 7n' \\
2.0704 &= k' + 8n' \\
\hline
7.5219 &= 4k' + 26n' \quad (2)
\end{aligned}
$$

Solving equations (1) and (2) simultaneously, we get $n' = 0.1265$ and $k' = 1.0582$. Hence $y' = 1.0582 + 0.1265x$.

Since $k' = \log k = 1.0582$, $k = 11.43$. Thus $y = 11.43(10)^{0.1265x}$. Using the relation $10 = e^{2.3026}$, we transform this at once into

$$y = 11.43e^{0.2913x}.$$

For computation purposes it is often better to leave this in the logarithmic form, $\log y = 1.0582 + 0.1265x$. This is also true for the type discussed in the previous section.

NOTE. The foregoing sections constitute only an introduction to the subject of empirical equations. Only a few of the simpler algebraic and exponential forms have been used and nothing has been given regarding periodic functions. For a more extensive treatment special textbooks on the subject should be consulted.

PROBLEMS

1. Find formulas of the type $y = kx^n$ approximately satisfied by the following sets of values.

(a) x	y
5	62
10	49
15	43
20	39
25	37
30	35

(b) x	y
5	0.57
10	0.87
25	1.50
50	2.29
100	3.47
150	4.42
200	5.25

(c) x	y
24	0.00305
26	0.00313
28	0.00321
30	0.00329
32	0.00336
34	0.00343

2. Find formulas of the type $y = ke^{nx}$ approximately satisfied by the following sets of values.

(a) x	y
0	64.9
1	59.9
2	55.3
3	51.0
4	47.2
6	40.1
8	34.2
10	29.2

(b) x	y
0	0.150
15	0.145
46	0.135
79	0.125
116	0.115
177	0.100

(c) x	y
0	73
5	89
10	108
15	131
20	163
25	197
30	241

3. The following table gives the number (N) of bacteria per unit volume in a certain culture at various times (t hr.). Express N as a function of t.   ($N = ke^{nt}$.)

t	0	1	2	3	4	5	6	7
N	20	26	33	42	54	70	90	115

4. The dip of the horizon (D'') at various heights (h ft.) is given in the following table.   Express D as a function of h.   ($D = kh^n$.)

h	10	20	30	40	50	60
D	186	263	322	372	416	455

5. The following table gives the intercollegiate track records for various distances (t sec., d yd.).   Express t as a function of d.   ($t = kd^n$.)

d	100	220	440	880	1760	3520
t	9.6	20.9	47.0	111.0	254.4	562.0

6. The following table gives the difference between the temperature of a certain heated body and that of the air ($T°$) for various times (t min.). Express T as a function of t. ($T = ke^{nt}$.)

t	0	1	2	3	4	5	6	7
T	70.5	65.0	60.0	55.5	51.0	47.5	43.5	40.5

7. The following table gives the elongation (E in.) of a strong rubber band stretched by various tensions (T lb.). Express E as a function of T. ($E = kT^n$.)

T	1	2	3	4	5	6	7	8
E	0.04	0.12	0.24	0.36	0.52	0.68	0.88	1.08

8. The following table gives the time of revolution about the sun (T yr.) and the radius of the orbit (R million miles) for each of the planets. Express T as a function of R. ($T = kR^n$.)

R	36.0	67.2	92.9	141.5	483.3	886.0	1781.9	2791.6
T	0.24	0.62	1.00	1.88	11.86	29.46	84.02	164.78

9. The following table gives the population of the United States (N millions) for various years (t). Express N as a function of t. ($N = ke^{n(t-1800)}$.)

t	1800	1810	1820	1830	1840	1850	1860	1870
N	5.3	7.2	9.6	12.9	17.1	23.2	31.4	38.6

10. Find a formula of the type $p = Ce^{-kh}$ approximately satisfied by the data of Problem 9, page 244.

CHAPTER XIII

SOLID ANALYTIC GEOMETRY

171. Introduction. Plane analytic geometry deals with the properties of figures which are wholly contained in a single plane; in solid analytic geometry this restriction is removed. The effect of the addition of one dimension is to generalize the work of the previous chapters, the number of variables being increased to three, the loci of equations being surfaces, etc. As might be expected, many of the formulas can be inferred at once from the corresponding formulas of plane analytic geometry, but in other cases the generalization is not so obvious. The following sections contain an outline of the principal features, such as those encountered in elementary courses in the calculus; for a detailed treatment more advanced texts should be consulted.

172. Cartesian coördinates. The position of a point is determined with reference to three mutually perpendicular planes, *XOY*, *YOZ*, and *XOZ*. These are called the *coördinate planes*, and designated as the *xy-*, *yz-*, and *xz-planes* respectively. Their lines of intersection, *OX*, *OY*, and *OZ*, are called *coördinate axes* and designated as the *x-*, *y-*, and *z-axes* respectively; and their common point, *O*, is called the *origin*.

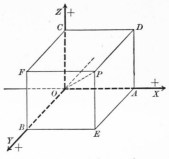

The *coördinates* of a point *P* are its distances from the respective coördinate planes measured parallel to the coördinate axes. The *x-coördinate* is the distance from the *yz*-plane parallel to the *x*-axis, the *y-coördinate* that from the *xz*-plane parallel to the *y*-axis, and the *z-coördinate* that from the *xy*-

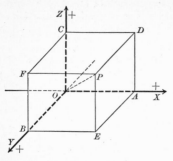

plane parallel to the *z*-axis. For the point *P* in the figure,

$$x = FP = BE = CD = OA,$$
$$y = DP = AE = CF = OB,$$
$$z = EP = BF = AD = OC.$$

Corresponding to each point there are evidently always three coördinates. Conversely, a point is completely located by its coördinates, which are written in the order (x, y, z). For the *x*-coördinate fixes it in a plane parallel to the *yz*-plane (or perpendicular to the *x*-axis), and similarly for the other coordinates; and these three planes meet in but one point. In plotting a point, we usually take

$$x = OA, \quad y = AE, \quad z = EP.$$

The positive directions are as indicated in the figure. The coördinate planes divide space into eight *octants*, which are distinguished by the signs of the coördinates of the points within them. For example, the octant containing *P* in the figure has all the coördinates positive in sign; it is often called the first octant.

173. Radius vector and direction cosines. The distance from the origin to a point is called the *radius vector* of the point, and is denoted by ρ.

For the point *P* in the figure $\rho = OP$. It is evident that

$$\rho^2 = \overline{OE}^2 + \overline{EP}^2$$
$$= \overline{OA}^2 + \overline{AE}^2 + \overline{EP}^2.$$

Hence $\rho^2 = x^2 + y^2 + z^2.$ **(54)**

The angles between the line *OP* and the positive halves of

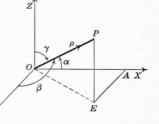

the x-, y- and z-axes are called the *direction angles* of the line OP and are denoted by α, β, and γ, respectively. The cosines of these angles are called the *direction cosines* of the line. They evidently fix its direction. From the figure it is readily seen that

$$x = \rho \cos \alpha, \qquad y = \rho \cos \beta, \qquad z = \rho \cos \gamma. \qquad (55)$$

Formulas 54 and 55 give at once the important relation

$$\cos^2 \alpha + \cos^2 \beta + \cos^2 \gamma = 1. \qquad (56)$$

It is sometimes convenient to locate a point by means of its radius vector and its direction angles. In this case we write

$$P(x, y, z) \equiv P(\rho, \alpha, \beta, \gamma).$$

This mode of representation is analogous to the polar coördinate system in plane analytic geometry.

Exercise 1. Explain why, in spite of Formula 56, the position of a point is not completely determined by the values of ρ and two direction cosines.

174. Distance between two points. Theorem. *The distance between any two points $P_1(x_1, y_1, z_1)$ and $P_2(x_2, y_2, z_2)$ is given by the formula,*

$$d = \sqrt{(x_1 - x_2)^2 + (y_1 - y_2)^2 + (z_1 - z_2)^2}. \qquad (57)$$

To prove this, pass planes through the given points P_1 and P_2, parallel to the coördinate planes. These will form a rectangular parallelopiped, of which P_1P_2 is the diagonal.

By elementary geometry,

$$\overline{P_1P_2}^2 = \overline{P_2A}^2 + \overline{AD}^2 + \overline{DP_1}^2.$$

But $P_2A = x_1 - x_2$, $AD = y_1 - y_2$, and $DP_1 = z_1 - z_2$. Hence we have the required formula.

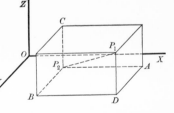

175. Direction of a line. *The direction angles of a line not passing through the origin are defined as the direction angles of a parallel line through the origin with the same positive direction.*

The positive direction on a line is arbitrary and indicated by the order in which its end points are read.* It is evident that if the direction is changed, the direction angles are replaced by their supplements. Thus, if the direction angles of P_2P_1 are α, β, and γ, those of P_1P_2 are $\pi - \alpha$, $\pi - \beta$, and $\pi - \gamma$. In all cases the direction angles are in value between 0 and π.

In the figure of § 174 the edges of the parallelopiped are parallel to the coördinate axes; hence the direction angles of the line P_2P_1 are:

$$\alpha = AP_2P_1, \qquad \beta = BP_2P_1, \qquad \gamma = CP_2P_1.$$

Then we have at once

$$\cos \alpha = \frac{x_1 - x_2}{d}, \quad \cos \beta = \frac{y_1 - y_2}{d}, \quad \cos \gamma = \frac{z_1 - z_2}{d}. \quad (58)$$

Since the direction cosines are connected by Formula 56, they may be found if three numbers to which they are proportional are known. For if

$$\cos \alpha : \cos \beta : \cos \gamma = a : b : c,$$

then

$$\frac{\cos^2 \alpha}{a^2} = \frac{\cos^2 \beta}{b^2} = \frac{\cos^2 \gamma}{c^2} = \frac{\cos^2 \alpha + \cos^2 \beta + \cos^2 \gamma}{a^2 + b^2 + c^2}$$

$$= \frac{1}{a^2 + b^2 + c^2},$$

whence

$$\cos \alpha = \frac{a}{\sqrt{a^2 + b^2 + c^2}}, \quad \cos \beta = \frac{b}{\sqrt{a^2 + b^2 + c^2}},$$

$$\cos \gamma = \frac{c}{\sqrt{a^2 + b^2 + c^2}}.$$

Any three numbers proportional to the direction cosines of a line are called *direction numbers* of the line.

* If it is desired to establish conventions defining the positive direction on any line, the following agree with those of § 6. If $\cos \gamma \neq 0$, the positive direction is that for which $\cos \gamma$ is positive; if $\cos \gamma = 0$ and $\cos \beta \neq 0$, the positive direction is that for which $\cos \beta$ is positive; if $\cos \gamma$ and $\cos \beta$ are both zero, the positive direction is that for which $\cos \alpha$ is positive, i.e., $\alpha = 0$.

176. Angle between two lines. *The angle between two lines which do not meet is defined as the angle between two intersecting lines parallel to the given lines and having the same positive directions.* If the lines are parallel, the angle between them is 0 or π, according to their directions.

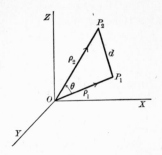

We now derive a formula for the angle between two lines in terms of their direction cosines. Let the lines through the origin parallel to the given lines be OP_1 and OP_2, where the coördinates of P_1 and P_2 are (x_1, y_1, z_1) and (x_2, y_2, z_2) respectively. Let d be the distance between these points, let ρ_1 and ρ_2 be their radii vectores, and let θ be the angle between the lines. Then

$$\cos \theta = \frac{\rho_1{}^2 + \rho_2{}^2 - d^2}{2\rho_1\rho_2}.$$

But

$$\rho_1{}^2 = x_1{}^2 + y_1{}^2 + z_1{}^2,$$
$$\rho_2{}^2 = x_2{}^2 + y_2{}^2 + z_2{}^2,$$
$$d^2 = (x_1 - x_2)^2 + (y_1 - y_2)^2 + (z_1 - z_2)^2.$$

$$\therefore \cos \theta = \frac{x_1x_2 + y_1y_2 + z_1z_2}{\rho_1\rho_2}.$$

Now Formula (55) gives $\dfrac{x_1}{\rho_1} = \cos \alpha_1$, etc. Hence this last equation becomes

$$\cos \theta = \cos \alpha_1 \cos \alpha_2 + \cos \beta_1 \cos \beta_2 + \cos \gamma_1 \cos \gamma_2. \quad \textbf{(59)}$$

When the two lines are parallel, we have

$$\alpha_1 = \alpha_2, \qquad \beta_1 = \beta_2, \qquad \text{and} \quad \gamma_1 = \gamma_2,$$
$$\text{or} \quad \alpha_1 = \pi - \alpha_2, \quad \beta_1 = \pi - \beta_2, \quad \text{and} \quad \gamma_1 = \pi - \gamma_2.$$

When the two lines are perpendicular, $\theta = \dfrac{\pi}{2}$ and (59) becomes

$$\cos \alpha_1 \cos \alpha_2 + \cos \beta_1 \cos \beta_2 + \cos \gamma_1 \cos \gamma_2 = 0. \quad \textbf{(60)}$$

PROBLEMS

1. Plot each of the following sets of points and for each point find the radius vector and its direction cosines.

(a) (4, 3, 5), (0, 6, 0), (− 8, 1, 4);

(b) (− 2, 3, − 6), (3, − 4, 12), (4, 1, 8);

(c) (16, 2, 8), (− 6, 3, − 2), (5, 2, 14).

2. Plot each of the following sets of points and for each point find the radius vector and its direction cosines.

(a) (0, 0, 1), (0, 4, 0), (− 8, 0, 0);

(b) (− 4, 8, 1), (14, 5, − 2), (3, − 2, 6);

(c) (0, 3, 4), (− 5, 12, 0), (8, 0, 15).

3. For each set of points in Problem 2 find the angle between the line segments joining the first point to the other two.

4. Find the perimeters of the triangles whose vertices are given in Problem 1.

5. Generalize the definition of symmetry with respect to a line so that it will apply to symmetry with respect to a plane. Show that the point (x, y, z) is symmetrical to $(− x, y, z)$ with respect to the yz-plane; to $(x, − y, z)$ with respect to the xz-plane; to $(x, y, − z)$ with respect to the xy-plane.

6. Show that the point (x, y, z) is symmetrical to $(− x, − y, z)$ with respect to the z-axis; to $(− x, y, − z)$ with respect to the y-axis; to $(x, − y, − z)$ with respect to the x-axis.

7. Find the coördinates of the points for which $\rho = 8$, $\cos \alpha = \frac{2}{7}$, and $\cos \beta = − \frac{3}{7}$.

8. Show by two methods that the following are the vertices of a right triangle:

(a) (6, 7, 0), (3, 1, − 2), (8, 4, 6);

(b) (0, 4, − 2), (− 3, − 2, − 4), (2, 1, 4).

9. Find the area of each triangle in Problem 8.

10. Show that the following points are vertices of a regular tetrahedron:

(a) (− 4, 12, 2), (2, 6, 2), (− 4, 6, 8), (− 6, 4, 0);

(b) (a, 0, 0), (0, a, 0), (0, 0, a), (a, a, a).

11. Show that the points $(6, -2, 1)$, $(3, 1, 1)$, and $(3, -2, 4)$ are the vertices of an equilateral triangle. Also find the fourth vertex of a regular tetrahedron which has these points as three of its vertices.

12. Show that the coördinates of the point P_0 dividing the line P_1P_2 in the ratio $r_1 : r_2$ are

$$x_0 = \frac{r_2x_1 + r_1x_2}{r_1 + r_2}, \qquad y_0 = \frac{r_2y_1 + r_1y_2}{r_1 + r_2}, \qquad z_0 = \frac{r_2z_1 + r_1z_2}{r_1 + r_2}.$$

13. What is the locus of points for which

(a) $z = 0$;

(b) $y = k$;

(c) $y = x = 0$;

(d) $x = y$;

(e) $x = 3, z = -2$;

(f) $\rho = 6$;

(g) $\cos \alpha = 0$;

(h) $\cos \alpha = \cos \beta = 0$?

14. Show that the points $(1, 4, -2)$, $(5, 8, 1)$, and $(-7, -4, -8)$ are in a straight line.

15. Find the lengths of the medians of the triangle whose vertices are $(6, 3, -2)$, $(4, 5, 4)$, and $(-2, 1, 6)$.

16. Show that the points $(-3, -1, 5)$, $(3, -4, 7)$, $(0, 5, -1)$, and $(6, 2, 1)$ are the vertices of a parallelogram.

17. Three vertices of a parallelogram in order are $(4, 3, 5)$, $(0, 6, 0)$, and $(-8, 1, 4)$. Find the fourth vertex.

18. Two lines have direction numbers 2, 3, 6 and 3, 4, 12. Find the direction cosines of a line perpendicular to both of them.

19. A regular tetrahedron has edges of length a. Find formulas for (a) the volume; (b) the radius of the circumscribed sphere.

Hint. Problem 10(b) may be used, but note that the length of each edge in that problem is $a\sqrt{2}$.

20. Show that in any tetrahedron the lines from each vertex to the intersection of the medians of the opposite face meet in a point dividing these lines in the ratio $3 : 1$.

Hint. Take the vertices of the tetrahedron as $(3a, 0, 0)$, $(3b, 0, 0)$, $(0, 3c, 0)$, and $(3d, 3e, 3f)$, and use Problem 12.

21. Show that the three lines joining the mid-points of opposite edges of a tetrahedron bisect each other.

177. The locus in solid geometry. *The locus of a point in space satisfying a given condition is in general a surface.* To illustrate, consider the locus of a point at a given distance a from a given fixed point C. This is evidently the definition of the surface of a sphere of radius a and center C. Again the locus of a point at a constant distance a from a given straight line l is evidently a circular cylindrical surface having l as an axis and a as a radius.

Extending the definition of the equation of a locus given in Chapter II, this shows that the locus of a single equation in the three variables, x, y, and z, is in general a surface.

If the coördinates of a point satisfy *two* equations simultaneously, its locus must be common to the two surfaces which are the loci of the equations, i.e., it must be their intersection, which is a curve or set of curves. Finally the points determined by a set of *three* equations will be the intersections of the surface determined by the third with the curves determined by the first two, and hence will be isolated points. Note the analogy to plane analytic geometry, where *one* equation determines a curve, and *two* equations the isolated points in which the curves meet.

178. The normal equation of the plane.

The perpendicular upon a plane from the origin is known as the *normal axis* and

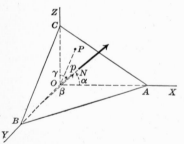

the distance of the plane from the origin is known as the *normal intercept*. A plane is completely determined if the length of the normal intercept p, and the direction angles, α, β, and γ, of the normal axis are known.

To find the normal equation of a plane, take any point $P(x, y, z)$ in the plane and join it to the origin. Draw the normal axis ON. Let ρ_1 be the radius vector of P, and α_1, β_1, γ_1 be its direction angles; let α, β, γ be the direction angles of ON; and let θ be the angle between OP and ON.

Then by Formula 59,

$$\cos \theta = \cos \alpha_1 \cos \alpha + \cos \beta_1 \cos \beta + \cos \gamma_1 \cos \gamma.$$

But $$\cos \theta = \frac{ON}{OP} = \frac{p}{\rho_1}.$$

Eliminating θ between these equations,

$$\rho_1[\cos \alpha_1 \cos \alpha + \cos \beta_1 \cos \beta + \cos \gamma_1 \cos \gamma] = p.$$

This becomes on applying (55),

$$x \cos \alpha + y \cos \beta + z \cos \gamma = p, \tag{61}$$

which is the *normal equation.**

Exercise 2. Show that for any point $P(x, y, z)$ not in the plane

$$x \cos \alpha + y \cos \beta + z \cos \gamma \gtrless p.$$

Exercise 3. Show that the distance from the plane

$$x \cos \alpha + y \cos \beta + z \cos \gamma - p = 0$$

to the point (x_1, y_1, z_1) is $x_1 \cos \alpha + y_1 \cos \beta + z_1 \cos \gamma - p$. Explain the significance of positive and negative results obtained by the use of this formula.

179. Plane parallel to one or more coördinate axes. Suppose that the plane is parallel to the z-axis. In this case the normal axis will lie in the xy-plane and $\gamma = \dfrac{\pi}{2}$. Hence (61) reduces to the form

$$x \cos \alpha + y \cos \beta = p. \tag{61a}$$

Similar equations are obtained for planes parallel to either of the other axes.

If the plane is parallel to both the y- and z-axes, the normal axis is the x-axis. Then $\beta = \gamma = \dfrac{\pi}{2}$, and $\alpha = 0$ or π. For this case (61) reduces to one of the forms

$$x = p \quad \text{or} \quad x = -p,$$

a result obvious from the definition of coördinates.

---

* This equation has been derived under the tacit assumption that the positive direction on the normal axis has been so chosen that p is positive. If it is desired to follow the conventions of the footnote on page 258, p may be negative. There will, however, be no change in the form of the equation. For reversing the direction of the normal axis merely changes the sign of each term, since each direction angle is replaced by its supplement.

180. The general equation of the first degree. The normal equation (61) of the plane is of the first degree. We shall now prove conversely that the locus of the general equation of the first degree

$$Ax + By + Cz + D = 0 \tag{62}$$

is a plane. To do this we simply show that (62) can always be reduced to the form (61).

Dividing both sides of the equation by $\pm \sqrt{A^2 + B^2 + C^2}$, we have

$$\frac{A}{\pm \sqrt{A^2 + B^2 + C^2}} x + \frac{B}{\pm \sqrt{A^2 + B^2 + C^2}} y$$

$$+ \frac{C}{\pm \sqrt{A^2 + B^2 + C^2}} z = \frac{-D}{\pm \sqrt{A^2 + B^2 + C^2}}.$$

By § 175 the coefficients of x, y, and z are direction cosines of a line. Hence this equation has the same form as (61) and its locus is a plane. The direction cosines of its normal axis are

$$\frac{A}{\pm \sqrt{A^2 + B^2 + C^2}}, \qquad \frac{B}{\pm \sqrt{A^2 + B^2 + C^2}},$$

$$\frac{C}{\pm \sqrt{A^2 + B^2 + C^2}}$$

and the length of its normal intercept is

$$\frac{-D}{\pm \sqrt{A^2 + B^2 + C^2}}.$$

The sign of the radical is taken opposite to that of D so that the normal intercept p shall be positive.* Comparison with (61a) shows that if any one of the three variables is missing the locus is a plane parallel to the corresponding axis.

---

* If it is desired to use the conventions in the footnotes of pp. 258 and 263, the sign of the radical should be taken the same as that of C if $C \neq 0$, the same as that of B if $C = 0$ and $B \neq 0$, or the same as that of A if both $C = 0$ and $B = 0$.

181. Plane perpendicular to a given line and passing through a given point. As a by-product of the previous section we note that in the general equation of the plane,

$$Ax + By + Cz + D = 0,$$

A, B, and C are direction numbers of the normal axis and any other line perpendicular to the plane. This enables us to write down at once the equation of a plane which passes through a given point and is perpendicular to a given line.

If the given line has direction numbers A, B, and C, any plane perpendicular to it has an equation of the form

$$Ax + By + Cz = k.$$

If the plane passes through the point (x_1, y_1, z_1), these coördinates satisfy this equation; hence

$$Ax_1 + By_1 + Cz_1 = k.$$

Subtracting these equations, we have the desired result:

$$A(x - x_1) + B(y - y_1) + C(z - z_1) = 0. \qquad (63)$$

This result can also be obtained from Formula 60.

182. Angle between two planes. When two planes intersect, two pairs of equal dihedral angles are formed, of which one pair are equal to the angle between the normal axes of the planes. We therefore define the angle between two planes as the angle between their normal axes. This can be found at once by Formula 59. If we wish to express $\cos \theta$ in terms of the coefficients of (62), substitution of the above values of the direction cosines gives

$$\cos \theta = \frac{AA' + BB' + CC'}{\sqrt{A^2 + B^2 + C^2} \cdot \sqrt{A'^2 + B'^2 + C'^2}}. \qquad (64)$$

Parallel planes. If two planes are parallel, their normal axes are the same. Hence their direction cosines are the same or numerically equal with unlike signs. This gives

$$\frac{A}{\sqrt{A^2 + B^2 + C^2}} = \frac{\pm A'}{\sqrt{A'^2 + B'^2 + C'^2}},$$

$$\frac{B}{\sqrt{A^2 + B^2 + C^2}} = \text{etc.}$$

By alternation we have

$$\frac{A}{A'} = \frac{\sqrt{A^2 + B^2 + C^2}}{\sqrt{A'^2 + B'^2 + C'^2}}, \qquad \frac{B}{B'} = \frac{\sqrt{A^2 + B^2 + C^2}}{\sqrt{A'^2 + B'^2 + C'^2}},$$

$$\frac{C}{C'} = \frac{\sqrt{A^2 + B^2 + C^2}}{\sqrt{A'^2 + B'^2 + C'^2}}.$$

This gives as the condition for parallelism,

$$\frac{A}{A'} = \frac{B}{B'} = \frac{C}{C'}. \tag{65}$$

Perpendicular planes. If the two planes are perpendicular to each other, cos θ = 0. Then from (64) we have at once

$$AA' + BB' + CC' = 0. \tag{66}$$

183. The intercept equation. The *intercepts* of a plane are the distances from the origin to the points in which it meets the x-, y-, and z-axes. They are denoted by a, b, and c, respectively.

If in equation (62) we set $y = z = 0$, we find that the x-intercept, a, is $-\dfrac{D}{A}$. Similarly $b = -\dfrac{D}{B}$, and $c = -\dfrac{D}{C}$. Hence by transposing D and dividing both sides by $-D$, equation (62) may be reduced at once to the form

$$\frac{x}{a} + \frac{y}{b} + \frac{z}{c} = 1, \tag{67}$$

which is known as the *intercept form* of the equation.

PROBLEMS

1. Write each of the following equations in the normal form and in the intercept form. In each case draw the lines of intersection of the given plane and the coördinate planes.

(a) $x - 4y + 8z = 36$;

(b) $3x + 4y - 12z = 52$;

(c) $2x - 8y + 16z = 81$;

(d) $4x - 3y = 100$;

(e) $2x - y + 2z + 81 = 0$;

(f) $3x - 2y + 6z + 49 = 0$.

2. The same as Problem 1 for the following equations:

(a) $2x + 3y - 6z = 56$; (d) $x + 2y - 2z + 36 = 0$;

(b) $2x - 5y + 14z = 60$; (e) $5x + 12z = 338$;

(c) $4x + 6y - 12z = 49$; (f) $5x + 2y - 14z + 225 = 0$.

3. Find the intersection of each plane in Problem 1 with its normal axis.

4. Find the intersection of each plane in Problem 2 with its normal axis.

5. Write the equations of the planes determined by the following data:

(a) $a = -9$, $b = \frac{9}{4}$, $c = -\frac{9}{8}$;

(b) $p = 8$, $\cos \alpha = \frac{2}{7}$, $\cos \gamma = -\frac{6}{7}$;

(c) passing through the points $(1, 1, 1)$, $(1, -2, 3)$, and $(-3, -4, 2)$;

(d) parallel to the plane $4x - 3y + 12z = 24$ and containing the point $(1, -4, 2)$.

6. Write the equations of the planes determined by the following data:

(a) perpendicular to the plane $2x + 3y - 6z = 56$, and containing the origin and the point $(2, 1, -4)$;

(b) meeting its normal axis at the point $(-2, -3, 6)$;

(c) parallel to the x-axis and containing the points $(-2, 1, 4)$ and $(-3, 2, -5)$;

(d) perpendicular to a line which has direction numbers 4, -3, and 12, and containing the point $(-5, 0, 8)$.

7. Find the angle between each of the planes in Problem 1 and the plane $2x + y - 2z = 18$.

8. Find the angle between each of the planes in Problem 2 and the plane $2x + y - 2z = 18$.

9. Find the angles at which each of the planes in Problem 2 meets the coördinate planes.

10. Using Exercise 3, find the distance from each of the planes of Problem 1 to the point $(3, 0, -2)$.

11. Using Exercise 3, find the distance from each of the planes of Problem 2 to the point $(3, -1, 4)$.

12. Find the locus of points equidistant from the points $(-2, 3, 1)$ and $(2, -2, -13)$.

13. Find the point of intersection of the following planes:

(a) Problem 1, (a), (b), (d);   (b) Problem 1, (d), (e), (f).

14. Show that the planes bisecting and perpendicular to the edges of the tetrahedron whose vertices are $(2, 4, 6)$, $(4, 2, 8)$, $(2, 10, -12)$, and $(6, -4, 2)$ meet in a point.

15. Find the locus of points which are equidistant from the planes $x - 4y + 8z = 36$ and $2x + y - 2z = 56$.

16. Find the volume of the tetrahedron in Problem 14.

17. What is the locus of each of the following equations:

(a) $z^2 - 5z + 6 = 0$;   (c) $x^2 - 2xy + y^2 - 4z^2 = 0$?

(b) $y^2 - z^2 = 0$;

18. Name all pairs of the following planes which are (i) parallel; (ii) perpendicular to each other:

(a) $3x - 5y - 2z = 80$;   (d) $2x + 4y - 7z = 28$;

(b) $x + 3y - 3z = 18$;   (e) $9x - 15y - 6z = 81$;

(c) $6x + 2y + 4z = 27$;   (f) $2x - 6y + 6z = 45$.

19. Prove that the sum of the lengths of the perpendiculars drawn to the faces of a regular tetrahedron from any point within it is equal to the altitude of the tetrahedron.

Hint. Use Exercise 3 and Problem 10(b), page 260.

184. Equations of the line. Since any straight line may be regarded as the intersection of two planes, it will be seen from §§ 177 and 180 that it requires *two* equations of the form

$$Ax + By + Cz + D = 0$$

to determine a straight line.

It is more convenient, however, to determine a line from two given points upon it, or from one point and its direction angles. From these we derive equations for the line. It should be noted that in each case *two* equations are required.

185. The symmetrical equations. Let the line pass through the point $P_1(x_1, y_1, z_1)$ and have direction angles α, β, and γ. If $P(x, y, z)$ is any point on the line and d denotes the distance P_1P, then by Formula 58

$$\cos \alpha = \frac{x - x_1}{d}, \qquad \cos \beta = \frac{y - y_1}{d}, \qquad \cos \gamma = \frac{z - z_1}{d}.$$

These relations give

$$\frac{x - x_1}{\cos \alpha} = \frac{y - y_1}{\cos \beta} = \frac{z - z_1}{\cos \gamma}, \tag{68}$$

which are the *symmetrical equations.*

If a point P_1 and the direction numbers of the line a, b. and c are known, a more convenient form to use is

$$\frac{x - x_1}{a} = \frac{y - y_1}{b} = \frac{z - z_1}{c}. \tag{68a}$$

186. The two-point equations. Let the line be determined by the points $P_1(x_1, y_1, z_1)$ and $P_2(x_2, y_2, z_2)$. Then from (58) the difference of the respective coördinates are direction numbers. Hence by substituting $x_1 - x_2$, $y_1 - y_2$, and $z_1 - z_2$ for a, b, and c, respectively, in (68a) we obtain the *two-point equations*

$$\frac{x - x_1}{x_1 - x_2} = \frac{y - y_1}{y_1 - y_2} = \frac{z - z_1}{z_1 - z_2}. \tag{68b}$$

187. The parametric equations. If we set t equal to the common value of the three fractions in (68a) and solve for x, y, and z, we obtain the *parametric equations:*

$$x = x_1 + at,$$
$$y = y_1 + bt, \tag{68c}$$
$$z = z_1 + ct.$$

Note that, if a, b, and c are the direction cosines of the line, the parameter t is the (directed) distance along the line from the fixed point (x_1, y_1, z_1) to the tracing point (x, y, z).

188. The projection forms. Let the equations of the projections of the given line on the xy- and xz-planes respectively be

$$y = kx + m,$$
$$z = lx + n. \tag{69}$$

These equations taken together determine the line.

For each equation may be regarded as the equation of the projecting plane. For example, the first by Formula 61a is the equation of a plane parallel to the z-axis and hence perpendicular to the xy-plane. But it contains all points satisfying the relation $y = kx + m$ and so must contain the given projection. Similarly, the other equation is that of the plane projecting the line on the xz-plane. Thus the line is determined as the intersection of its projecting planes.

189. Reduction of the general equations of a line to the standard forms. Consider the line determined by the equations

$$4x + y - z + 2 = 0,$$
$$x + 4y + 2z - 1 = 0.$$

To reduce these to the projection forms, eliminate first z and then y between the equations. We have at once,

$$3x + 2y + 1 = 0, \qquad 5x - 2z + 3 = 0.$$

That the locus of these equations is the same as the locus of those given is obvious, since coördinates satisfying the first pair of equations must satisfy the last.

To reduce the given equations to the symmetrical form solve the projection forms for x. We have

$$x = \frac{2y + 1}{-3}, \qquad x = \frac{2z - 3}{5}.$$

Equating these, we have

$$\frac{x}{1} = \frac{y + \frac{1}{2}}{-\frac{3}{2}} = \frac{z - \frac{3}{2}}{\frac{5}{2}}.$$

The denominators are direction numbers, and if we divide each one by $\sqrt{1^2 + (-\frac{3}{2})^2 + (\frac{5}{2})^2} = \frac{1}{2}\sqrt{38}$ they become direction cosines by § 175. Doing so, we get

$$\frac{x}{\frac{2}{\sqrt{38}}} = \frac{y + \frac{1}{2}}{\frac{-3}{\sqrt{38}}} = \frac{z - \frac{3}{2}}{\frac{5}{\sqrt{38}}},$$

which are the symmetrical equations of a line having direction cosines $\dfrac{2}{\sqrt{38}}, \dfrac{-3}{\sqrt{38}}, \dfrac{5}{\sqrt{38}}$, and passing through the point $(0, -\frac{1}{2}, \frac{3}{2})$.

But these are merely transformations of the original equations, and hence are the forms required.

Exercise 4. A line has the equations $A_1x + B_1y + C_1z + D_1 = 0$ and $A_2x + B_2y + C_2z + D_2 = 0$. Show that this line has direction numbers $B_1C_2 - B_2C_1$, $C_1A_2 - C_2A_1$, and $A_1B_2 - A_2B_1$.

PROBLEMS

1. Find the points where the following lines cut the coördinate planes and draw the lines:

(a) $3x - 2y - 6z + 9 = 0$, $x + 4y - 8z + 16 = 0$;

(b) $4x - 2z + 15 = 0$, $3x - y = 6$;

(c) $4x - 3y - 3z = 7$, $2x + y + 6z = 6$;

(d) $5x + z = 13$, $3y + 3z + 1 = 0$.

2. Reduce the equations in Problem 1 to the projection forms, the projecting planes being perpendicular to the xy- and yz-planes.

3. Reduce the equations in Problem 1 to the symmetrical forms.

4. Write in parametric form the equations of each line in Problem 1, taking (x_1, y_1, z_1) as the point where the line meets the xy-plane.

5. Find the equations of the straight lines determined as follows:

(a) passing through the points $(1, -5, -8)$ and $(3, -2, -2)$;

(b) passing through the point $(3, 2, -5)$ and parallel to the z-axis;

(c) passing through the point $(3, 2, -5)$ and having direction numbers 3, 4, and 12;

(d) passing through the point $(3, 2, -5)$ and perpendicular to the z-axis;

(e) passing through the point $(3, 2, -5)$ and having $\cos \alpha = \frac{1}{9}$ and $\cos \gamma = \frac{4}{9}$;

(f) passing through the point $(3, 2, -5)$ and parallel to the line of Problem 1(c);

(g) passing through the point $(3, 2, -5)$ and perpendicular to the plane $3x - 2y - 6z + 9 = 0$;

(h) passing through the point $(3, 2, -5)$ and perpendicular to two lines having direction numbers 2, 3, 6 and 2, 5, 14.

6. Do the lines of Problem 1(a) and (b) meet?

7. Find the equation of the plane which contains the line of Problem 1(c) and is perpendicular to the plane $2x - 5y - 4z = 20$.

Hint. Write the equation of a system of planes containing the given line and use Formula 66.

8. A line has direction numbers a, b, and c, and a plane has the equation $Ax + By + Cz + D = 0$. Show that the line and the plane are

(a) parallel if $aA + bB + cC = 0$;

(b) perpendicular if $a : A = b : B = c : C$.

9. Find in the symmetrical form the equations of the locus of points which are equidistant from the points $(3, -2, 4)$, $(5, 3, -2)$, and $(0, 4, 2)$.

10. Show that the line $x - 3y + 7 = 0$, $x - 2z - 4 = 0$

(a) is parallel to the plane $3x - 6y - 2z = 12$;

(b) lies in the plane $2x - 3y - 2z + 3 = 0$;

(c) is perpendicular to the plane $6x + 2y + 3z = 15$.

11. Find the perpendicular distance between the point $(4, 2, -3)$ and the line $x - 3y + 7 = 0$, $x - 2z - 4 = 0$.

12. Write the special cases of the forms of the equations of a straight line

(a) if it is parallel to the xy-plane;

(b) if it is parallel to the z-axis.

13. Three edges of a cube AB, AC, and AD meet at the vertex A. Prove that the plane containing the vertex D and the line joining the mid-points of the edges AB and AC is tangent to the sphere inscribed in the cube.

190. Cylindrical surfaces. *A cylindrical surface is a surface generated by a moving straight line which constantly intersects a given fixed curve and remains parallel to a fixed straight line.*

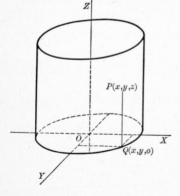

The fixed curve is called the *directrix* and the generating line the *generatrix*.

Let the directrix of a cylindrical surface ˈbe an ellipse in the xy-plane symmetrical with respect to the coördinate axes, and let the generatrix remain parallel to the z-axis. Then the equation of the ellipse in its plane will be

$$b^2x^2 + a^2y^2 = a^2b^2.$$

Let $P(x, y, z)$ be any point on the surface, and Q the corresponding point on the ellipse. Evidently the coördinates of Q will be $(x, y, 0)$; i.e., the x- and y-coördinates of every point on the line PQ are the same as those of Q. But the coördinates of Q satisfy the equation of the ellipse. Hence for any point on the cylindrical surface,

$$b^2x^2 + a^2y^2 = a^2b^2.$$

The preceding is perfectly general, and we see that it leads at once to the theorem:

A cylindrical surface whose directrix is a curve in the xy-plane and whose generatrix moves parallel to the z-axis, has the same equation as the directrix.

The converse, which is readily established, is:

The locus of an equation in two variables, x and y, is a cylindrical surface, whose directrix is the curve in the xy-plane which has the same equation, and whose generatrix moves parallel to the z-axis.

Similar theorems hold of course for cylinders whose generatrices are parallel to either the x- or y-axes.

Exercise 5. What is the locus of any equation in *one* variable?

191. Surfaces of revolution. *A surface generated by revolving a plane curve about a fixed line in its plane as an axis is called a surface of revolution.*

The curve is called the *generatrix;* its position with reference to the axis is unchanged during the revolution. Sections of the surface made by planes through the axis are called *meridional sections.* From the definition of such a surface it is evident that

(a) sections made by planes perpendicular to the axis are circles;

(b) any meridional section consists of two positions of the generatrix.

Let us first consider a conical surface generated by revolving a straight line about the z-axis. Let the position of the generatrix in the xz-plane be AB, of which the equation is

$$2x + z = 5.$$

Let $P(x, y, z)$ be any point of the locus. As the line turns about the z-axis, P describes a circle of radius $r = LP$ in a

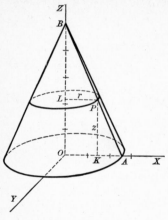

plane parallel to the xy-plane and distant from it $KP = z$. Now when the line is in the xz-plane, $x = r$; hence for all positions of the line,

$$2r + z = 5.$$

But, as P describes a circle of radius r in a plane parallel to the xy-plane,

$$x^2 + y^2 = r^2.$$

Substitution above gives

$$2\sqrt{x^2 + y^2} + z = 5.$$

Simplifying, we have the equation

$$4(x^2 + y^2) = (z - 5)^2.$$

Consider the surface generated by revolving about the x-axis a circle of radius a whose center is the origin. The equation of the generatrix in the xz-plane is

$$x^2 + z^2 = a^2.$$

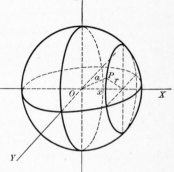

Evidently the point P describes a circle with its center on the x-axis and of radius r; hence

$$x^2 + r^2 = a^2.$$

But $\quad y^2 + z^2 = r^2.$

Hence we have at once,

$$x^2 + y^2 + z^2 = a^2. \quad \textbf{(70)}$$

This equation is important, as it is the equation of a sphere of radius a and with its center at the origin.

Exercise 6. What is the locus of any equation of the form $x^2 + y^2 = f(z)$?

PROBLEMS

1. Find the equation of the surface of a cone if its vertex is at the origin, the z-axis is its axis of revolution, and opposite elements are perpendicular to each other.

2. Describe and sketch the following surfaces:

(a) $x^2 + 4y^2 = 36$;

(b) $x^2 - 9y^2 = 36$;

(c) $y^2 + z^2 - 4y = 29$;

(d) $xy = 24$;

(e) $y^2 = 12z$;

(f) $x^2 + x - 6 = 0$.

3. Find the equation of the surface generated by revolving each plane curve about the axis indicated:

(a) $2x - y = 10$, x-axis;

(b) $x^2 = 2pz$, z-axis;   (Paraboloid of revolution)

(c) $b^2x^2 + a^2y^2 = a^2b^2$, x-axis;   (Ellipsoid of revolution)

(d) $b^2x^2 - a^2z^2 = a^2b^2$, z-axis;   (Hyperboloid of revolution)

(e) $yz = k$, y-axis;

(f) $z = e^{-x^2}$, z-axis;

(g) $z = e^{-x^2}$, x-axis.

4. Describe the following surfaces of revolution:

(a) $x^2 + z^2 = mx$;

(b) $b^2x^2 + a^2y^2 + a^2z^2 = a^2b^2$;

(c) $b^2x^2 + b^2y^2 - a^2z^2 = a^2b^2$;

(d) $x^2 + y^2 = 2pz$;

(e) $z(x^2 + y^2 + 4a^2) = 8a^3$;

(f) $x^2y^2 + x^2z^2 = 144$.

5. Find the equation of the locus of a point which is equidistant from a given plane and a given line parallel to the plane.

Hint. Let $x = -\dfrac{p}{2}$ be the given plane and $x = \dfrac{p}{2}$, $y = 0$ be the given line.

6. Show that the locus of a point equidistant from the point $(p, 0, 0)$ and the yz-plane is the paraboloid of revolution $y^2 + z^2 = 2px - p^2$.

7. Find the equation of the locus of a point in space such that the difference of its distances from the points $(0, 0, \pm c)$ is $2a$.

8. How may the hyperboloid $\dfrac{x^2}{a^2} - \dfrac{y^2}{b^2} - \dfrac{z^2}{b^2} = 1$ be defined as a locus?

9. Show that the locus of a point in space the sum of whose distances from the points $(\pm c, 0, 0)$ is $2a$ is the prolate spheroid

$$\frac{x^2}{a^2} + \frac{y^2}{b^2} + \frac{z^2}{b^2} = 1.$$

10. The ellipse $(x - 3)^2 + 4z^2 = 36$ is revolved about its minor axis. Find the equation of the ellipsoid of revolution thus generated.

11. Find the equation of the surface generated by revolving the circle $(x - h)^2 + z^2 = r^2$ about the z-axis. (This is called the *torus* or *anchor ring*.)

12. Find the equation of the surface generated by revolving the lemniscate $(x^2 + y^2)^2 = a^2(x^2 - y^2)$ about (a) the x-axis; (b) the y-axis. Describe the surface in each case.

192. Discussion of surfaces. The discussion of a surface is in general a more complicated matter than that of a curve. The notions of intercepts, symmetry, and extent are readily generalized. Besides these, however, we have two other methods which help to determine the nature of a surface. The first is to find the section of the surface by any of the coördinate planes; the second is to find the section of the surface by any plane parallel to one of the coördinate planes. The former is called a *trace* of the surface.

To illustrate these, consider the sphere, with equation

$$x^2 + y^2 + z^2 = a^2.$$

To find the equations of the traces, set x, y, and z successively equal to 0. When $x = 0$, we have

$$y^2 + z^2 = a^2.$$

Thus the yz-trace is a circle of radius a. The xy- and xz-traces are also circles of the same radius, with equations

$$x^2 + y^2 = a^2$$

and $\qquad x^2 + z^2 = a^2$, respectively.

The section made by a plane parallel to the yz-plane and at a distance c from it is the curve determined by the given equation and the equation $x = c$. Eliminating x between the two equations, we have

$$y^2 + z^2 = a^2 - c^2,$$

which shows that the section is a circle having the point $(c, 0, 0)$ as a center and $\sqrt{a^2 - c^2}$ as the radius. If $c > a$, this is imaginary, indicating that the surface lies wholly within the planes $x = \pm a$. A similar discussion holds for sections parallel to the other coördinate planes.

To sketch a surface when only two variables of its equation are of the same degree, or of the same degree and sign, first draw sections parallel to the plane of the two variables. These sections and the traces give the best representation of the locus.

193. Quadric surfaces. By analogy to the conics, the locus of the general equation of the second degree

$$Ax^2 + By^2 + Cz^2 + Dxy + Eyz + Fxz + Gx + Hy + Kz + L = 0$$

is called a *quadric surface*. It is evident that each of the three traces is a conic. Moreover, it can be shown that every plane section is a conic. For the degree of the equation is not changed by a translation or a rotation of the axes, and by a proper translation or rotation, or both, the cutting plane can be made a coördinate plane.* We shall not go into these details, but will confine our discussion to the simpler forms to which the general equation can be reduced.

194. The ellipsoid. The locus of the equation

$$\frac{x^2}{a^2} + \frac{y^2}{b^2} + \frac{z^2}{c^2} = 1 \qquad (71)$$

is called an ellipsoid.

* Let (x, y, z) and (x', y', z') be the coördinates of a point with respect to the old and the new axes, respectively. For a translation of the old origin to the point (h, k, l), we have

$$x = x' + h, \quad y = y' + k, \quad z = z' + l.$$

If the axes are rotated, and α_1, β_1, γ_1 are the direction angles of OX', α_2, β_2, γ_2 those of OY', and α_3, β_3, γ_3 those of OZ', with respect to the old axes, the formulas of rotation are:

$$x = x' \cos \alpha_1 + y' \cos \alpha_2 + z' \cos \alpha_3;$$
$$y = x' \cos \beta_1 + y' \cos \beta_2 + z' \cos \beta_3;$$
$$z = x' \cos \gamma_1 + y' \cos \gamma_2 + z' \cos \gamma_3.$$

These can be proved by observing that α_1, α_2, α_3 are the direction angles of OX, β_1, β_2, β_3 those of OY, and γ_1, γ_2, γ_3 those of OZ, with respect to the new axes, and using Exercise 3, page 263.

The form of the equation shows that the surface is symmetrical with respect to all of the coördinate planes and coördinate axes. The intercepts on the axes are

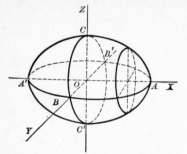

$$x = \pm a,$$
$$y = \pm b,$$
$$z = \pm c.$$

Setting $x = 0$, the equation becomes

$$\frac{y^2}{b^2} + \frac{z^2}{c^2} = 1;$$

hence the yz-trace is an ellipse with semiaxes b and c. In like manner the traces on the other coördinate planes are ellipses.

Setting $x = k$, the equation becomes $\dfrac{y^2}{b^2} + \dfrac{z^2}{c^2} = \dfrac{a^2 - k^2}{a^2}$, a form which shows that there is no section for k numerically greater than a. Dividing by the right-hand member, we obtain

$$\frac{y^2}{\dfrac{b^2}{a^2}(a^2 - k^2)} + \frac{z^2}{\dfrac{c^2}{a^2}(a^2 - k^2)} = 1.$$

Hence the various sections are ellipses symmetrical with respect to the x-axis. The semiaxes, $\dfrac{b}{a}\sqrt{a^2 - k^2}$ and $\dfrac{c}{a}\sqrt{a^2 - k^2}$, grow smaller as k increases, until the ellipse becomes a point when $k = a$. Similarly the sections parallel to the other coördinate planes are ellipses.

The values a, b, and c are called the semiaxes of the ellipsoid. When $a = b = c$, the ellipsoid is evidently a sphere with the center at the origin. Ordinarily the semiaxes are unequal, and in this form of the equation it is usually assumed that $a > b > c$. When $b = c$, but $a > b$ or c, the ellipsoid is called a prolate spheroid. In this case the sections parallel to the yz-plane are circles. The locus is then a surface of revolution since it is generated by revolving the xz-trace (or the xy-trace) about the

x-axis. When $a = b$, but $c < a$ or b, the surface is that of an oblate spheroid. This is also a surface of revolution and the sections parallel to the xy-plane are circles.

195. Hyperboloid of one sheet. The locus of the equation

$$\frac{x^2}{a^2} + \frac{y^2}{b^2} - \frac{z^2}{c^2} = 1 \qquad (72)$$

is called a hyperboloid of one sheet.

In this case sections parallel to the xy-plane, made by the planes $z = k$, have equations

$$\frac{x^2}{a^2} + \frac{y^2}{b^2} = 1 + \frac{k^2}{c^2}$$

and hence are ellipses which increase in size as the numerical value of k increases.

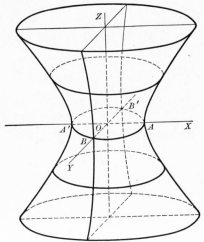

The xz-trace and the yz-trace are the hyperbolas

$$\frac{x^2}{a^2} - \frac{z^2}{c^2} = 1 \quad \text{and} \quad \frac{y^2}{b^2} - \frac{z^2}{c^2} = 1, \text{ respectively.}$$

If $a = b$, the locus is a surface of revolution about the z-axis.

Exercise 7. Describe the locus of the equation obtained from Formula 72 by substituting 0 for 1. How is this surface related to the hyperboloid?

196. Hyperboloid of two sheets. The locus of the equation

$$\frac{x^2}{a^2} - \frac{y^2}{b^2} - \frac{z^2}{c^2} = 1 \qquad (73)$$

is called the hyperboloid of two sheets.

In this case we consider sections parallel to the yz-plane made by the planes $x = k$. These are the ellipses

$$\frac{y^2}{b^2} + \frac{z^2}{c^2} = \frac{k^2}{a^2} - 1.$$

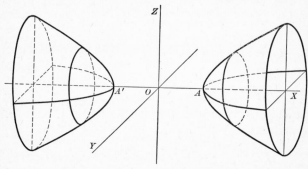

If $k^2 < a^2$ the right-hand member is negative. Hence no part of the locus is between the two planes $x = \pm a$. If $k = \pm a$, each corresponding section is a point ellipse. As k increases numerically from a to ∞ the section increases indefinitely.

The xy-trace and the xz-trace are the hyperbolas

$$\frac{x^2}{a^2} - \frac{y^2}{b^2} = 1 \quad \text{and} \quad \frac{x^2}{a^2} - \frac{z^2}{c^2} = 1, \text{respectively.}$$

If $b = c$, the locus is a surface of revolution.

Exercise 8. Describe the locus of the equation obtained from Formula 73 by substituting 0 for 1. How is this surface related to the hyperboloid?

197. Elliptic paraboloid. This is the locus of the equation

$$\frac{x^2}{a^2} + \frac{y^2}{b^2} = 2cz. \qquad (74)$$

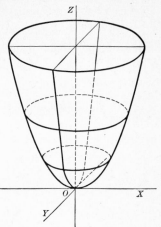

Proceeding as before, we observe that sections made by the planes $z = k$ are ellipses whose axes increase indefinitely as k increases. The surface lies wholly above or wholly below the xy-plane, according as c is positive or negative. The xz- and yz-traces are parabolas. If $a = b$, the locus is a surface of revolution.

198. Hyperbolic paraboloid. This is the locus of the equation

$$\frac{x^2}{a^2} - \frac{y^2}{b^2} = 2cz. \qquad (75)$$

Consider c positive. Sections made by the planes $z = k$ are the hyperbolas

$$\frac{x^2}{a^2} - \frac{y^2}{b^2} = 2ck.$$

As k increases from 0 to ∞ the vertices of the corresponding sections lie in the xz-plane and recede indefinitely from the

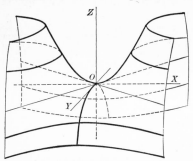

z-axis. As k decreases from 0 to $-\infty$ the vertices of the sections are in the yz-plane and recede indefinitely from the z-axis. The xz- and yz-traces are parabolas, each having its vertex at the origin, the former extending above the xy-plane, the latter below. The xy-trace is a pair of lines intersecting at the origin.

PROBLEMS

1. Identify and sketch each of the following quadric surfaces:

(a) $4x^2 + 9y^2 + 24z = 0$; (f) $4x^2 + y^2 - z^2 + 64 = 0$;

(b) $x^2 + 4y^2 - 9z^2 = 144$; (g) $x^2 + 4y^2 + 4z^2 = 64$;

(c) $x^2 + 4y^2 + 9z^2 = 144$; (h) $4x^2 - y^2 + 12z = 0$;

(d) $x^2 - 4y^2 = 16z$; (i) $x^2 + z^2 = 12y$;

(e) $x^2 - 4y^2 - 9z^2 = 144$; (j) $9x^2 + 25y^2 - 16z^2 = 225$.

2. Discuss and sketch each of the following surfaces:

(a) $x^2 = y^2 + 9z^2$; (f) $y^2 - x^2 - 4z^2 = 64$;

(b) $x^2 + 4z^2 = 16y$; (g) $x^{\frac{2}{3}} + y^{\frac{2}{3}} + z^{\frac{2}{3}} = a^{\frac{2}{3}}$;

(c) $z = 4 - y - x^2$; (h) $xyz = a^3$;

(d) $x^2 - y^2 + 4z^2 = 36$; (i) $(x - y)^2 = 4z$;

(e) $\sqrt{x} + \sqrt{y} + \sqrt{z} = \sqrt{a}$; (j) $x^2 + y^2 + z^2 - 8x = 0$.

3. Name each quadric surface in Problem 2.

4. What is the equation of a sphere which has the center (h, k, l) and the radius r?

5. The surfaces in Exercises 7 and 8, §§ 195, 196, are called *quadric cones.* Show that the line joining each point P of a quadric cone to the origin O (the vertex) lies wholly in the surface.

Hint. How are the coördinates of any point Q on OP related to those of P?

6. Find the traces of the surface

$$4k^2(y^2 + z^2) = (x^2 + y^2 + z^2 + k^2 - r^2)^2$$

and describe the surface.

Hint. The equation of each trace can be factored.

7. Show that the section of the surface in Problem 6 by the plane $z = r$ is a Cassinian curve. (See § 137.)

8. Show that the section of the special type of torus

$$(x^2 + y^2 + z^2 + 3r^2)^2 = 16r^2(x^2 + y^2)$$

made by the plane $x = r$ is a lemniscate. (See § 137.)

9. Similar rectangular parallelopipeds with faces parallel to the coördinate planes are inscribed in and circumscribed about the ellipsoid $\dfrac{x^2}{a^2} + \dfrac{y^2}{b^2} + \dfrac{z^2}{c^2} = 1$. Find the volume of the inscribed parallelopiped.

10. Find the equation of the sphere circumscribed about the regular tetrahedron whose vertices are $(a, 0, 0)$, $(0, a, 0)$, $(0, 0, a)$, and (a, a, a).

11. Find the locus of a point whose distance from the x-axis is twice its distance from the y-axis.

12. The base of a solid is a circle of radius a and cross sections perpendicular to a fixed diameter of the base are equilateral triangles. Choosing coördinate axes in a suitable manner, find the equations of the surfaces bounding the solid.

13. The same as Problem 12, except that each cross section is an isosceles triangle whose altitude is a and whose base is a chord of the circle.

199. Cylindrical coördinates. Polar coördinates in space were described in § 173. Two other somewhat similar systems

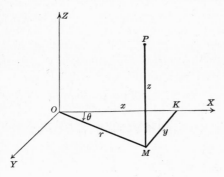

of coördinates which are useful in applications of analytic geometry will be described in this and the following section. In the cylindrical system the point $P(x, y, z)$ is located by coördinates r, θ, and z, where r and θ are the polar coördinates in the xy-plane of the projection $(x, y, 0)$ of the point P. These coördinates are written (r, θ, z). The relations between cylindrical and rectangular coördinates are:

$$x = r \cos \theta, \quad y = r \sin \theta, \quad z = z; \qquad (76)$$

or $$r^2 = x^2 + y^2, \quad \theta = \arc \tan \frac{y}{x}. \qquad (76a)$$

Cylindrical coördinates are convenient in problems involving surfaces of revolution, where the axis of revolution is the z-axis or a line parallel to it. Thus the equation of a cylindrical surface whose axis is the z-axis and whose radius is a is simply $r = a$; if the axis is the line $x = a$, $y = 0$, the equation is $r = 2a \cos \theta$.

200. Spherical coördinates.

The spherical coördinates of a point are its radius vector ρ, the angle ϕ between the radius vector and the z-axis, and the angle θ between the projection of the radius vector on the xy-plane and the x-axis. They are written (ρ, θ, ϕ). The angle ϕ is called the *colatitude* and θ the *longitude* of the point. It is clear that angle ϕ is identical with the direction angle γ of the radius vector and has any value between 0 and π. Angle θ may have any value, as in polar coördinates in the plane, the positive direction of rotation being from OX to OY.

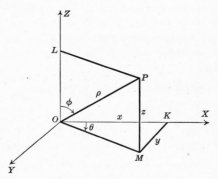

From the right triangles OMP, OKM, and OLP we obtain the formulas:

$$x = \rho \sin \phi \cos \theta, \quad y = \rho \sin \phi \sin \theta, \quad z = \rho \cos \phi. \qquad (77)$$

These may be transformed into

$$\rho^2 = x^2 + y^2 + z^2, \; \theta = \arctan \frac{y}{x}, \; \phi = \arccos \frac{z}{\sqrt{x^2 + y^2 + z^2}}. \qquad (77a)$$

PROBLEMS

1. Find spherical coördinates for the following points:

(a) $(4, 2, -4)$;   (c) $(1, -\sqrt{3}, 4)$;

(b) $(-3, 4, 12)$;   (d) $(8, 2, 16)$.

2. Find cylindrical coördinates for the points in Problem 1.

3. Find rectangular coördinates for the following points given in cylindrical coördinates:

(a) $\left(6, \dfrac{2\pi}{3}, -2\right)$;   (c) $\left(12, -\dfrac{\pi}{2}, 5\right)$;

(b) $(10, \text{arc cos } \tfrac{3}{5}, 4)$;   (d) $\left(8, \dfrac{4\pi}{3}, -4\right)$.

4. Find rectangular coördinates for the following points given in spherical coördinates:

(a) $(8, 45°, 60°)$;   (c) $(10, 150°, 120°)$;

(b) $\left(6, -\dfrac{\pi}{2}, \dfrac{\pi}{6}\right)$;   (d) $\left(8, \dfrac{7\pi}{6}, \dfrac{3\pi}{4}\right)$.

5. A right circular cone is generated by revolving about the z-axis the triangle whose vertices are $(0, 0, 0)$, $(0, 0, 8)$, and $(6, 0, 8)$. Find the equation of the conical surface generated by the line containing the hypotenuse of this triangle (a) in cylindrical coördinates; (b) in spherical coördinates.

6. Find the equations in cylindrical coördinates of the following surfaces:

(a) $4(x^2 + y^2) = (z - 5)^2$;   (d) $z = e^{-(x^2+y^2)}$;

(b) $x^2 + y^2 = 8y$;   (e) $x^2z^2 + y^2z^2 = 144$;

(c) $x^2 + y^2 = 2pz$;   (f) $x^2 + y^2 = 16z^2$.

7. The following surfaces are given in cylindrical coördinates. Describe the surfaces and find the equations in rectangular coördinates.

(a) $r^2 + 4z^2 = 36$;   (e) $r^2 - 9z^2 = 144$;

(b) $r = z$;   (f) $r = -6 \sin \theta$;

(c) $z^2 - 9r^2 = 144$;   (g) $r^2 = -12z$;

(d) $z = a\theta$;   (h) $(r^2 + z^2)^2 = 4a^2r^2$.

8. Find the equations in spherical coördinates of the following surfaces:

(a) $x^2 + y^2 + 4z^2 = 16$;   (c) $x^2 + y^2 = 16$;

(b) $x^2 + y^2 = 4z^2$;   (d) $z = x^2 + y^2$.

9. The following surfaces are given in spherical coördinates. Describe the surfaces and find their equations in rectangular coördinates.

(a) $\rho = 10$;   (c) $\rho^2 \cos 2\phi = a^2$;

(b) $\rho = a \cot \phi \csc \phi$;   (d) $\rho = a \sin \phi \sin \theta$.

201. Curves in space. The path of a point moving about in space may be extremely complicated and correspondingly difficult to express analytically. Many of the simpler curves, however, can be given as the intersection of some pair of surfaces, as in the case of a straight line, and in general the locus of a pair of equations is a curve or set of curves. Thus $x^2 + y^2 + z^2 = 169$ and $x - 3y + 4z = 12$ are equations of the circle which is the intersection of the spherical surface and the plane defined by these equations.

When a curve is given by the equations of two surfaces, elimination of any one of the variables gives the equation of a cylindrical surface which contains the curve and has its elements perpendicular to the coördinate plane of the other variables. This cylinder is called a *projecting cylinder* of the curve and its equation is also the equation of the projection of the curve on the coördinate plane. For example, the equations of the projecting cylinders of the curve $3x^2 + 2y^2 + 2z^2 = 48$, $2x^2 + 3y^2 - 2z^2 = 32$ are $x^2 + y^2 = 16$, $x^2 + 2z^2 = 16$, and $y^2 - 2z^2 = 0$. Any two of these define the curve, but it is usually best to get all three, so as to be able to choose the simplest pair. In this case the curve consists of the two ellipses which are the intersection of the circular cylinder $x^2 + y^2 = 16$ and the pair of planes $y = \pm \sqrt{2}z$.

In many cases the best way of defining a curve is by three parametric equations of the form $x = f(t)$, $y = g(t)$, $z = h(t)$. It is easy to verify that parametric equations for the curve given in the previous paragraph are $x = 4 \cos t$, $y = 4 \sin t$, $z = \pm 2\sqrt{2} \sin t$. As a final example consider the equations

$$x = a \cos kt, \quad y = a \sin kt, \quad z = ct,$$

where t is the parameter. The curve defined by these equations is called a *helix*. It is the locus of a point which revolves about the z-axis with a uniform angular velocity k and at the same time moves parallel to the z-axis with a uniform linear velocity c. The thread of a bolt has the shape of a helix.* Elimination of t between various pairs of the equations gives

$$x^2 + y^2 = a^2, \quad x = a \cos \frac{kz}{c}, \quad y = a \sin \frac{kz}{c}.$$

These equations show that the helix lies on a circular cylinder and that its projection on the xz-plane is a cosine curve.

PROBLEMS

1. Sketch the following curves. In each case find the equations of the projecting cylinders.

(a) $x^2 + y^2 + z^2 = 4a^2, x^2 + y^2 - 2ax = 0$;

(b) $z^2 = xy, z^2 - y^2 = 2xy$;

(c) $4x^2 + 4y^2 = z^2, x^2 - 6x + y^2 = 0$;

(d) $x^2 + 2y^2 + 2z^2 = 32, x^2 - y^2 - z^2 = 16$;

(e) $y^2 = 8z, x^2 = 8y$;

(f) $x^2 + 4y^2 - 2z^2 = 36, 2x^2 - y^2 - z^2 = 18$.

2. Find rectangular equations for the following curves and sketch the curves:

(a) $x = \cos^2 \theta, y = \sin^2 \theta, z = \cos \theta$;

(b) $x = \sin \theta, y = \theta, z = 1 - \cos \theta$;

(c) $x = t, y = 2t^2, z = -\dfrac{1}{t}$;

(d) $x = t, y = t^2, z = t^3$;

(e) $x = at \cos kt, y = at \sin kt, z = bt$.

3. Find the center and the radius of the circle $x^2 + y^2 + z^2 = 169$, $x - 2y + 2z = 36$.

4. Find equations of the circle which passes through the points $(3, 0, 1)$, $(6, 2, 1)$, and $(0, -6, -1)$.

5. The axes of two cylinders of radius a meet and are mutually perpendicular. Find equations of the curve of intersection. Show that it lies in two mutually perpendicular planes.

---

* Apollonius is said to have proved that any part of a helix will fit any other part. This is the property needed here.

6. The axes of two cylinders of radii a and b respectively meet and are mutually perpendicular. Find equations of the curve of intersection.

7. Two cylinders have radii a and b, respectively, where $a > b$. Their axes are perpendicular, but do not meet, the distance between them being c, where $c < a - b$. Choose axes conveniently and find equations of the curve of intersection.

8. A right circular cone has a radius r and a height h. A right circular cylinder has a radius a, where $a < \dfrac{h}{2}$, and its axis meets the axis of the cone at right angles at a point midway between the vertex and the base. Choose axes conveniently and write equations of the curve of intersection of the surfaces.

9. A right circular cone has a radius r and a height h. A right circular cylinder has a radius of the base of the cone as a diameter. Choose axes conveniently and write equations of the curve of intersection of the surfaces.

10. The rectangle $ABCD$ has the length $AB = 10\pi$ and the width $AD = 5$. It is rolled up into a cylinder so that BC coincides with AD. Choosing the axes so that the circumference AB has its center at the origin and lies in the xy-plane, with the point A on the x-axis, find equations of the curve into which the diagonal AC is bent.

11. A cylindrical surface has the radius a. A sphere of radius a has its center in the cylindrical surface. Choose axes conveniently and write equations of the curve of intersection.

12. Show that $x = a(\sin\ \alpha\ \cos\ \theta - \cos\ \alpha\ \cos\ \beta\ \sin\ \theta)$, $y = a(\cos\ \alpha\ \cos\ \theta + \sin\ \alpha\ \cos\ \beta\ \sin\ \theta)$, $z = a\ \sin\ \beta\ \sin\ \theta$, where θ is the parameter, are equations of a circle whose center is the origin.

13. If the cylindrical surface in Problem 11 is unrolled and spread on a plane, find the equation of the curve in this problem.

14. A point moves along a great circle on the surface of the sphere whose radius is r and whose center is the origin between the points whose spherical coördinates are $\left(r,\ 0,\ \dfrac{\pi}{2}\right)$ and $\left(r,\ \dfrac{3\pi}{4},\ \dfrac{\pi}{3}\right)$. Find equations of the path in rectangular coördinates.

FORMULAS AND EQUATIONS

FORMULAS OF DISTANCE AND DIRECTION

	No.	PAGE

Distance: $\quad d = \sqrt{(x_1 - x_2)^2 + (y_1 - y_2)^2}.$ (1)   8

Point dividing line in the ratio $r_1 : r_2$:

$$x_0 = \frac{r_1 x_2 + r_2 x_1}{r_1 + r_2}, \; y_0 = \frac{r_1 y_2 + r_2 y_1}{r_1 + r_2}. \qquad (2) \qquad 8$$

Mid-point:

$$x_0 = \tfrac{1}{2}(x_1 + x_2), \; y_0 = \tfrac{1}{2}(y_1 + y_2). \qquad (2a) \qquad 9$$

Slope: $\quad m = \dfrac{y_1 - y_2}{x_1 - x_2}.$ (3)   15

Test for parallelism: $\quad m_1 = m_2.$ (4)   17

Test for perpendicularity:

$$m_1 m_2 = -1. \qquad (5) \qquad 17$$

Angle between two lines:

$$\tan \beta = \frac{m_1 - m_2}{1 + m_1 m_2}. \qquad (6) \qquad 17$$

THE STRAIGHT LINE

Equations:

Point slope form: $\quad y - y_1 = m(x - x_1).$ (7)   47

Two-point form: $\quad \dfrac{y - y_1}{x - x_1} = \dfrac{y_1 - y_2}{x_1 - x_2}.$ (7a)   48

Slope intercept form:

$$y = mx + b. \qquad (8) \qquad 48$$

Intercept form: $\quad \dfrac{x}{a} + \dfrac{y}{b} = 1.$ (9)   49

General form: $\quad Ax + By + C = 0.$ (10)   53

Test for parallelism:

$$A : A' = B : B' \neq C : C'. \qquad 54$$

The Hyperbola

Formulas connecting the fundamental constants:

Equations of the asymptotes:

Equilateral hyperbolas:

Transformation of Coördinates

Equation of the conic with the directrix as the
y-axis and the focus on the x-axis:

$$(1 - e^2)x^2 - 2px + y^2 + p^2 = 0.$$ (29) 139

Generalized standard equations of the conics:

Parabola: $(y - k)^2 = 2p(x - h).$ (30) 141

$(x - h)^2 = 2p(y - k).$ (30a) 141

Ellipse: $\dfrac{(x - h)^2}{a^2} + \dfrac{(y - k)^2}{b^2} = 1.$ (31) 141

$\dfrac{(y - k)^2}{a^2} + \dfrac{(x - h)^2}{b^2} = 1.$ (31a) 141

Hyperbola: $\dfrac{(x - h)^2}{a^2} - \dfrac{(y - k)^2}{b^2} = 1.$ (32) 141

$\dfrac{(y - k)^2}{a^2} - \dfrac{(x - h)^2}{b^2} = 1.$ (32a) 141

Angle of rotation for eliminating the xy term:

$$\tan 2\theta = \frac{B}{A - C}.$$ (33) 145

Polar Coördinates

Relation to rectangular coördinates:

$$x = \rho \cos \theta, \quad y = \rho \sin \theta.$$ (34) 155

$$\rho^2 = x^2 + y^2, \quad \theta = \text{arc} \tan \frac{y}{x}.$$ (35) 155

Equations of the straight line:

$\rho \cos \theta = a.$ (36) 158

$\rho \sin \theta = a.$ (36a) 158

$\theta = c.$ (37) 158

Equations of the circle:

$\rho = r.$ (38) 158

$\rho = 2r \cos \theta.$ (39) 158

$\rho = 2r \sin \theta.$ (39a) 158

$\rho = a \cos \theta + b \sin \theta.$ (40) 158

* These formulas apply to the standard forms $b^2 x^2 + a^2 y^2 = a^2 b^2$, $y^2 = 2px$, and $b^2 x^2 - a^2 y^2 = a^2 b^2$.

Solid Analytic Geometry

Cylindrical and rectangular coördinates:

$$x = r \cos \theta, \quad y = r \sin \theta, \quad z = z. \qquad (76) \quad 283$$

$$r^2 = x^2 + y^2, \quad \theta = \text{arc tan } \frac{y}{x}. \qquad (76a) \quad 283$$

Spherical and rectangular coördinates:

$$x = \rho \sin \phi \cos \theta, \, y = \rho \sin \phi \sin \theta, \, z = \rho \cos \phi. \qquad (77) \quad 284$$

$$\rho^2 = x^2 + y^2 + z^2, \, \theta = \text{arc tan } \frac{y}{x},$$

$$\phi = \text{arc cos } \frac{z}{\sqrt{x^2 + y^2 + z^2}}. \qquad (77a) \quad 284$$

Pages 50, 51, 52

3. (a) $x - 2y + 7 = 0$; (b) $8x + 3y = 38$; (c) $x - y = 1$;
(d) $3x + 2y = 13$; (e) $5x + 8y + 30 = 0$; (f) $3x + 2y = 5$;
(g) $5x + 4y = 27$; (h) $3x - 4y + 16 = 0$.

5. (a) $x - y = 2$; (b) $x + y = 9$; (c) $x - \sqrt{3}y = 5 - 4\sqrt{3}$;
(d) $2x + y + 6 = 0$; (e) $2x - y + 6 = 0$; (f) $3x + y = 12$;
(g) $x - y + 5 = 0$; (h) $x + y = 6$; (i) $\sqrt{3}x - y = 4$;
(j) $x + \sqrt{3}y = 5\sqrt{3}$.

7. (a) $45°$; (b) $4° 58'$; (c) $119° 45'$; (d) $72° 15'$; (e) $11° 53'$; (f) $90°$;
(g) $33° 41'$; (h) $135°$.

9. 45.   **11.** $4x + 3y = \pm 50$.   **13*.** $2x + 3y = 24, 6x + y = 24$.

15. $\dfrac{cm - d}{m} \sqrt{1 + m^2}$.

17. (a) $2x - y + 2 = 0, x + y = 8, x - 2y = 2$;
(b) $x + 2y = 4, x = y, 2x + y = 4$;
(c) $x + 2y = 10, x = y, 2x + y = 10$; (d) $y = 2, x = y, x = 2$.

23*. (a) $x = 2a$ and $x = -a$; (b) $y = 2a$ and $y = -a$.

Pages 57, 58, 59

3. (a) $x - 2y + 5 = 0, 2x + y = 15$; (b) $3x - 4y + 26 = 0, 4x + 3y = 7$;
(c) $3x - y = 29, x + 3y = 13$; (d) $2x - 3y + 34 = 0, 3x + 2y = 14$;
(e) $5x + 12y + 103 = 0, 12x - 5y = 57$;
(f) $2x + y + 7 = 0, x - 2y + 1 = 0$; (g) $x + 3y = 35, 3x - y = 5$;
(h) $3x + 5y + 72 = 0, 5x - 3y = 16$.

5. (a) $4\sqrt{5}$; (b) 10; (c) $2\sqrt{10}$; (d) $4\sqrt{13}$; (e) 13; (f) $\frac{19}{5}\sqrt{5}$; (g) $2\sqrt{10}$;
(h) 17.49.

9. (a) 36; (b) 64.

11. (a) $(1, \frac{15}{2})$, $\frac{5}{2}\sqrt{13}$; (b) $(\frac{11}{2}, 4)$, $\frac{1}{2}\sqrt{185}$; (c) $(-3, 4)$, 10;
(d) $(\frac{15}{16}, \frac{29}{4})$, 8.25.

13. (a) $(13, 12)$; (b) $(15, 2)$.

15. $(-\frac{1}{2}, -\frac{5}{2})$, $(\frac{9}{2}, \frac{19}{2})$, $7x - 17y = 39$, $7x - 17y = -130$,
$17x + 7y = 143, 17x + 7y + 26 = 0$.

17. (a) $x = 2, 4x - 3y + 1 = 0$; (b) $x + y = 5, 7x + y = 17$;
(c) $x - y + 1 = 0, x - 7y + 19 = 0$;
(d) $2x - 9y + 23 = 0, 7x - 6y + 4 = 0$;
(e) $x + y = 5, 7x + y = 17$; (f) $6x - 7y + 9 = 0, 9x - 2y = 12$;
(g) $x + y = 5, 7x + y = 17$; (h) $x = 2, 4x - 3y + 1 = 0$.

19. $(-6, 5), (10, -3)$.   **21.** $(-1, 12)$.

Pages 62, 63, 64

1. (a) $x = 6$; (b) $\sqrt{3}x + y + 16 = 0$; (c) $x + y = 10\sqrt{2}$;
(d) $x + \sqrt{3}y + 16 = 0$; (e) $y = 5$; (f) $x - \sqrt{3}y = 24$;
(g) $x - y + 16\sqrt{2} = 0$; (h) $\sqrt{3}x - y = 12$.

3. (a) $3x + 4y = 50$; (b) $12x - 5y + 156 = 0$; (c) $2x + y = 6\sqrt{5}$;
(d) $x - y + 8 = 0$; (e) $4x + 3y = 60$; (f) $4x - 3y = 15$.

5. (a) $-\frac{3}{5}x + \frac{4}{5}y = -\frac{24}{5}$; (b) $-\frac{12}{13}x + \frac{5}{13}y = -\frac{60}{13}$;

(c) $\frac{15}{17}x + \frac{8}{17}y = \frac{120}{17}$; (d) $\frac{4}{5}x + \frac{3}{5}y = 0$; (e) $\frac{x}{\sqrt{2}} + \frac{y}{\sqrt{2}} = 8\sqrt{2}$;

(f) $-\frac{2}{\sqrt{13}}x + \frac{3}{\sqrt{13}}y = -\frac{15}{\sqrt{13}}$; (g) $-\frac{\sqrt{3}}{2}x + \frac{1}{2}y = -6$;

(h) $\frac{x}{\sqrt{5}} + \frac{2}{\sqrt{5}}y = \frac{16}{\sqrt{5}}$.

7. (a) $36° 52'$; (b) $112° 37'$; (c) $118° 4'$; (d) $153° 26'$; (e) $59° 2'$; (f) $135°$;
(g) $53° 8'$; (h) $18° 26'$.

9. (a) $x + y = 5$; (b) $\sqrt{3}x - y = 10\sqrt{3} + 5$; (c) $5x - 12y = 110$;
(d) $4x + 3y = 25$; (e) $3x + 4y = 10$; (f) $4x - 3y = 55$.

11. $p = \pm \dfrac{ab}{\sqrt{a^2 + b^2}}$, $\tan \omega = \dfrac{a}{b}$.   **13.** $\left(\dfrac{ab^2}{a^2 + b^2}, \dfrac{a^2 b}{a^2 + b^2} \right)$.

Pages 67, 68

1. (a) -12; (b) $5\sqrt{5}$; (c) $\dfrac{196}{13}$; (d) $10\sqrt{2}$; (e) $\dfrac{-43}{\sqrt{13}}$; (f) 8.

3. (a) $\dfrac{13}{\sqrt{5}}$; (b) $\dfrac{12}{\sqrt{13}}$; (c) 7.2; (d) $\dfrac{30}{\sqrt{34}}$.

5. (a) 21.61; (b) 73.5; (c) 84.   **7.** (a) 99; (b) 118; (c) 70; (d) 115.

9. (a) $19x + 2y = 105$, $29x - 22y = 35$;
(b) $128x + 99y = 48$, $4x + 67y + 256 = 0$;
(c) $5x - 4y = 18$, $x = 4$; (d) $89x + 68y = 424$, $11x + 172y = 216$.

11*. (a) $4x - 3y + 5 = 0$; (b) $5x + 12y = 125$; (c) $8x - 15y = 5$;
(d) $x - y = 10 - 5\sqrt{2}$.

13. $y = mx + \dfrac{r_1 b_2 - r_2 b_1}{r_1 - r_2}$.   **15.** $\left(14, \dfrac{14}{3} \right), \dfrac{14}{3}$.

Pages 70, 71

3. (a) $x + \sqrt{3}y = 10$; (b) $\sqrt{3}x - y = 6$; (c) $x - \sqrt{3}y + 10 = 0$;

(d) $x - \sqrt{3}y = 8$; (e) $x + \sqrt{3}y = 6\sqrt{3}$; (f) $x - y = 6\sqrt{2}$;

(g) $4x + 3y = 60$; (h) $4x \mp 3y = \pm 30$; (i) $3x - y + 5\sqrt{10} = 0$;

(j) $2x - y + 20 = 0$.

5*. (a) $x + 2y = k$; (b) $x + y = k$; (c) $(10 - a)x + ay = a(10 - a)$;

(d) $y = mx + \dfrac{1}{m}$; (e) $ax + y = a^2$; (f) $x + \sqrt{3}y = a$.

7. (a) -5; (b) -19; (c) $-\frac{4}{5}$; (d) $-\frac{27}{4}$; (f) -2; (g) -5.

9. (a) -5; (b) -15; (c) $-\frac{12}{5}$; (f) $-\frac{6}{5}$; (g) $\frac{5}{3}$; (h) $\frac{8}{5}$.

11. $4x - 3y = k$. **17.** $2x + 3y = 24, x - 3y = 30$.

Pages 73, 74

1. $5x - 10y + 1 = 0$.

3. (a) $13x + 22y = 4$; (b) $13x + 8y = 112$; (c) $x - 3y + 9 = 0$;

(d) $146x - 253y = 360$.

5. (a) $6x + 19y + 30 = 0$; (b) $4x + 125y + 20 = 0$;

(c) $3x - 7y + 15 = 0$; (d) $96x - 353y + 480 = 0$.

7. (a) $3x + 6y = 29, 12x + 6y = 71, 6x - 6y = 13$;

(b) $2x + 3y - 50 = 0, 44x - 66y + 445 = 0, 16x - 20y + 115 = 0$;

(c) $2x - 3y = 15, 5x + 3y = 12, 7x + 7y = 10$;

(d) $54x + 45y = 430, 37x - 148y + 170 = 0, 145x - 58y = 690$.

Page 76

3. (a) 16; (b) 64; (c) 50.

7. (a) $9x^2 - y^2 - 30x + 25 = 0$; (b) $x^2 - 4xy + 4y^2 - 7x + 14y = 0$;

(c) $4x^2 - y^2 - 8y - 16 = 0$; (d) $4x^2 - 4xy + y^2 - 10x + 5y - 50 = 0$.

11. $2xy + 3y - 6x - 9 = 0$.

Pages 78, 79

1. (a) $x^2 + y^2 - 10x - 16y + 25 = 0$; (b) $x^2 + y^2 - 10x + 24y = 0$;

(c) $x^2 + y^2 + 14y = 0$; (d) $x^2 + y^2 - 10x - 12y - 39 = 0$;

(e) $x^2 + y^2 - 16x + 12y = 0$; (f) $x^2 + y^2 + 16x = 0$;

(g) $x^2 + y^2 + 14x - 10y + 25 = 0$;

(h) $x^2 + y^2 + 24x - 14y + 24 = 0$; (i) $x^2 + y^2 + 6x + 6y - 7 = 0$.

3. (a) $x^2 + y^2 \pm 16x + 12y = 0$; (b) $x^2 + y^2 + 16x - 16y + 64 = 0$;

(c) $x^2 + y^2 - 12x \pm 16y = 0$; (d) $x^2 + y^2 - 8x + 12y = 0$;

(e) $x^2 + y^2 - 4x \pm 16y - 32 = 0$; (f) $x^2 + y^2 \pm 8x - 10y + 16 = 0$.

5. $x^2 + y^2 - ax - by = 0$. **7.** $x^2 + y^2 - 15x + 2y - 79 = 0$.

9. $r\sqrt{2 - \sqrt{2}}$.

Pages 82, 83, 84

1. (a) $(4, -2)$, 8;   (b) $(3, 5)$, 10;   (c) $(-8, -6)$, 10;   (d) $(\frac{9}{4}, 0)$, $\frac{9}{4}$;
     (e) $(-8, 6)$, 8;   (f) $(5, -\frac{7}{2})$, $\frac{1}{2}\sqrt{113}$;   (g) $(0, -8)$, 6;
     (h) $(-2, 3)$, $\sqrt{46}$;   (j) $(3, -4)$, 0.

5. A point if (a) $k = \pm 8$;   (b) $k = \pm 4\sqrt{5}$.

7. (a) $(8, 0)$, $(\frac{8}{5}, \frac{24}{5})$;   (b) $(3, 2)$, $(-\frac{17}{5}, \frac{26}{5})$.   **9.** $2x + 3y = 16$, $2\sqrt{13}$.

11. (a) $3x - 4y + 41 = 0$;   (b) $5x + 12y = 121$;
     (c) $9x + 2y = 40$;   (d) $x - y = 6$.

13. (a) $(6, 4)$, $(-2, 8)$;   (b) $(4, -10)$, $(12, -6)$;   (c) $(5, 4)$, $(-12, -3)$.

15. (a) $(2, -4)$, $(-2, 8)$;   (b) $(-4, 6)$, $(12, -6)$;
     (c) $(12, -3)$, $(-12, -13)$.

17. $\pm \dfrac{1}{3} \sqrt{\dfrac{a^2 - 9r^2}{r^2 - a^2}}$, $a > 3r$, $a < r$.   **19.** $x^2 + y^2 = 2r^2$.

21. $4x^2 + 4y^2 - 4ax + a^2 - r^2 = 0$.   **23*.** $2x^2 + 2y^2 = k - 2c^2$.

25*. (a) $2x^2 + 2y^2 = k - 4a^2$;   (b) $4x^2 + 4y^2 = k - 8a^2$.

27. $x^2 + y^2 - 24x = 0$.

Pages 87, 88

1. (a) $x^2 + y^2 - 6x - 28y + 99 = 0$;   (b) $3x^2 + 3y^2 - 24x + 28y = 0$;
     (c) $4x^2 + 4y^2 - 15x - 40y - 150 = 0$;
     (d) $x^2 + y^2 + 4x + 6y - 87 = 0$;
     (e) $x^2 + y^2 + 10x + 6y - 135 = 0$;   (f) $x^2 + y^2 - 8x - 6y = 0$.

3. (a) $x^2 + y^2 \pm 12x - 15y + 36 = 0$;
     (b) $x^2 + y^2 - 8x + 2y - 33 = 0$, or $x^2 + y^2 + 4x - 14y + 3 = 0$;
     (c) $4x^2 + 4y^2 - 8x + 19y - 140 = 0$;
     (d) $x^2 + y^2 - 8x + 8y - 36 = 0$;   (e) $x^2 + y^2 + 2x - 4y - 20 = 0$;
     (f) $x^2 + y^2 + 2x - 6y - 3 = 0$;
     (g) $x^2 + y^2 - 2x - 4y = 0$, or $x^2 + y^2 + 118x + 116y = 0$;
     (h) $441(x^2 + y^2) - 4368(x + y) + 18496 = 0$;
     (i) $3x^2 + 3y^2 - 18x - 16y - 160 = 0$, or $x^2 + y^2 + 2x - 16y + 40 = 0$;
     (j) $(5x - 97)^2 + (5y - 54)^2 = 4225$, or $(5x + 7)^2 + (5y + 24)^2 = 4225$.

Pages 93, 94

1. (a) 5.53;   (b) 4.92;   (c) 9;   (d) 4.02;   (e) 10.72;   (f) 7.60;   (g) $15 - 5\sqrt{5}$;
     (h) 5.62.

7. (a) $(11, -\frac{29}{2})$;   (b) $(-\frac{11}{2}, 0)$.

11. (c) $5x^2 + 5y^2 + 14x - 68 = 0$;   (d) $2x^2 + 2y^2 + 17x - 71 = 0$;
     (e) $x^2 + y^2 - 4x - 32 = 0$;   (f) $x^2 + y^2 + 16x + 27 = 0$.

Pages 100, 101, 102, 103, 104

1. (a) $(4, 0)$, $x = -4, 16$; (b) $(0, 3)$, $y = -3, 12$;

(c) $(0, -3)$, $y = 3, 12$; (d) $(-\frac{9}{8}, 0)$, $x = \frac{9}{8}, \frac{36}{5}$; (e) $(-\frac{3}{2}, 0)$, $2x = 3, 6$;

(f) $(\frac{1}{36}, 0)$, $36x + 1 = 0, \frac{1}{3}$; (g) $(0, 6)$, $y = -6, 24$;

(h) $(0, -4)$, $y = 4, 16$; (i) $(a, 0)$, $x = -a, 4a$;

(j) $\left(0, \dfrac{1}{16a}\right)$, $16ay + 1 = 0, \dfrac{1}{4a}$.

3. (a) $x^2 = -16y$; (b) $y^2 = 20x$; (c) $x^2 = 4ay$;

(d) $y^2 = 10x$, or $x^2 = -10y$; (e) $x^2 = 24y$; (f) $y^2 = -24x$.

5. $4p\sqrt{3}$. **7.** $4p$. **9.** $2x^2 + 2y^2 - 5py = 0$.

11. $(0, 0)$, $(a\sqrt[3]{2},\ a\sqrt[3]{4})$. **13.** $(7, \pm 2\sqrt{21})$. **15.** $(\frac{3}{2}p,\ p\sqrt{3})$.

23. $ON = \frac{25}{6}$ in the figure of page 98. **25.** $x^2 = -20y$. **27*.** $x^2 = 4ay$.

29. $x^2 = 4py$. **31*.** $\pm x = 2y$. **33.** $x^2 = 2ay$.

35. (a) $y^2 = 2px - p^2$, or $y^2 = -2px - p^2$;

(b) $x^2 = 2py + p^2$, or $x^2 = -2py + p^2$.

39. (a) $y^2 - 4y + 8x + 68 = 0$; (b) $x^2 - 8x - 24y + 16 = 0$;

(c) $y^2 - 4y - 12x + 40 = 0$; (d) $x^2 - 16y + 32 = 0$.

41. $(y - k)^2 = 2p(x - h)$.

Pages 108, 109

1. (b) $10, 5, 5, \dfrac{\sqrt{3}}{2}$, $(\pm 5\sqrt{3}, 0)$, $(\pm 10, 0)$;

(c) $6, 4, \dfrac{16}{3}, \dfrac{\sqrt{5}}{3}$, $(\pm 2\sqrt{5}, 0)$, $(\pm 6, 0)$;

(d) $6, 2, \dfrac{4}{3}, \dfrac{2\sqrt{2}}{3}$, $(\pm 4\sqrt{2}, 0)$, $(\pm 6, 0)$;

(e) $8, 2\sqrt{7}, 7, \frac{3}{4}$, $(\pm 6, 0)$, $(\pm 8, 0)$;

(f) $13, 5, \frac{50}{13}, \frac{12}{13}$, $(\pm 12, 0)$, $(\pm 13, 0)$;

(g) $6\sqrt{2}, 6, 6\sqrt{2}, \dfrac{1}{\sqrt{2}}$, $(\pm 6, 0)$, $(\pm 6\sqrt{2}, 0)$;

(h) $7, 3, \dfrac{18}{7}, \dfrac{2\sqrt{10}}{7}$, $(\pm 2\sqrt{10}, 0)$, $(\pm 7, 0)$;

(i) $10, 4, \dfrac{16}{5}, \dfrac{\sqrt{21}}{5}$, $(\pm 2\sqrt{21}, 0)$, $(\pm 10, 0)$.

3. (a) $x^2 + 4y^2 = 36$; (b) $3x^2 + 4y^2 = 192$; (c) $x^2 + 2y^2 = 100$;

(d) $9x^2 + 25y^2 = 625$; (e) $4x^2 + 5y^2 = 500$.

5. (a) $a = b\sqrt{2}$; (b) $a = 2b$. **7.** $\dfrac{c}{e}\sqrt{1 - e^2}$. **9.** $7x^2 + 16y^2 = 256$.

11. $\left(\pm \sqrt{90\sqrt{2} - 99},\ \pm 5(\sqrt{2} - 1)\right)$.

13. $9x^2 + 25y^2 = 225$. **15*.** $9x^2 + 16y^2 = 324$.

Pages 114, 115, 116

1. (b) $(0, \pm 5)$, $(0, \pm \sqrt{21})$, $\dfrac{\sqrt{21}}{5}$, $\dfrac{8}{5}$; (c) $(\pm 6, 0)$, $(\pm 3\sqrt{3}, 0)$, $\dfrac{\sqrt{3}}{2}$, 3;

(d) $(0, \pm 12)$, $(0, \pm 8\sqrt{2})$, $\dfrac{2\sqrt{2}}{3}$, $\dfrac{8}{3}$; (e) $(0, \pm 8)$, $(0, \pm 6)$, $\dfrac{3}{4}$, 7;

(f) $(0, \pm 8)$, $(0, \pm \sqrt{39})$, $\dfrac{\sqrt{39}}{8}$, $\dfrac{25}{4}$; (g) $(0, \pm 8)$, $(0, \pm 4\sqrt{2})$, $\dfrac{\sqrt{2}}{2}$, 8.

3. (a) $9x^2 + 5y^2 = 180$; (b) $5x^2 + 2y^2 = 200$; (c) $25x^2 + 9y^2 = 900$;
(d) $2x^2 + y^2 = 128$; (e) $74x^2 + 25y^2 = 1850$.

5. (a) $\sqrt{3}y = \pm 16$; (b) $3y = \pm 25$; (c) $\sqrt{33}y = \pm 49$;
(d) $\sqrt{2}y = \pm 9$; (e) $2x = \pm 5\sqrt{15}$; (f) $y = \pm 9$.

7*. $24x^2 + 49y^2 = 1176$.   **9.** $\left(\pm \dfrac{a}{e}\sqrt{2e^2 - 1}, \pm \dfrac{a}{e}(1 - e^2) \right)$.

11. (a) $\dfrac{\sqrt{7}}{4}$; (b) $\dfrac{1}{\sqrt{3}}$.   **13.** $2ab$.   **15.** $4b^2x^2 + a^2y^2 = a^2b^2$.

19*. $b^2x^2 + a^2y^2 = a^2b^2$.   **21.** $b^2x^2 + a^2y^2 = a^2b^2$.

Pages 120, 121, 122

1. (b) 4, 6, 18, $(\pm 2\sqrt{13}, 0)$; (c) $\frac{5}{2}$, 5, 20, $(0, \pm \frac{5}{2}\sqrt{5})$;
(d) 6, $3\sqrt{2}$, 6, $(\pm 3\sqrt{6}, 0)$; (e) 4, $2\sqrt{3}$, 6, $(0, \pm 2\sqrt{7})$;
(f) 5, 5, 10, $(0, \pm 5\sqrt{2})$; (g) 5, $\sqrt{15}$, 6, $(\pm 2\sqrt{10}, 0)$;
(h) 3, 4, $\frac{3\cdot 2}{3}$, $(0, \pm 5)$; (i) 4, $4\sqrt{3}$, 24, $(\pm 8, 0)$.

3. (a) $9x^2 - 4y^2 = 144$, $9y^2 - 4x^2 = 144$;
(b) $9x^2 - 16y^2 = 144$, $9y^2 - 16x^2 = 144$;
(c) $4x^2 - 5y^2 = 180$, $4y^2 - 5x^2 = 180$;
(d) $3x^2 - y^2 = 75$, $3y^2 - x^2 = 75$;
(e) $7x^2 - 9y^2 = 144$, $7y^2 - 9x^2 = 144$;
(f) $5x^2 - 4y^2 = 80$, $5y^2 - 4x^2 = 80$; (g) $x^2 - y^2 = 25$, $y^2 - x^2 = 25$;
(h) $25x^2 - 20y^2 = 576$, $25y^2 - 20x^2 = 576$.

5. (a) $\dfrac{\sqrt{5}}{2}$, $\sqrt{5}x = \pm 12$; (b) $\dfrac{\sqrt{13}}{3}$, $\sqrt{13}y = \pm 18$; (c) $\dfrac{5}{4}$, $5x = \pm 16$;

(d) $\dfrac{\sqrt{10}}{3}$, $\sqrt{10}x = \pm 18$; (e) $\sqrt{3}$, $y = \pm \sqrt{3}$; (f) $\sqrt{2}$, $\sqrt{2}y = \pm 7$;

(g) $\dfrac{\sqrt{15}}{3}$, $\sqrt{15}x = \pm 18$; (h) $\dfrac{3}{\sqrt{5}}$, $3x = \pm 5\sqrt{5}$.

7. (a) $3x^2 - 4y^2 = 48$; (b) $7x^2 - 4y^2 = 108$.

9. $9y^2 + 25x^2 = 900$, $225y^2 - 400x^2 = 9216$.

11. $(\pm 8, \pm 6)$.   **15.** $3x^2 - y^2 = 108$.   **17.** $2y^2 - 2x^2 = c^2$.

Pages 127, 128, 129

1. (b) $2\sqrt{5}$, 4, $\dfrac{3}{\sqrt{5}}$, $(\pm 6, 0)$, $2x = \pm \sqrt{5}y$;

(c) 6, 4, $\dfrac{\sqrt{13}}{3}$, $(0, \pm 2\sqrt{13})$, $2y = \pm 3x$;

(d) 4, 5, $\dfrac{\sqrt{41}}{4}$, $(\pm \sqrt{41}, 0)$, $4y = \pm 5x$;

(e) 2, 6, $\sqrt{10}$, $(0, \pm 2\sqrt{10})$, $3y = \pm x$;

(f) 5, 2, $\dfrac{\sqrt{29}}{5}$, $(\pm \sqrt{29}, 0)$, $5y = \pm 2x$;

(g) $2\sqrt{15}$, 6, $\dfrac{4}{\sqrt{10}}$, $(0, \pm 4\sqrt{6})$, $\sqrt{3}y = \pm \sqrt{5}x$;

(h) 8, $8\sqrt{3}$, 2, $(0, \pm 16)$, $x = \pm \sqrt{3}y$;

(i) 5, 10, $\sqrt{5}$, $(\pm 5\sqrt{5}, 0)$, $y = \pm 2x$.

3. (b) $5y^2 - 4x^2 = 80$, $\frac{3}{2}$, $(0, \pm 6)$;

(c) $9x^2 - 4y^2 = 144$, $\dfrac{\sqrt{13}}{2}$, $(\pm 2\sqrt{13}, 0)$;

(d) $16y^2 - 25x^2 = 400$, $\dfrac{\sqrt{41}}{5}$, $(0, \pm \sqrt{41})$;

(e) $x^2 - 9y^2 = 36$, $\dfrac{\sqrt{10}}{3}$, $(\pm 2\sqrt{10}, 0)$;

(f) $25y^2 - 4x^2 = 100$, $\dfrac{\sqrt{29}}{2}$, $(0, \pm \sqrt{29})$;

(g) $5x^2 - 3y^2 = 180$, $\dfrac{4}{\sqrt{6}}$, $(\pm 4\sqrt{6}, 0)$;

(h) $x^2 - 3y^2 = 192$, $\dfrac{2}{\sqrt{3}}$, $(\pm 16, 0)$;

(i) $y^2 - 4x^2 = 100$, $\dfrac{\sqrt{5}}{2}$, $(0, \pm 5\sqrt{5})$.

5*. $3x^2 - y^2 = 3a^2$.   **7.** $(\pm 6, \mp 6)$, $(\pm 6\sqrt{2}, \mp 6\sqrt{2})$.

9. $\dfrac{a^2b^2}{c^2}$.   **15.** $2a$.   **17*.** $2(x^2 - y^2) = a^2 - b^2$.

19. (a) $(2, 1)$, $(2, -9)$, $(2, -1)$, $(2, -7)$, $\frac{5}{3}$;

(b) $(12, 1)$, $(-8, 1)$, $(10, 1)$, $(-6, 1)$, $\frac{5}{4}$.

21. (a) $9x^2 - 16y^2 - 36x - 128y - 364 = 0$;

(b) $9x^2 - 16y^2 - 36x + 32y + 596 = 0$.

Pages 132, 133

1. (a) $y'^2 = 12x'$; (b) $25x'^2 + 9y'^2 = 225$; (c) $9x'^2 - 16y'^2 = 144$;

(d) $x'y' = 24$; (e) $x'^2 = -4y'$; (f) $y' = x'^3$.

3. (a) $y'^2 = 8x'$; (b) $x'^2 + 4y'^2 = 36$; (c) $y'^2 - x'^2 = 25$;
(d) $x'y' = -18$; (e) $x'^2 - y'^2 = \pm a^2$; (f) $2y'^2 = 2\sqrt{2}ax' - a^2$.

5. (a) $(-2, -10)$; (b) $(5, -8)$; (c) $(7, -2)$; (d) $(-2, 0)$.

7. (a) $(4, 2)$; (b) $(3, -6)$; (c) $(-\frac{16}{5}, \frac{12}{5})$.

Pages 135, 136, 137

1. (a) $4x'^2 + y'^2 = 64$; (b) $16x'^2 - 9y'^2 = 121$; (c) $9x'^2 + 4y'^2 = 144$;
(d) $4x'^2 - y'^2 = -36$; (e) $x'^2 + y'^2 = 13$.

3. (a) $y'^2 = -4x'$; (b) $9x'^2 + 4y'^2 = 36$; (c) $x'^2 = -12y'$;
(d) $16x'^2 - 4y'^2 = 81$; (e) $9x'^2 + 25y'^2 = 225$.

7. $y' = x'^3 - 4x'^2$ or $y' = x'^3 + 4x'^2$.

9. (a) $y'^2 = -12x'$; (b) $x'^2 = 16y'$; (c) $y'^2 = -10x'$; (d) $x'^2 = -20y'$

11. (a) $7x'^2 + 16y'^2 = 448$; (b) $25x'^2 + 9y'^2 = 225$.

13. (a) $x'^2 = -24y'$; (b) $y'^2 = -24x'$; (c) $x'^2 - 3y'^2 = -192$;
(d) $4x'^2 + 3y'^2 = 192$; (e) $x'^2 = 4y'$; (f) $9x'^2 - 3y'^2 = 100$.

17. $x'^2 = 2by'$.

Pages 142, 143, 144

1. (a) $5x^2 + 9(y + 2)^2 = 180$; (b) $25(x - 1)^2 + 9(y - 3)^2 = 225$;
(c) $5(x - 2)^2 + 9(y - 3)^2 = 180$; (d) $36(x - 2)^2 + 11(y - 3)^2 = 396$.

3. (a) $16x^2 - 9(y - 4)^2 = 144$; (b) $5(y - 2)^2 - 4(x - 2)^2 = 80$;
(c) $7x^2 - 9(y - 2)^2 = 252$; (d) $3(x - 2)^2 - (y - 2)^2 = 192$.

5. (a) $4x + 3y = 12, 4x - 3y = -12$; (b) $2x = 4 \pm \sqrt{5}(y - 2)$;
(c) $3y = 6 \pm \sqrt{7}x$; (d) $y = 2 \pm \sqrt{3}(x - 2)$.

7. (a) $(y - 3)^2 = -24(x - 4)$; (b) $(x + 4)^2 = 16(y + 2)$;
(c) $(y - 1)^2 = -10(x - \frac{9}{2})$; (d) $x^2 = -4a(y - a)$;
(e) $x^2 = -2a\left(y - \dfrac{a}{2}\right)$.

11. (a) $(-2, 3 \pm 4\sqrt{3})$, $\dfrac{\sqrt{3}}{2}$, $y = 3 \pm \dfrac{16}{\sqrt{3}}$;

(b) $\left(-\dfrac{1}{2} \pm \dfrac{9\sqrt{5}}{4}, -2\right)$, $\sqrt{5}$, $x = -\dfrac{1}{2} \pm \dfrac{9}{4\sqrt{5}}$;

(c) $(-\frac{1}{4}, -3)$, 1, $4x = -7$; (d) $(-1, 2 \pm \frac{55}{12})$, $\frac{5}{3}$, $y = 2 \pm \frac{33}{20}$;

(e) $(-2, 1)$, 1, $y = 3$; (f) $\left(-3, 4 \pm 2\sqrt{5}\right)$, $\dfrac{\sqrt{5}}{3}$, $y = 4 \pm \dfrac{18}{2\sqrt{5}}$.

13. $x^2 + y^2 = e^2(x + p)^2$.

19*. (a) $9(x + 4)^2 + 25y^2 = 225$; (b) $(x + 3)^2 + 4(y - 2)^2 = 25$;

(c) $x^2 = 2b\left(y - \dfrac{b}{2} + \dfrac{c^2}{8b}\right)$; (d) $x^2 = -2(a + r)\left(y - \dfrac{a + r}{2}\right)$.

Pages 148, 149

1. $x''^2 + 4y''^2 = 64$.   **3.** $2x''^2 + 3y''^2 = 0$.   **5.** $x''^2 = 10y''$.

7. $9x''^2 - 16y''^2 = 144$.   **11.** $x''^2 - y''^2 = 49$.   **13.** $x''^2 = -4y''$.

15. $16x''^2 - 9y''^2 = 0$.   **17.** $4x''^2 + y''^2 = 100$.   **19.** $4y''^2 = 9$.

21*. $x''^2 - y''^2 = 8\sqrt{2}$.

25. $2x^2 - 5xy + 2y^2 - 4x + 5y = 0$, $(1, 0)$, $2x - y = 2$, $x - 2y = 1$.

Pages 151, 152

1. (a) $37x^2 + 168xy - 12y^2 - 800x - 600y = 0$;

    (b) $7x^2 - 8xy + 13y^2 - 40x - 20y = 0$.

3. (a) $x^2 + 4xy + 4y^2 - 2x - 8y - 7 = 0$, or

    $25x^2 + 60xy + 36y^2 - 90x - 96y - 7 = 0$;

    (b) $y^2 - 2y - 8 = 0$, or $x^2 - 2xy + y^2 - 2x - 7 = 0$.

5. (a) $x^2 - 2xy + 2y^2 = 20$; (b) $x^2 - xy = 16$; (c) $x^2 - xy + y^2 = 12$.

7. (a) $2x = 36 - 29y + 5y^2$; (b) $2x = 26 - 17y + 3y^2$;

    (c) $2x = y^2 - 3y$; (d) $2x = y^2 - 4$.

Page 157

5. (a) $(4\sqrt{3}, -4)$; (b) $(-8, 0)$; (c) $(5, -5\sqrt{3})$; (d) $(6\sqrt{2}, 6\sqrt{2})$;

    (e) $(-5, -5\sqrt{3})$; (f) $(-6\sqrt{3}, 6)$.

7*. (a) $\left(10, -\dfrac{\pi}{6}\right)$, $\left(-10, \dfrac{5\pi}{6}\right)$; (b) $\left(6\sqrt{2}, \dfrac{3\pi}{4}\right)$, $\left(-6\sqrt{2}, -\dfrac{\pi}{4}\right)$;

    (c) $\left(16, \dfrac{7\pi}{6}\right)$, $\left(-16, \dfrac{\pi}{6}\right)$; (d) $\left(10\sqrt{2}, \dfrac{\pi}{4}\right)$, $\left(-10\sqrt{2}, \dfrac{5\pi}{4}\right)$;

    (e) $(10, -36° 52')$, $(-10, 143° 8')$; (f) $(8, \pi)$, $(-8, 0)$.

9. (a) $x^2 + y^2 = 100$; (b) $2y = x$; (c) $x^2 + y^2 + 10y = 0$;

    (d) $x^2 + y^2 = 25$; (e) $4y = \pm 3x$; (f) $y = 6$; (g) $x^2 + y^2 - 2ax = 0$;

    (h) $x^2 + y^2 - 8x - 6y = 0$; (i) $x = a$.

Pages 165, 166

1. (a) $\rho = a \cos \theta$; (b) $\rho = a \cos 3\theta$; (c) $\rho^2 = a^2 \cos 2\theta$;

    (d) $\rho = 2a \tan \theta \sin \theta$; (e) $\rho = a \csc \theta \pm b$; (f) $\rho = \sqrt{a^2 + b^2} \cos \theta$.

3*. (a) $\rho = a(1 - \cos \theta)$; (b) $\rho = -a \cos 3\theta$; (c) $\rho = -2a \tan \theta \sin \theta$;

    (d) $\rho = -a \cos \theta$; (e) $\rho = -a \cos \theta + b \sin \theta$; (f) $\rho^2 = -a^2 \sin 2\theta$.

7*. (a) $(0, 0)$, $\left(\dfrac{\sqrt{3}}{2}\,a,\,\dfrac{\pi}{3}\right)$, $\left(\dfrac{\sqrt{3}}{2}\,a,\,\dfrac{2\pi}{3}\right)$; (b) $(0, 0)$, $\left(\dfrac{8a}{5},\,53°\,8'\right)$;

   (c) $(0, 0)$, $\left(\pm 1,\,\dfrac{\pi}{2}\right)$, $(.2192,\,\pm 141°\,20')$;

   (d) $(0, 0)$, $\left(a - \dfrac{a}{\sqrt{2}},\,\dfrac{\pi}{4}\right)$, $\left(a + \dfrac{a}{\sqrt{2}},\,\dfrac{5\pi}{4}\right)$;

   (e) $\left(6,\,\dfrac{\pi}{6}\right)$, $\left(2,\,-\dfrac{\pi}{6}\right)$, $\left(6,\,\dfrac{5\pi}{6}\right)$, $\left(2,\,-\dfrac{5\pi}{6}\right)$.

Pages 168, 169, 170

3. $2ep$.

5. (a) 16, $8\sqrt{3}$; (d) 16, $4\sqrt{7}$; (g) $\frac{25}{2}$, 10; (j) 18, $6\sqrt{5}$; (m) $\frac{50}{3}$, 10;
   (p) 16, $8\sqrt{3}$.

9. (a) $\rho^2(1 - e^2 \cos^2 \theta) = b^2$; (b) $\rho^2(e^2 \cos^2 \theta - 1) = b^2$.

13. $\dfrac{2ep}{1 - e^2}$.

Pages 170, 171, 172

1. $\rho = 2(b + a \cos \theta)$.   **3.** $d = \sqrt{\rho_1{}^2 + \rho_2{}^2 - 2\rho_1\rho_2 \cos (\theta_2 - \theta_1)}$.

5*. $\rho^2(1 - e^2 \cos^2 \theta) = b^2$.   **7*.** $\rho = a(1 + 2 \cos \theta)$.

9. $\rho^3 - 3a^2\rho - 2a^3 \cos^2 \theta = 0$.   **11*.** $\rho \sin 2\theta = a$.   **13*.** $\rho = a \sin 2\theta$.

15*. $\rho^2 = 2a^2 \cos 2\theta$.   **17*.** $\rho = a \cos \dfrac{\theta}{3}$.   **19*.** $\rho + a = \dfrac{4a\theta}{\pi}$.

Page 174

31. (a) $(x^2 + y^2 + ax)^2 = a^2(x^2 + y^2)$; (b) $(x^2 + y^2 - bx)^2 = a^2(x^2 + y^2)$;
   (c) $ay^2 = x^3$; (d) $(x^2 + y^2)(x - a)^2 = b^2x^2$; (e) $y^2(2a - x) = x^3$;
   (f) $(x^2 + y^2)^3 = 4a^2x^2y^2$; (g) $(x^2 + y^2)^2 = a(3x^2y - y^3)$;

   (h) $(x^2 + y^2)^2 = 2a^2xy$; (i) $y = x \tan \dfrac{\sqrt{x^2 + y^2}}{a}$;

   (j) $y = x \tan \dfrac{a}{\sqrt{x^2 + y^2}}$; (k) $(x^2 - y^2)^2 = a^2(x^2 + y^2)$;

   (l) $4x^2y^2 = a^2(x^2 + y^2)$; (m) $x(x^2 - 3y^2) = a(x^2 + y^2)$.

Pages 179, 180

5. (a) $x = -\log_3 y$; (b) $x = -\log_4 y$; (c) $x = -\log_3 y$;
   (d) $x = 4 + \log_2 y$; (e) $x = 1 - \log_3 y$; (f) $x = -\log_e y$;
   (g) $x = 5 \log_e \dfrac{5}{y}$; (h) $x = -\log_e (-y)$.

7. (a) $x = 2^y$; (b) $x = \pm 10^{\frac{y}{2}}$; (c) $x = 5 + 10^y$; (d) $x = 10^y - 5$;

(e) $x = 5 - 10^y$; (f) $x = e^{\frac{y}{2}}$; (g) $x = \pm \sqrt{e^y - 1}$;

(h) $x = \pm \sqrt{10 - 10^y}$.

9. (a) $x = \log_e (y \pm \sqrt{y^2 - 1})$; (b) $x = \log_e (y + \sqrt{y^2 + 1})$;

(c) $x = a \log_e \dfrac{y \pm \sqrt{y^2 - a^2}}{a}$.

Pages 193, 194, 195

3. (a) $y = 1 - 2x + x^2$; (b) $y^2 = x^3$; (c) $9y = 18x - x^2$;

(d) $64y^2 = x(16 - x)^2$; (e) $x^2 - y^2 = 4$; (f) $x(x^2 + y^2) = 2(y^2 - x^2)$;

(g) $x(x^2 + y^2) = 2ay^2$; (h) $x = y^{\frac{2}{3}} + 2y^{\frac{1}{3}}$; (i) $x^2 + 4y^2 = 400$;

(j) $y = 1 - 2x^2$; (k) $x^2 + y^2 - 6x + 8y = 0$; (l) $x^2 - y^2 = a^2$;

(m) $625y^2 = 36x^2(25 - x^2)$; (n) $a^4y^2 = 4b^2x^2(a^2 - x^2)$;

(o) $\sqrt{x} + \sqrt{y} = \sqrt{a}$; (p) $y(1 + x^2) = 2x$; (q) $y(x^2 + 4a^2) = 8a^3$;

(r) $\left(\dfrac{x}{a}\right)^{\frac{2}{3}} + \left(\dfrac{y}{b}\right)^{\frac{2}{3}} = 1$; (s) $\left(\dfrac{x}{a}\right)^2 + \left(\dfrac{y}{b}\right)^{\frac{2}{3}} = 1$;

(t) $ay = x\sqrt{x^2 - a^2}$; (u) $(x^2 + y^2)^2 - 6a^2(x^2 + y^2) + 8a^3x - 3a^4 = 0$.

5. $x = 6 + \frac{4}{5}t$, $y = 4 + \frac{3}{5}t$.

7. (a) $x = 64\sqrt{2}t$, $y = 64\sqrt{2}t - 16t^2$, 512, (256, 128);

(b) $x = 40t$, $y = 40\sqrt{3}t - 16t^2$, $100\sqrt{3}$, $(50\sqrt{3}, 75)$;

(c) $x = 80t$, $y = 60t - 16t^2$, 300, (150, 56.25);

(d) $x = 120t$, $y = 160t - 16t^2$, 1200, (600, 400).

9. 182.0.   **11.** $y = x \tan \alpha - \dfrac{gx^2}{2u^2} \sec^2 \alpha$.

17. (a) $x = at^2$, $y = a^2t^3$; (b) $x = a \sec \theta$, $y = b \tan \theta$;

(c) $x = \dfrac{2at^2}{1 + t^2}$, $y = \dfrac{2at^3}{1 + t^2}$; (d) $x = a \sec^3 \theta$, $y = a \tan^3 \theta$;

(e) $x = \dfrac{a(t^2 - 1)}{t^2 + 1}$, $y = \dfrac{2at^3}{t^2 + 1}$; (f) $x = \dfrac{3a - at^2}{1 + t^2}$, $y = \dfrac{3at - at^3}{1 + t^2}$;

(g) $x = \dfrac{a(t^2 - 1)}{t^2 + 1}$, $y = \dfrac{at(t^2 - 1)}{t^2 + 1}$; (h) $x = \dfrac{at}{(1 + t^2)^2}$, $y = \dfrac{at^2}{(1 + t^2)^2}$;

(i) $x = \dfrac{a}{1 + t^3}$, $y = \dfrac{at}{1 + t^3}$; (j) $x = \dfrac{t^2 - 1}{t^3}$, $y = \dfrac{(t^2 - 1)^2}{t^5}$.

Pages 196, 197

3. $x = r \text{ arc vers } \dfrac{y}{r} - \sqrt{2ry - y^2}$.   **7.** $- 2, 3.7435$; ± 0.8520.

11. $x = \frac{7}{6}\left(\frac{8.8}{7}t - \sin \frac{8.8}{7}t\right)$, $y = \frac{7}{6}(1 - \cos \frac{8.8}{7}t)$.

Pages 203, 204, 205

1. (a) $(x^2 + y^2 - bx)^2 = a^2(x^2 + y^2)$;   (b) $(x^2 + y^2 + ax)^2 = a^2(x^2 + y^2)$;
   (c) $(x^2 + y^2)(x - a)^2 = b^2x^2$;   (d) $y^2(2a - x) = x^3$;
   (e) $(x^2 + y^2)^3 = 4a^2x^2y^2$;   (f) $(x^2 + y^2)^2 = a(3x^2y - y^3)$.

7*. (a) $\rho = a(\sec \theta + \tan \theta)$;   (b) $\rho^4 - 2a^2\rho^2 \cos 2\theta = c^4 - a^4$.

9*. $x = \sqrt{3}y$.   **11.** $x = \sqrt{r^2 - 4y^2} + \frac{1}{2}\sqrt{a^2 - 4y^2}$.

13. $2y^2 - 2px + 2py + p^2 = 0$.   **15.** $(x^2 + y^2)^2 = ax^2y$.

17*. $y^2(a^2 - x^2) = x^4$.

Pages 209, 210

1. (a) $-\dfrac{y_1}{x_1}$;   (b) $3ax_1^2$;   (c) $\dfrac{x_1 - h}{p}$;   (d) $-\dfrac{p}{y_1}$;   (e) $-\dfrac{x_1 - h}{y_1 - k}$;   (f) $-\dfrac{a^2x_1}{b^2y_1}$;

   (g) $\dfrac{a^2x_1}{b^2y_1}$.

3. (a) $\frac{2}{9}$, $-\frac{9}{2}$;   (b) $\frac{4}{5}$, $-\frac{5}{4}$;   (c) -3, $\frac{1}{3}$;   (d) -1, 1;   (e) $\frac{3}{4}$, $-\frac{4}{3}$;

   (f) $\frac{3}{2}$, $-\frac{2}{3}$;   (g) 6, $-\frac{1}{6}$;   (h) $\frac{1}{8}$, -8;   (i) $\dfrac{1}{a^2}$, $-a^2$;   (j) $-\frac{16}{25}$, $\frac{25}{16}$.

5. (a) $3x - 4y + 26 = 0$, $4x + 3y + 18 = 0$;
   (b) $5x - 3y = 9$, $9x + 15y = 125$;   (c) $x + 4y = 10$, $4x - y + 45 = 0$;
   (d) $x + y + 3 = 0$, $x - y = 9$;   (e) $2x - 3y = 12$, $3x + 2y = 5$;
   (f) $x + 2y = 12$, $2x - y = 9$;   (g) $3x - 2y = 2$, $2x + 3y = 10$;
   (h) $3x - 4y = 10$, $4x + 3y = 30$.

9. (a) $36° 52'$, $71° 34'$;   (b) $109° 28'$;   (c) $63° 26'$, $153° 26'$;   (d) $32° 28'$.

11. $\dfrac{2m}{1 - m^2}$.

Pages 214, 215

1. (a) $-\frac{8}{3}$, -6;   (b) -1, -4;   (c) $\frac{4}{3}$, 48;   (d) -4, $-\frac{9}{4}$;   (e) 2, 2;
   (f) 32, $\frac{1}{2}$;   (g) $-\frac{9}{4}$, $-\frac{64}{9}$;   (h) $-\frac{9}{2}$, -2.

3. (a) $4x - 3y = \pm 50$;   (b) $x + y + 6 = 0$;   (c) $2x - 9y = \pm 26$;
   (d) $3x - y = \pm 10$;   (e) $x + 2y = \pm 12$;   (f) $6x - y = \pm 8$;
   (g) $x + 2y = 8$;   (h) $3x - 2y = \pm 12$.

5. (a) $4x - 3y = 50$, $3x + 4y = 50$;   (b) $x + y + 6 = 0$, $3x + y + 2 = 0$;
   (c) $2x - 9y + 26 = 0$, $46x + 27y = 338$;   (d) $3x - y = 10$;
   (e) $x + 2y = 12$;   (f) $6x - y = 8$;   (g) $x - y = 2$, $x + 2y = 8$;
   (h) $3x - 2y = 12$, $3x - 14y + 60 = 0$.

7. (a) $2x_1$, p, $\sqrt{4x_1^2 + y_1^2}$, $\sqrt{y_1^2 + p^2}$;

   (b) $-\dfrac{a^2y_1^2}{b^2x_1}$, $-\dfrac{b^2x_1}{a^2}$, $\dfrac{y_1}{b^2x_1}\sqrt{a^4y_1^2 + b^4x_1^2}$, $\dfrac{1}{a^2}\sqrt{a^4y_1^2 + b^4x_1^2}$;

   (c) $\dfrac{a^2y_1^2}{b^2x_1}$, $\dfrac{b^2x_1}{a^2}$, $\dfrac{y_1}{b^2x_1}\sqrt{a^4y_1^2 + b^4x_1^2}$, $\dfrac{1}{a^2}\sqrt{a^4y_1^2 + b^4x_1^2}$;

(d) $-\dfrac{y_1{}^2}{x_1}$, $-x_1$, $\dfrac{y_1 r}{x_1}$, r.

9. (a) $y_1 x + py = y_1(p + x_1)$; (b) $\dfrac{a^2 x}{x_1} - \dfrac{b^2 y}{y_1} = a^2 - b^2$;

(c) $\dfrac{a^2 x}{x_1} + \dfrac{b^2 y}{y_1} = a^2 + b^2$; (d) $y_1 x - x_1 y = 0$.

13. a^2. **17.** $x^2 + y^2 = a^2 + b^2$.

Page 221

1. (a) $-\frac{1}{8}$; (b) $\frac{9}{2}$; (c) ∞; (d) 0; (e) $-\frac{25}{18}$; (f) $\frac{9}{32}$.

3. $mm' = -\dfrac{a^2}{b^2}$. **5.** $x = mp$. **7.** $a = \sqrt{2}b$. **11.** $4ab$.

Pages 233, 234, 235, 236

1. $A = \dfrac{\sqrt{3}x^2}{4}$. **3.** $V = \dfrac{\pi}{3}x^2(3r - x)$. **5.** 25. **7.** 10. **9.** $S = 2x^2 + \dfrac{4k}{x}$.

11. $\dfrac{32\pi R^3}{81}$. **13.** 5. **15.** 0.3663 cu. ft. per degree.

17. $L = 30 + 0.0000326T$. **19.** $v = 100 - 4t$. **25.** $g = 512 \cdot 10^6 \cdot d^{-2}$.

27. $C = \dfrac{80000}{v} + 0.05v^3$. **29.** $I = \dfrac{a}{x^2} + \dfrac{b}{(c - x)^2}$.

Pages 243, 244 ☩

2. (a) $y = 1.538 + 0.0086x$; (b) $y = 109.948 + 0.01996x$;
(c) $d = 0.007627 + 0.0000119t$; (d) $y = 61.807 + 0.3002x$;
(e) $v = 3.307 + 0.358u$; (f) $s = 28.93 - 0.442t$;
(g) $y = 13.17 + 1.545x$; (h) $y = 100.10 + 0.1437x$.

3†. (a) $y = 1.528 + 0.0088x$; (b) $y = 109.953 + 0.01988x$;
(c) $d = 0.007631 + 0.0000118t$; (d) $y = 61.814 + 0.3x$;
(e) $v = 3.317 + 0.356u$; (f) $s = 28.94 - 0.443t$;
(g) $y = 13.09 + 1.556x$; (h) $y = 100.10 + 0.1433x$.

7†. $y = 0.9921 + 0.00749x$. **8†.** $F = 4.97 + 0.05694w$.

9†. $p = 29.857 - 0.0006114h$.

Pages 248, 249, 250 ☩

1. (a) $y = 2.801 - 0.3125x^2$; (b) $y = 0.2024 + 0.00165x^2$;
(c) $y = 3.242 + 0.05x^2$; (d) $y = 10.21 + 0.3024x^2$.

☩ NOTE. In calculating these answers the values of the variables were substituted in the appropriate type of equation and the resulting equations were grouped exactly as in the model examples. A variation in this grouping will lead to somewhat different results. To determine which of several results is the best it is necessary to calculate the residuals. Answers obtained by the method of moments are marked by a dagger (†).

2. (a) $y = 16.30 - \dfrac{22.36}{x}$; (b) $y = 3.519 + \dfrac{4.452}{x}$;

(c) $y = 0.01653 - \dfrac{0.0754}{x}$; (d) $y = 10.85 + \dfrac{15.03}{x}$.

3. (a) $y = 369.9 - 18.16x - 0.1406x^2$;

(b) $y = 0.0273 + 0.03691x + 0.001685x^2$;

(c) $y = 8.46 + 0.644x + 0.03677x^2$.

4. $n = 0.325 + \dfrac{69.35}{i}$.   **5.** $T = 134.3 + 0.819x + 0.01187x^2$.

6. $W = 137.4 + 3.42(h - 64) + 0.145(h - 64)^2$.

7. $t = -0.14 + 2.02R + 0.206R^2$ or $t = 1.92R + 0.219R^2$ if we take $a = 0$.

8. $T = 12.55 + 0.01881x - 0.00000344x^2$.

9. $v = 2.903 + 0.5063x - 0.10148x^2$.

Pages 253, 254 +

1. (a) $y = 102.2x^{-0.3172}$; (b) $y = 0.217x^{0.6015}$; (c) $y = 0.001031x^{0.34095}$.

2. (a) $y = 64.87e^{-0.0799x}$; (b) $y = 0.1500e^{-0.0023x}$; (c) $y = 72.44e^{0.0402x}$.

3. $N = 20.04e^{0.2496t}$.   **4.** $D = 58.8h^{0.5}$.   **5.** $t = 0.03924d^{1.1728}$.

6. $T = 70.43e^{-0.0796t}$.   **7.** $E = 0.0408T^{1.576}$.   **8.** $T = 0.001119R^{1.4998}$.

9. $N = 5.37e^{0.02889(t-1800)}$.   **10.** $p = 29.95e^{-0.00002285h}$.

Pages 260, 261

1. (a) $5\sqrt{2}, \dfrac{2\sqrt{2}}{5}, \dfrac{3\sqrt{2}}{10}, \dfrac{\sqrt{2}}{2}$; 6, 0, 1, 0; 9, $-\frac{8}{9}, \frac{1}{9}, \frac{4}{9}$;

(b) 7, $-\frac{2}{7}, \frac{3}{7}, -\frac{6}{7}$; 13, $\frac{3}{13}, -\frac{4}{13}, \frac{12}{13}$; 9, $\frac{4}{9}, \frac{1}{9}, \frac{8}{9}$;

(c) 18, $\frac{8}{9}, \frac{1}{9}, \frac{4}{9}$; 7, $-\frac{6}{7}, \frac{3}{7}, -\frac{2}{7}$; 15, $\frac{1}{3}, \frac{2}{15}, \frac{14}{15}$.

3. (a) $88° 17'$; (b) $54° 41'$; (c) $136° 11'$.   **7.** $(\frac{16}{7}, -\frac{24}{7}, \pm\frac{48}{7})$.

9. (a) 24.5; (b) 24.5.   **11.** (6, 1, 4) or (2, -3, 0).

15. $\sqrt{17}, \sqrt{74}, \sqrt{83}$.   **17.** $(-4, -2, 9)$.   **19.** (a) $\dfrac{a^3\sqrt{2}}{12}$; (b) $\dfrac{a\sqrt{6}}{4}$.

Pages 266, 267, 268

1. (a) $\dfrac{x}{9} - \dfrac{4y}{9} + \dfrac{8z}{9} = 4$, $\dfrac{x}{36} + \dfrac{y}{-9} + \dfrac{z}{\frac{9}{2}} = 1$;

(b) $\dfrac{3x}{13} + \dfrac{4y}{13} - \dfrac{12z}{13} = 4$, $\dfrac{x}{\frac{52}{3}} + \dfrac{y}{13} + \dfrac{z}{-\frac{13}{3}} = 1$;

(c) $\dfrac{x}{9} - \dfrac{4y}{9} + \dfrac{8z}{9} = \dfrac{9}{2}$, $\dfrac{x}{\frac{81}{2}} + \dfrac{y}{-\frac{81}{8}} + \dfrac{z}{\frac{81}{16}} = 1$; (d) $\dfrac{4x}{5} - \dfrac{3y}{5} = 20$;

+ See note on page 15.